ROADSIDE GEOLOGY
of WEST VIRGINIA

ROADSIDE GEOLOGY
of WEST VIRGINIA

JOSEPH G. LEBOLD AND
CHRISTOPHER WILKINSON

PHOTOGRAPHS BY Maria af Rolén

2018
Mountain Press Publishing Company
Missoula, Montana

Maps constructed by Chelsea Feeney (www.cmcfeeney.com)
using GIS data from the West Virginia GIS Technical Center.

Roadside Geology is a registered trademark
of Mountain Press Publishing Company

Library of Congress Cataloging-in-Publication Data

Names: Lebold, Joseph G., 1972- author. | Wilkinson, Christopher, 1946-
  author. | Rolen, Maria af, photographer.
Title: Roadside geology of West Virginia / Joseph G. Lebold and Christopher
  Wilkinson ; photographs by Maria af Rolen.
Description: Missoula, Montana : Mountain Press Publishing Company, 2018. |
  Series: Roadside geology series | Includes bibliographical references and
  index.
Identifiers: LCCN 2018022837 | ISBN 9780878426836 (pbk. : alk. paper)
Subjects: LCSH: Geology—West Virginia—Guidebooks. | West
  Virginia—Guidebooks.
Classification: LCC QE177 .L43 2018 | DDC 557.54—dc23
LC record available at https://lccn.loc.gov/2018022837

PRINTED IN HONG KONG BY MANTEC PRODUCTION COMPANY

P.O. Box 2399 • Missoula, MT 59806 • 406-728-1900
800-234-5308 • info@mtnpress.com
www.mountain-press.com

To my parents, Jack and Jennie, who faithfully supported me in whatever path I chose to follow. To Dr. Robert Behling (Dr. Bob) and Dr. Thomas Kammer, who taught my first geology classes at West Virginia University and opened a whole new world to me. And finally, to my many students over the years who have let me share my passion for geology and motivate me to explain even the more complicated aspects of the Earth in simple yet dynamic ways.

—Joseph G. Lebold

In memory of Donald Brandreth Potter (1923–2015), professor of geology, Hamilton College, who for reasons neither of us fully understood instilled a lifelong interest in his field; to John McPhee for sustaining that interest through his *New Yorker* essays on the subject; and, as always, to my wife, Carroll Wetzel Wilkinson.

—Christopher Wilkinson

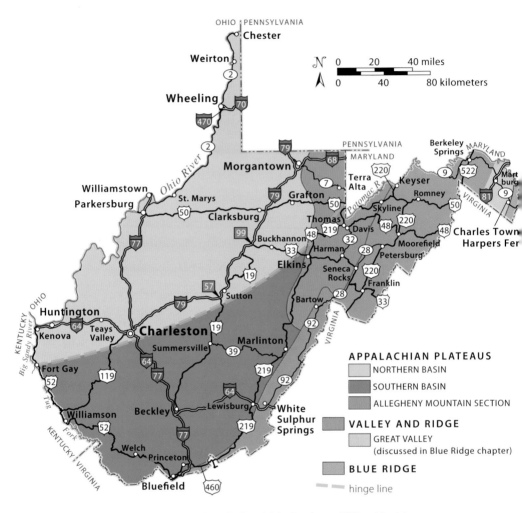

Routes and sections in Roadside Geology of West Virginia.

As you read this book, be aware that, with few exceptions, each highway for which we have provided a guide connects at one end or the other with another highway discussed in this guide. This will enable those who are interested in organizing "geo-tours" to do so and will enlarge their understanding of the geology and topography of West Virginia. We encourage readers to travel through our state and enjoy its extraordinary beauty.

TABLE OF CONTENTS

ACKNOWLEDGMENTS

Fundamentally, any writing worth reading is the product of collaboration, and in no instance is this more true than with this book. Beyond the obvious partnership of the coauthors, a number of other individuals contributed in significant ways to the preparation of the text, and their assistance was invaluable.

Our deepest thanks goes to Maria af Rolén, the photographer for the book. A graduate of Fotoskolan i Stockholm, the leading institution of its kind in her native Sweden, Maria brought her extraordinary gifts to the challenge of capturing images of unmistakable clarity and precision to illustrate the descriptions of geological and topographical phenomena to be seen along West Virginia's highways. Each of her pictures is worth at least one thousand words, if not more.

With deepest appreciation, we must also thank professor emeritus of geology at West Virginia University, Dr. Robert Schumaker, who took an interest in this project almost from the beginning and who, through the Robert and Beverly Shumaker Fund for Geologic Research, underwrote the succession of road trips required to bring into focus the geology of the state.

Mitch Blake, director and state geologist for the West Virginia Geological and Economic Survey, provided important information concerning a variety of issues, with particular attention to the coal deposits of the state, and moreover he read a complete early draft of the book. His subsequent recommendations proved invaluable in clarifying various issues and, in general, improving our text.

Numerous faculty members of the department of geology and geography at West Virginia University provided support in various forms. Professors Jaime Toro and J. Steven Kite provided invaluable suggestions concerning geologic cross sections and maps. Professor Jack Renton provided a library of helpful figures. Dr. Aaron Maxwell provided the GIS files used as base maps for figures. In addition, Professor Gregory Elmes lent his skills at map-making to early drafts of several chapters.

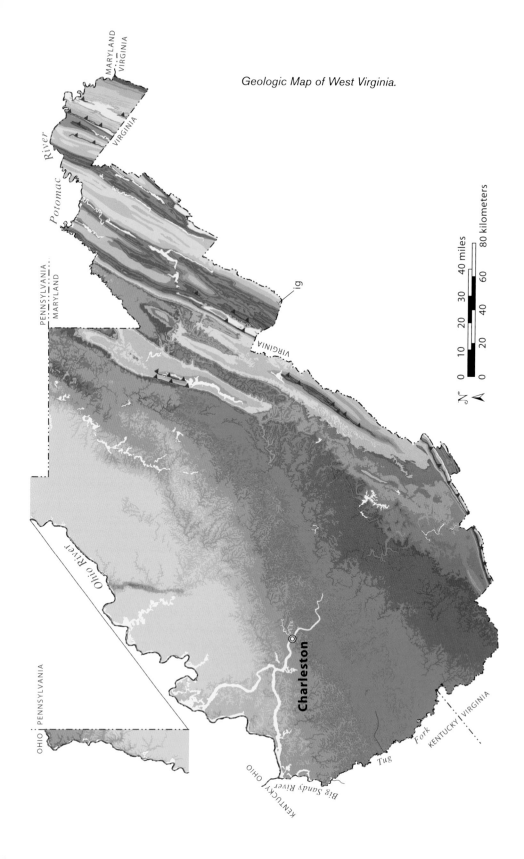

Geologic Map of West Virginia.

CENOZOIC

QUATERNARY

Qal alluvium

MESOZOIC AND CENOZOIC

Ig intrusive igneous rocks

PALEOZOIC

PENNSYLVANIAN-PERMIAN

IPPd Dunkard Group

PENNSYLVANIAN

IPm Monongahela Formation
IPc Conemaugh Group
IPa Allegheny Formation
IPpv Pottsville Sandstone
IPk Kanawha Formation — Pottsville Group
IPnr New River Formation — Pottsville Group
IPp Pocahontas Formation — Pottsville Group

MISSISSIPPIAN

Mmc Mauch Chunk Formation
Mbp Bluestone and Princeton Formations — Mauch Chunk Group
Mh Hinton Formation — Mauch Chunk Group
Mbf Bluefield Formation — Mauch Chunk Group
Mg Greenbrier Limestone
Mmc Maccrady Formation
Mp Price Formation
Mmp Maccrady and Price Formations, undivided

DEVONIAN

Dhs Hampshire Formation
Dgg Greenland Gap Group
Db Brallier Formation
Dh Harrell Shale
Dmt Mahantango Shale
Dm Marcellus Shale
Dmn Marcellus Shale and Needmore Shale, undivided
Do Oriskany Sandstone and Huntersville Chert
Dhl Helderberg Group
Dmu Middle and Upper Devonian, undivided
Dbh Brallier Formation and Harrell Shale, undivided
Dmb Millboro Shale
Dohl Oriskany Sandstone and Helderberg Group, undivided

SILURIAN

Stw Tonoloway, Wills Creek, and Williamsport Formations
Smc McKenzie Formation and Clinton Group
St Tuscarora Sandstone
Sct McKenzie Formation, Clinton Group, and Tuscarora Sandstone, undivided

ORDOVICIAN

Ojo Juniata and Oswego Formations
Om Martinsburg Shale
Ot Trenton Group
Obr Black River Group
Osp St. Paul Group
Obps Pinesburg Station Dolomite
Obrr Rockdale Run Formation
Obs Stonehenge Limestone
Otbr Trenton Group and Black River Group, undivided
Ob Beekmantown Group

CAMBRIAN

Cc Conococheague Formation
Ce Elbrook Formation
Cwy Waynesboro Formation
Ct Tomstown Dolomite
Ca Antietam Formation

CAMBRIAN-PRECAMBRIAN

Ch Harpers Formation
Cw Weverton-Loudon Formation
CpCc Catoctin Formation

—— fault
⊣⊣ thrust fault
✢ syncline
✢ anticline

GEOLOGIC TIME SCALE

ERA	PERIOD / EPOCH		AGE (millions of years)	GEOLOGIC EVENTS IN WEST VIRGINIA
CENOZOIC	QUATERNARY	HOLOCENE	0.01	Ice sheets to the north and west of West Virginia block the ancient Teays and Monongahela Rivers, forming glacial lakes in the Mountain State. As they melted, outwash deposits partially fill Ohio River valley.
		PLEISTOCENE	2.6	Uplift throughout the Cenozoic, caused by isostatic adjustment to erosion, induces streams to begin carving the modern Appalachian Mountains within the last 10 million years.
	NEOGENE		23	
	PALEOGENE		66	A brief period of igneous activity occurs around 45 to 50 million years ago.
MESOZOIC	CRETACEOUS		145	Mesozoic sedimentary rocks were either eroded or never deposited even as Pangea rifted to the east and the Atlantic Ocean opened around 200 million years ago.
	JURASSIC		201	
	TRIASSIC		252	Minor igneous intrusions associated with early rifting of Pangea in eastern West Virginia.
PALEOZOIC	PERMIAN		299	The Alleghanian Orogeny comes to a close as Pangea is assembled. Low-relief coastal environments persist, but arid conditions reduce the amount of plant material available for coal formation.
	PENNSYLVANIAN		323	The Alleghanian Orogeny and assembly of Pangea continue. Uplift from the collision forms the ancestral Appalachian Mountains. West Virginia is now between the mountains to the east and a shallow sea to the west. Rivers draining the mountains flow to the sea, which is bordered by vast coastal swamps now preserved as coal beds.
	MISSISSIPPIAN		359	LATE: Late Paleozoic ice age begins as vast ice sheets form in the southern hemisphere and cause the shallow sea to recede. Present-day Africa begins a slow collision with eastern Laurentia, starting the Alleghanian Orogeny to the east of West Virginia, which lasts until the end of the Paleozoic Era as the supercontinent Pangea is assembled. MIDDLE: Shallow sea covers much of ancient North America. EARLY: Acadian Mountains are eroded to a low-relief plain.
	DEVONIAN		419	MIDDLE to LATE: Eastern edge of Laurentia becomes an active margin again as a collision with a microcontinent produces the Acadian Orogeny between 380 and 340 million years ago. Sediments eroded from Acadian Mountains form the Catskill clastic wedge, which accumulates in the Catskill foreland basin in a pattern similar to the Queenston clastic wedge during the Taconic Orogeny. EARLY: Passive margin conditions continue.
	SILURIAN		444	Taconic Mountains eroded to a low-relief plain; return to passive margin conditions.
	ORDOVICIAN		485	LATE: Active margin develops as a volcanic arc in the Iapetus Ocean collides with eastern Laurentia during the Taconic Orogeny between 460 and 435 million years ago, producing a mountainous clastic source area and foreland basin. Sediments of the Queenston clastic wedge deposited west of the mountains record the transition from deep to shallow marine, and eventually continental environments are established in and around the Taconic foreland basin. EARLY to MIDDLE: Warm, shallow marine environments continue on the passive margin.
	CAMBRIAN		541	Waters of the newly opened Iapetus Ocean slowly advance over the eastern, passive margin of Laurentia drowning the continental shelf and covering West Virginia in a warm, shallow sea.
PRECAMBRIAN / PROTEROZOIC			1,600	Rifting of Rodinia splits Grenville basement rocks around 680 to 550 million years ago. Continued rifting forms the Iapetus Ocean and the continent of Laurentia, which eventually becomes North America.
			2,500	Grenville Orogeny 1.3 to 1.0 billion years ago during the assembly of the supercontinent Rodinia; Grenville basement rocks added to present-day North American continent.
				Earth forms 4.56 billion years ago.

Precambrian is an informal time unit ranging from the Earth's formation to 541 million years ago.

Geologic time scale with major events that shaped the rocks and landscape in and around West Virginia. –Modified from Ashton, 2008

INTRODUCTION

In West Virginia, geologic and human history are inseparable. The Mountain State was formed during the Civil War when a number of western counties of Virginia were recognized by the Union as a new state, and its subsequent economic and cultural development was deeply influenced by its geology. To this day, West Virginia has been associated with coal and the mining of this resource. Its importance for the newly formed state was acknowledged as early as September 1863, when, just three months after West Virginia became the thirty-fifth state, its Great Seal was adopted by the legislature. In its center are two figures, one a farmer, the other a coal miner.

In the mid-nineteenth century, particularly in the southern part of the state, coal was found in great abundance, was easily accessible at the surface, and was valued for its high quality. Industrialists moved quickly to exploit this resource beginning around 1870, both to fuel their factories and to power the increasingly complex network of railroads crisscrossing the country. Their accomplishments have shaped much of the subsequent economic, political, labor, racial, and cultural history of the state and still do so to a great extent even as extensive drilling for natural gas threatens to dethrone king coal.

In truth, however, the state's geology encompasses more than its vast coal fields and has a long history extending back hundreds of millions of years before the materials that would be transformed into coal and natural gas began to accumulate. Before telling that story, an orientation to the state is in order. Examination of a map reveals several notable facts. At the top is a narrow, finger-shaped extension, a consequence of the survey that created the Mason-Dixon Line, originally intended to define the boundaries separating the colonies of Maryland, Pennsylvania, and Virginia in 1767 and extended farther west in 1784. Where the survey ended would also determine Pennsylvania's western border, as from that point a line was projected due north to Lake Erie. About 19 miles due west of that point runs the Ohio River, perhaps a more practical stopping point for the survey. However, as a consequence of the decision to end the boundary between those three states 5 degrees west of the point where the Delaware River flows into Chesapeake Bay, this thin strip of territory, belonging first to Virginia and after 1863 to West Virginia, lies west of Pennsylvania and constitutes what is known locally as "the northern panhandle."

About three-quarters of the Mountain State's western boundary is formed by the Ohio River, the balance by the Big Sandy River and its tributary the Tug Fork, which constitute most of the southwestern and southern boundary with Kentucky. Continuing east and then turning north, the border with Virginia is marked by mountain ridges extending all the way to the "eastern panhandle," which includes counties through which ran the Baltimore & Ohio Railroad, now part of CSX. So great was the railroad's military value to the Union during the Civil War that, when the time came to carve out Virginia's western counties to form the new state of West Virginia, these counties were included. The Potomac River marks the boundary with Maryland to the river's headwaters high in the mountains of Tucker County. From that point due north to the Mason-Dixon Line runs the border between western Maryland and north-central West Virginia.

Almost reflexively, many will associate the Mountain State with the South; its association with Virginia both in history and in name makes that logical. Indeed, the southernmost point in the state is approximately due west of the second capital of the Confederacy: Richmond, Virginia. But consider this: the town of Chester, which sits at the tip of the northern panhandle, lies approximately due west of New York City. Perhaps even more counterintuitive is the fact that the westernmost part of the state lies near the longitude on which Detroit, Michigan, is located. Moreover, since the Civil War, the combination of the state's political, racial, and labor history suggests a more northerly

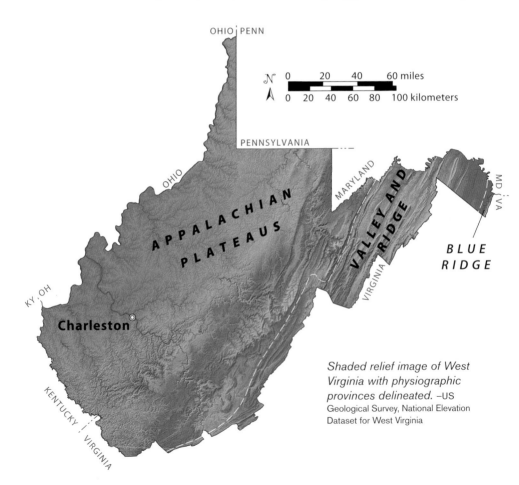

Shaded relief image of West Virginia with physiographic provinces delineated. –US Geological Survey, National Elevation Dataset for West Virginia

orientation. Perhaps the best compromise is simply to think of West Virginia as part of the mid-Atlantic region of the eastern United States.

Within its borders, the landscape of the Mountain State can be divided into three regions, or *physiographic provinces*, each with its own characteristic topography—a function of its climate and underlying geology. More than three-quarters of the state is located on what is formally known as the Appalachian Plateaus (also called the Allegheny Plateau in some publications). To the east lies the Valley and Ridge Province that constitutes most of the northeastern quarter of the state. Finally, at the edge of the eastern panhandle lies a very small sliver of the Blue Ridge Province. The underlying geology responsible for the unique topography of these three provinces has been a work in progress for over 1 billion years. In order to understand its evolution fully, we need to understand both the history of the Earth and the geologic history of what would one day be named West Virginia.

Formation of the Earth

While the Earth might seem to be a vast, complex system, its formation and continuing evolution can be partly attributed to two processes that helped shape our solar system as a whole: gravitational attraction and heat. *Gravity* is a force that attracts physical bodies that have mass toward one another. Although some of the greatest minds in human history have put forth various ideas for the nature of gravitational attraction, no single unifying theory has emerged to explain its presence. *Heat* is the energy of motion at the atomic or molecular level. Both phenomena can be difficult to visualize as they operate at scales difficult for humans to view, but their effects can be repeatedly measured, and laws have been developed that describe their consistent behavior in nature. For our purposes, only these effects need to be understood: gravity brings objects with mass closer together, and heat always flows from areas of more motion, creating more energy measured as higher temperatures, to areas of less motion, measured as lower temperatures.

Our solar system formed as the result of the interplay between these two processes acting on the raw materials contained within a low-density cloud of dust and gas known as a *nebula*. We now think that some external force triggered an inward collapse of the dust and gas, causing some of the particles to move closer to one another, forming a large rotating disk. The lightest material settled in the center of the disk and coalesced to form our sun. The heavier particles were hurled farther from the center, and the gravitational attraction among the particles caused them to collide, forming clumps of larger mass. The collisions produced heat that became more intense as the collisions proceeded, causing the clumps to remain as hot "sticky" blobs of material. Several of the clumps coalesced into planet-sized objects about 4.6 billion years ago, while others continued to smash into each other.

The Earth remained hot as additional heat was initially generated from within by gravity, which drew particles closer together, and subsequently by radioactive decay of some of that material. At first, the Earth's interior was molten, having more or less a uniform density from its center to the base of a thin, low-density crust cooling on the surface. The interior of the hot, early planet began to separate as higher-density material sank toward the gravitational center, and lower-density material floated outward. This eventually led to the formation of the Earth's internal layers and laid the groundwork for the evolution of our planet.

Plate Tectonics

After the dust had settled in the rather violent early days of the Earth, three main layers of different compositions stabilized: the innermost iron nickel core, the high-density rocky mantle in the middle, and the thin low-density rocky crust. However, differences in temperature and pressure, both of which increase toward the planet's center, cause regions of these layers to behave differently. The core has two distinct zones: a solid inner core and a liquid outer core. The mantle, which comprises 83 percent of the Earth's volume, can be separated into three zones. The lower and upper mantle behave like a solid, while the middle zone of the mantle can behave either like a rigid solid or a mobile liquid depending on how pressure is applied. Think of silly putty: Apply pressure to it quickly by striking it with a hammer, and it will crack like a brittle solid. Apply pressure slowly by gradually pulling the ends apart, and it will flow, stretching into a thin strand. Because pressure is applied slowly by the weight of the upper mantle and crust, the middle zone flows, causing those upper layers to "float" over this zone. This difference permits the division of the crust and mantle based on how the zones behave. The middle mantle is called the *asthenosphere*, from the Greek word *asthene,* meaning "weak," while the upper mantle and crust make up the *lithosphere*, from the Greek word *lithos,* meaning "rocky."

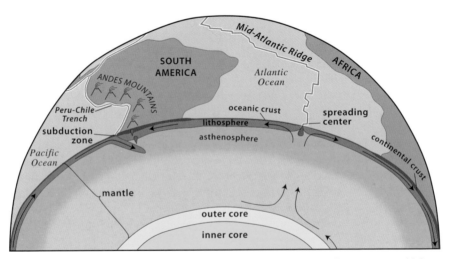

Currents of heat from the core elevate the lithosphere at spreading centers, which cause adjacent plates to slide down and apart from one another. This movement is balanced at subduction zones, where the cooler edges of the plates sink back into the asthenosphere.

The lithosphere is not a single continuous shell; rather, it is broken into about a dozen large pieces and numerous smaller pieces called *plates*. The plates move over the asthenosphere about as fast as fingernails grow, interacting with each other along their edges, or *plate boundaries*. The movement of the plates is driven by the same two processes that influenced the formation of the solar system and the Earth itself: gravity and heat. As heat flows from the core to outer space, it moves convection cells in the weak mantle very slowly in a manner similar to the way liquids develop swirling convection cells when heated in a pot. The lithosphere is warmed unevenly, with the greatest concentration of heat corresponding to the rising currents of convection cells. The lithosphere becomes more buoyant in areas of rising currents, and as a consequence it stretches and rides higher on the asthenosphere, lowering the pressure below. Lower pressure permits parts of the asthenosphere to expand into a liquid, generating enormous volumes of *magma*, or liquid rock, which rises through fractures in the stretched lithosphere and solidifies as thin, dense *oceanic crust*. The newly formed, heated, and elevated portions of the plates split and slide down and away from one another along mid-ocean ridges due to the force of gravity, creating *divergent boundaries* where the plates move apart.

The downward currents of convection cells are where the temperatures are coolest, causing the plates to ride lower on the asthenosphere. The cool, low

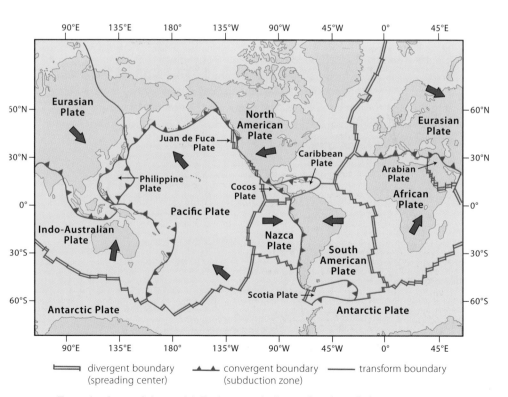

Tectonic plates of the world. Red arrows indicate direction of plate movement.
–Modified from the US Geological Survey

edges of oceanic plates sink into the asthenosphere under their own immense weight, creating the world's deep ocean trenches. Known as *subduction*, this sinking edge is one example of a *convergent boundary* where the plates come together. The two boundaries operate together because no gaps exist between the plates. The process resembles a bumper-to-bumper traffic jam: press the accelerator to move away from the car behind you, and you collide with the car in front.

As an oceanic plate descends in a subduction zone, water trapped in it is released, lowering the melting temperature of the surrounding mantle and causing it to melt. The rising magma then begins the long journey up through the lithosphere, and as it does, it melts portions of the overriding plate. The melting incorporates low-density minerals into the magma, which lowers its density. It can then solidify into thick, low-density *continental crust*.

Because of its increased buoyancy, lithosphere capped by continental crust does not subduct. When one plate is capped by continental crust, it forms the overriding plate. When both are capped by continental crust, neither subducts, resulting in a continental collision zone.

A third type of boundary, called a *transform boundary*, exists to allow the divergence and convergence of plates on the spherical Earth. At these boundaries, the plates slide past one another, neither rising nor descending, effectively accommodating the motion of plates around them.

On the Earth's surface these three types of boundaries are principal sites of mountain building, volcanism, and earthquakes, all by-products of the processes operating below the Earth's surface. The edges of continents that are close enough to the boundaries to be directly affected by them are called *active margins*, of which one prominent example is the Pacific Coast of North America. *Passive margins* are the continental edges that are too far from plate boundaries to be directly affected and tend to be the sites of vast sediment accumulation on continental shelves. The Atlantic Coast of North America is a good example of a passive margin.

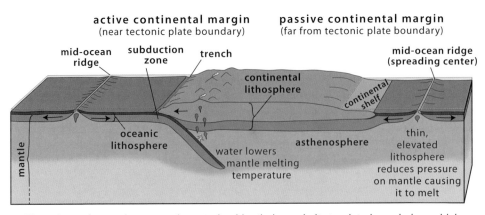

The edges of a continent are characterized by their proximity to plate boundaries, which generate magmas in very different ways at spreading centers and subduction zones.

Although the plates move at the rate of one to a few inches per year, the motion has been going on since the development of the Earth's layers, causing mountains to rise and ocean basins to open and close. Today, the Atlantic Ocean is getting wider as divergence along the Mid-Atlantic Ridge causes new crust to be added to the seafloor, while the Pacific Ocean is slowly shrinking as subduction along the Pacific Ring of Fire consumes old seafloor along its edges.

One other aspect of the lithosphere can also produce elevation differences. The crust that caps the lithosphere can either be thin, higher-density oceanic crust or thicker, low-density continental crust. Oceanic crust averages 4 miles in thickness while continental crust ranges from 20 to 30 miles thick. The thickness difference, combined with the density difference between the two, causes the lithosphere capped by oceanic crust to ride lower on the asthenosphere, creating the world's ocean basins; conversely, lithosphere capped by continental crust rides higher, often above sea level. The next time you look at a map of the world, do not think so much of oceans and land, but rather of thin and thick crust. Also, do not think of the highest elevations on the planet as just mountains; they are simply the surface expression of regions having the thickest crust!

Minerals and Rocks

Most rocks are the by-product of plate tectonics. They are combinations of minerals, the basic components of the solid Earth. On the largest scale, crustal rocks are formed at plate boundaries. Divergent margins produce oceanic crust when magma from the mantle rises to the surface at the boundary and solidifies to form basalt. Granite and andesite, components of continental crust, are generated above subduction zones. These rocks are classified as igneous rocks, those that solidify either from cooling magma at depth or as lavas extruded from volcanoes at the surface. Only a few small outcrops of igneous rock can be found in West Virginia.

Once formed, Earth processes can act upon igneous rocks and produce other types of rocks. If the crust is exposed at the surface, it can be broken down, or *weathered*, into smaller pieces called sediments, or *clasts*, which are the raw materials for clastic sedimentary rocks. The clasts are classified by size: from largest to smallest they are gravel, sand, and mud, the latter of which is a combination of silt and clay. Geologists often refer to small clast sizes, such as mud, as *fine*, and large clasts, such as gravel, as *coarse*.

Clasts can be removed, or eroded from bedrock, and transported by gravity, water, wind, or ice, and deposited in low regions, or basins, where they can accumulate in great thickness. In general, larger clasts are deposited by high-energy streams and rivers, whereas smaller clasts settle to the bottom of low-energy water bodies. Over time, these vast deposits of sediment are covered by younger layers, and by the time they are buried by at least a thickness of 1.5 miles of sediment, they are compacted and lithified to various degrees, depending on their grain size. At these depths minerals dissolved in water flowing through sediments precipitate, binding or cementing the grains together. Together, compaction and cementation lead to the *lithification* of sediments in the basins in which they are deposited. The resulting clastic rocks, like the sediments, are

In some clastic rocks, grains look like they have been glued together. This sample of the Pottsville Sandstone has large, easy-to-see, sand-sized grains that are cemented together by minerals. The texture becomes diffi-cult to recognize when the grains are smaller, such as in other clastic rocks like siltstone, mudstone, and shale, and can't be seen with the naked eye.

classified by the size of the clasts. From largest to smallest clasts, the rocks are conglomerate, sandstone, and mudstone or shale, some of the most common rocks at the surface in West Virginia

Producing clastic rocks ultimately requires a source area for the sediments, the most common of which is a mountainous region. In the absence of a source area, nonclastic sediments can accumulate in a basin either by the actions of organisms that secrete hard parts, like shells, bones, and teeth, or inorgani-cally by minerals precipitating out of water. The most common nonclastic rock is limestone, a rock composed of calcium carbonate. One nonclastic rock that does not quite fit into this simplified scheme is coal, one of the most impor-tant rocks to the cultural and economic history of the Mountain State. It forms when thick accumulations of plant material are buried by younger sediments that produce the necessary pressure and heat to compact and alter that plant material at depth.

Metamorphic rocks are any preexisting rock, called a *parent rock*, that is altered or changed by increased heat and/or pressure, most often at depth. The type of metamorphic rock produced depends on the composition of the parent rock, thus what you end up with is dependent on what you start with. Although metamorphic rocks can be found at great depth under the sedimentary layers in West Virginia, they are very rare at the surface, restricted to a thin band in the very easternmost part of the state.

Many limestones contain fossils or grains that are easy to see, such as in this sample from the Helderberg Group. Like clastic rocks, if the grains are too small to see, the rocks can have a rather nondescript appearance.

The black color and blocky fracture pattern makes coal easy to spot in outcrops. It is also less dense than rocks composed of minerals and feels much lighter when held.

Geologic Time

The vast expanse of geologic time is recorded in rocks, generally called the *rock record*. Just as in our everyday lives, geologic time can be either *relative*, which puts events in the order in which they occurred, or *absolute*, in which a numerical age is assigned to an event. Absolute ages are determined using *radiometric dating*, a suite of techniques that utilizes radioactive variations, or *isotopes,* of some isotopes. Generally speaking, radioactive isotopes are imperfect creations of nature. Unlike stable isotopes, radioactive isotopes fall apart, or *decay,* over time from the initial radioactive isotope, called a *parent*, to a stable isotope, called a *daughter.* The decay of isotopes occurs at a consistent, known rate over time. Thus geologists can measure the ratio of parent to daughter atoms initially trapped in the crystal structure of minerals when they formed. This ratio yields the absolute age of the magma or lava—that is, how long ago it solidified. Because the Earth initially solidified from liquid, geologists have been able to determine the age of the Earth and solar system.

Prior to the discovery of and application of radioactivity, geologists had to determine the relative ages of events by studying stacked sequences of layered sedimentary rocks, the study of which is called *stratigraphy*. A series of guiding principles of stratigraphy was developed in part by Nicolaus Steno (1638–1686), the most basic of which is the *law of superposition*, which states that in any undisturbed stack of sedimentary layers, the oldest layer lies at the bottom and the youngest is located at the top. Another useful law is that of *original*

Sediments and the layered rocks they form are generally horizontal, parallel to the Earth's surface, where the sediments accumulated.

Sedimentary rock layers that are tilted at an angle to the surface have been deformed, or folded, by tectonic stress after the layers were deposited, such as in these beds of the Mauch Chunk Formation.

horizontality, which assumes that all sedimentary rocks were deposited horizontally. If they are tilted or *dipping*, that must have been the result of a later tectonic event.

In addition to Steno's laws, another important guiding principle of stratigraphy is Walther's Law, developed by Johannes Walther in the late 1800s. It states that the environments recorded in sedimentary layers that are stacked vertically in the rock record were likely located next to each other at the time of deposition. If the environments could not have occurred next to each other, for instance desert sediments lying above a deep-sea deposit, then a gap in the rock record exists. This principle permits geologists to reconstruct the original lateral relationships between environments almost as if they were looking at a map of the ancient Earth while the sediments were still accumulating.

To visualize Walther's Law, imagine standing on a sandy beach looking out over the ocean. If sea level were to rise, what geologists call a *transgression*, progressively deeper water, with low-energy currents, would shift landward and deposit smaller, mud-sized grains on top of the beach sand. Environments that were adjacent are now recorded vertically in rocks as a *fining-upward sequence*, meaning the clasts get smaller upward. If sea level were to fall instead, what geologists call a *regression*, the high-energy currents and shallow water conditions on the beach would come to rest upon finer muds deposited offshore and produce a *coarsening-upward sequence*. Thus, changes in sea level that occurred in the past can be inferred by the presence of fining- or coarsening-upward sequences. The law may also be applied to other environments, such as river systems, that shift laterally across the Earth's surface.

Within the framework of these laws and patterns, fossils can be used to increase the resolution of relative geologic time. Biological evolution has produced a consistent vertical order of the appearance and extinction of organisms over time. Thus, fossils can be used to determine the sequence in which the rocks containing them were deposited. Normally, boundaries between time units are established using *index fossils,* or *guide fossils.* These fossils are generally abundant, easy to identify, and found over a large geographic area. These features make them relatively easy for geologists to find in many parts of the world. Another defining characteristic of an index fossil is that the organism existed for a relatively short period of time. For example, an organism that lived for only a few million years can provide stronger evidence that the rock layer in which it is found dates from a more specific time period than can a fossil of an organism that lived for many tens of millions of years. Typically, index fossils are marine, their habitats being the extensive oceans and seas of the world.

While it may not seem as precise as absolute time, the order of fossils was first used as the raw data for the geologic time scale, where segments of time are placed into a hierarchical classification that can be universally applied to rocks all over the world. Only after the relative ages had been determined were absolute ages applied to the time scale.

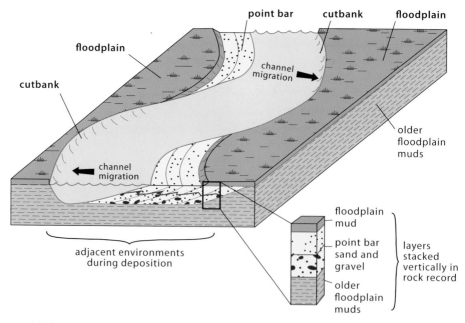

Walther's Law allows geologists to interpret the original lateral relationships of some depositional environments based on the vertical order of sedimentary rock layers. In the case of a meandering stream, the migration of the channel causes sand and gravel bars to accumulate over older mud deposited on the floodplain and, in turn, to be covered by younger floodplain muds.

SYSTEM	ROCK FORMATION (Northern Basin/Southern Basin)	DEPOSITIONAL ENVIRONMENT	EVENT
PENNSYLVANIAN / PERMIAN	Dunkard Group *(ALLEGHANIAN CLASTIC WEDGE)*	Clastic and minor peat deposition continues without the periodic sea level changes; the growth of plants in the coastal swamps is greatly reduced in the more arid, continental climate of Pangea; economically important coals no longer occur in the rock record.	final assembly of Pangea
PENNSYLVANIAN	Monongahela Formation, Conemaugh Group, Allegheny Formation, Pottsville Sandstone/Group	Thick peat deposits form coal as the melting and buildup of glaciers causes cyclic episodes of sea level rise that flood the coastal plain, depositing marine clastics and minor amounts of cabonate sediment.	Late Paleozoic ice age
DEVONIAN / MISSISSIPPIAN / MISSISSIPPIAN	Mauch Chunk Formation/Group	Clastic river and alluvial plain deposits with occasional marine carbonate layers.	Alleghanian Orogeny
	Greenbrier Limestone/Group	Carbonate sediments accumulate in a warm, shallow tropical sea.	
	Price Formation	Coastal plain and nearshore clastic deposition.	
DEVONIAN	Hampshire Formation, Foreknobs Formation, Brallier Formation, Harrell Shale, Mahantango Shale, Marcellus Shale, Needmore Shale *(CATSKILL CLASTIC WEDGE)*	Clastic sediments continue to accumulate in nearshore shelf and coastal plain environments. Clastic sediments shed from the Acadian Mountains accumulate in a series of offshore to nearshore marine environments in a pattern similar to the series deposited during the Taconic Orogeny.	Acadian Orogeny
	Oriskany Sandstone	Clastic shallow marine and beach settings.	
SILURIAN / DEVONIAN	Helderberg Group	Coral reefs and other carbonate-producing marine organisms thrive in a shallow sea.	passive margin
	Tonoloway Limestone, Wills Creek Formation, Williamsport Formation, McKenzie Formation, Rochester Shale, Keefer Sandstone, Rose Hill Formation, Tuscarora Sandstone *(QUEENSTON CLASTIC WEDGE)*	The inland sea becomes increasingly isolated from the open ocean. Salt deposits accumulate on tidal flats covered by microbial mats and form layers within cabonate sediments. Clastic coastal and shallow water environments persist in and around the inland sea as the Taconic Mountains are eroded.	
ORDOVICIAN	Juniata Formation, Martinsburg Shale, Trenton Group, Black River Group, St. Paul Group, Beekmantown Group	Clastic sediments shed from the Taconic Mountains accumulate in a series of offshore to nearshore marine environments in a shallow inland sea. Carbonate deposition continues in a warm, shallow sea.	Taconic Orogeny
CAMBRIAN	Conococheague Formation, Elbrook Formation, Waynesboro Formation, Tomstown Dolostone, Antietam Formation, Harpers Formation, Weverton Formation	Carbonate sediments accumulate in tropical settings as microbial mats cover broad tidal flats and parts of the shallow continental shelf. River and lake sediments give way to beach and shallow marine sands as global sea level rises rand the shoreline passes over West Virginia.	passive margin
PROTEROZOIC	Catoctin Formation, Swift Run Formation	Volcanic rocks, including lava flows mixed with sand and gravels eroded from rift valley walls and carried by rivers; lakes may have covered lowlands in the rift.	rifting and breakup of Rodinia
	Grenville crystalline rocks		Grenville Orogeny; assembly of Rodinia

Order and origin of the rock layers in West Virginia. Oldest rocks are located at the bottom and the youngest are on the top, in keeping with the order in which they were laid down. Layers laid down during times of mountain building and erosion are highlighted.

GEOLOGIC HISTORY OF WEST VIRGINIA

Inasmuch as it is important to understand the basic tenets of geology outlined above, the application of this knowledge to the physical rock record is far more exciting. It brings the inanimate rocks and fossils to life, each telling a story about what the Earth was like in the past. Understanding how to read these stories empowers humans to comprehend the timing and range of events that have shaped and continue to shape the planet. Perhaps more importantly, this knowledge fuels our curiosity to understand our existence within the context of the enormity of Earth's history. In order to simplify the vastness of time, we will divide the geologic history of West Virginia into three stages of development to provide travelers a solid understanding of the sequence of events that determined the state's rocks and, ultimately, its landforms.

LAYING THE FOUNDATION
Proterozoic time to 460 million years ago

The assembly of the continent that contains modern-day West Virginia began early in Earth's history. Like other continents, ours was initially assembled in the Archean and Proterozoic Eons, as smaller pieces of continental crust, riding on tectonic plates, collided with and joined one another. Each collision, called an *orogeny*, produced mountain chains, volcanism, and metamorphism where the continents overlapped and deformed the existing rock layers. One such event was the Grenville Orogeny, which occurred from 1.3 to 1.0 billion years ago and contributed to the assembly of the ancient supercontinent Rodinia. Although no Grenville-age rocks are exposed at the surface in West Virginia, the eroded surface of the crust added during that orogeny serves as the stable continental mass, or *basement*, upon which the sediments that make up West Virginia's surface rocks were deposited.

Like all supercontinents, Rodinia eventually broke apart, or *rifted*, during the last part of the Proterozoic Eon, from about 680 to 550 million years ago. The earliest stages of rifting, which occurred east of modern-day West Virginia, stretched the Grenville-age basement rocks. As they were stretched, large extensional fractures, called *normal faults*, developed in the crust, causing parts of it to slide down into a basin. The stretching produced a broad, flat-bottomed

A. RIFTING OF RODINIA
Late Proterozoic (680–550 million years ago)

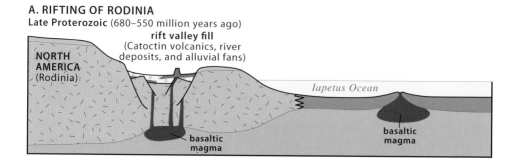

B. PASSIVE MARGIN
Middle Cambrian to Middle Ordovician (500–460 million years ago)

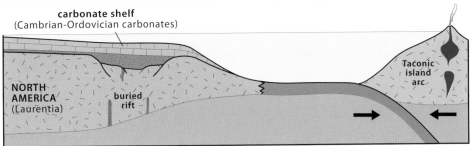

C. TACONIC OROGENY
Late Ordovician to Silurian (460–435 million years ago)

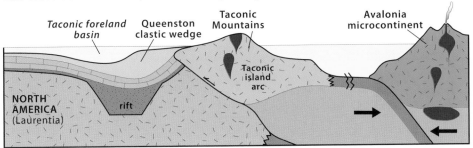

D. ACADIAN OROGENY
Middle Devonian to Middle Mississippian (380–340 million years ago)

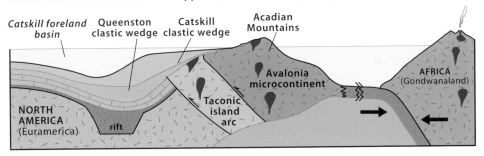

A. The breakup of Rodinia forms rift valleys and the Iapetus Ocean. Alluvial fan gravels and sands, along with lavas, cover the valley bottoms of the rifts and are the first layers to cover the Grenville-age basement rocks in present-day West Virginia. **B.** A broad, shallow water carbonate bank forms along the margin of Laurentia as a newly formed island arc approaches from the Iapetus Ocean. **C.** Collision of the island arc forms the Taconic Mountains, which load the edge of the Laurentian margin, forming the Taconic foreland basin. Sediments eroded from the mountains accumulate in the Queenston clastic wedge. **D.** In a similar style of convergence, the Avalonia microcontinent collides with Laurentia. Along with another large continental fragment to the north, the addition of these terranes enlarges Laurentia enough for it to earn a new name, Euramerica. Like the Taconic Orogeny, the addition of the Avalonia microcontinent forms a mountain range and a foreland basin, where sediments are deposited as the Catskill clastic wedge.
(Figure and caption continued on the following page.)

E. ALLEGHANIAN OROGENY
Late Mississippian to Permian (330–250 million years ago)

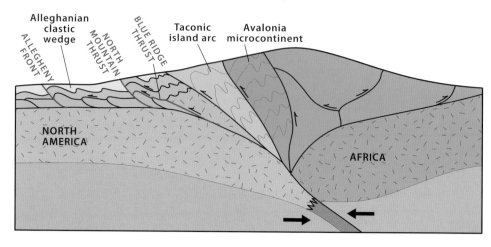

F. PASSIVE MARGIN
Today

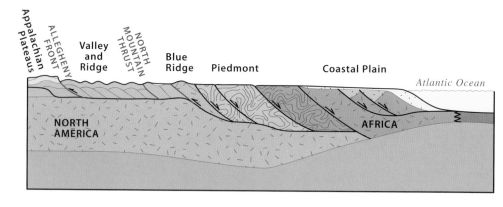

E. The African portion of Gondwanaland collides with Euramerica in the Alleghanian Orogeny, which along with other Paleozoic continental collisions assembles the supercontinent Pangea. Because this event involved two very large continental masses, the crust became very thick, forming the ancestral Appalachian Mountains. Sediments eroded from these mountains were deposited mainly in continental environments instead of the marine foreland basin environments that characterized the Taconic and Catskill clastic wedges. *F.* North America and the Atlantic Ocean emerge from the breakup of Pangea in the Mesozoic Era. Although the eastern seaboard is now a passive margin, erosion of the ancestral Appalachians causes uplift that promotes further erosion and sculpts the modern Appalachian Mountains. –Modified from Means, 2010

rift valley, similar to the East African Rift located in part in present-day Ethiopia. The valley began to fill rapidly with sediments as its walls were weathered and eroded. The rate of erosion is thought to have been accelerated during this time because several episodes of worldwide glaciation occurred between about 900 and 600 million years ago, increasing rates of weathering and erosion. The resulting sediments were carried by rivers and accumulated along the edges of the valley walls in large lobe-shaped piles called *alluvial fans*. Because the sediments were deposited very close to their source, they are composed of grains ranging from sand sized to large gravels, forming the conglomerates and sandstones of the Swift Run Formation of the Proterozoic Eon.

A side effect of rifting and thinning of the crust is that pressure is released on the underlying mantle, generating magmas. After the initial accumulation of the Swift Run gravels, these magmas migrated through fractures, producing extensive lava flows of the Catoctin Formation within the rift valleys. The lavas and alluvial fans began to build up simultaneously, alternating, or *interfingering*, with one another along the valley edges.

The rifting eventually produced the continent of Laurentia and initiated the opening of the Iapetus Ocean. West Virginia was located on Laurentia's *continental shelf*, the part of the continent that was covered by shallow water along the edge of the new ocean. As the Iapetus Ocean continued to widen, the land that would become West Virginia drifted farther away from the focus of rifting, becoming a tectonically quiet passive margin. The newly separated continents, which were heated near the rift, cooled and became denser as they moved away from the focus of rifting and slowly sank into the asthenosphere.

As they sank, or *subsided*, more and more of the continental surface was covered by the oceans, which invaded the rift valleys and crept upward to the adjacent highlands. The freshwater and land-based, or *terrestrial*, settings, collectively called continental environments, were replaced by saltwater, or marine, environments. This transition is recorded in the oldest rocks of latest Proterozoic to Early Cambrian age in West Virginia.

The subsidence also generated the necessary room for vast amounts of calcium carbonate sediment to accumulate on the passive margin almost continuously from the latest Early Cambrian to earliest Middle Ordovician time. The carbonate sediments were later transformed into a thick sequence of rocks, collectively known as the Cambro-Ordovician carbonates.

MOUNTAINS AND SEAS
460 to 250 million years ago

The second stage in West Virginia's geologic history began about 460 million years ago in the Late Ordovician Period of the Paleozoic Era, when the eastern margin of Laurentia was transformed from a passive to an active margin as the other plates moved toward it and the Iapetus Ocean slowly began to close. As the name implies, such margins are tectonically active. For the next 200 million years or so, West Virginia was in the shadow of a series of mountain ranges produced by three Paleozoic collisional events along this active margin: the Late Ordovician Taconic Orogeny, Middle Devonian Acadian Orogeny, and Pennsylvanian to Permian Alleghanian Orogeny.

A common outcome of mountain building begins with increased weight on the nearby crust, which causes it to subside, producing a *foreland basin* between the newly emerging mountain range and the stable interior of a continent. Within these basins, sediments shed from the mountains are carried by rivers, accumulating with the greatest thickness near the mountains and thinning farther away. Geologists refer to these accumulations as *clastic wedges*, so named after the asymmetrical, or wedge, shape of the clastic basin fill.

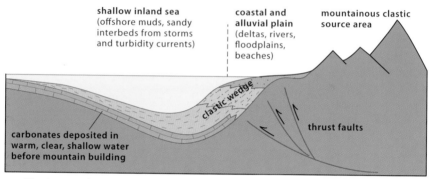

The forces of mountain building often shove slabs of crust into adjacent areas along thrust faults. The added weight of the slabs causes the crust to subside and can form a foreland basin. –Modified from Means, 2010

Each of the three Paleozoic orogenies produced a corresponding clastic wedge: the Taconic Orogeny produced the Queenston clastic wedge, the Acadian Orogeny the Catskill wedge, and the Alleghanian Orogeny the Alleghanian wedge. The three orogenies can thus be used to divide the sedimentary rock record of West Virginia into three cycles of mountain building, with each mountain range providing sources of clastic sediment. One interesting side effect of this correspondence is that even long after a mountain range is worn away, its presence can still be inferred from the sedimentary record by the presence of a clastic wedge.

The foreland basins in West Virginia's geological history contain a record of environments that range from continental to nearshore and offshore marine, where relatively shallow inland seas, known as *epicontinental seas*, covered parts of the basins. In contrast to oceans that have floors of thin oceanic crust and are thousands of feet deep, these inland seas rest upon continental crust and are only a few hundred feet deep. Epicontinental seas are rare today because much of the Earth's water is tied up in ice caps, but during warm climates of the past, these extensive, shallow seas extended over low-lying areas of continents. Hudson Bay is a modern example of an epicontinental sea. West Virginia was only in direct contact with a large, major ocean after the rifting of Rodinia in late Proterozoic time, and even then contact was limited to the shallow continental shelf.

The three orogenies and their corresponding clastic wedges dominate the state's rock record and account for the vast majority of the rocks at the surface. In between these wedges, passive margin conditions were established during which nonclastic sediments, usually composed of calcium carbonate, accumulated in shallow inland seas. Between the Taconic and Acadian events, from Late Silurian to Early Devonian time, carbonates of the Tonoloway Limestone through Helderberg Group were deposited. And between the Acadian and Alleghanian events, carbonates of the Middle Mississippian Greenbrier Limestone accumulated.

While each orogeny did produce a foreland basin in West Virginia, the effects of compressional forces varied in their extent and duration. During the Taconic and Acadian Orogenies, which lasted from 460 to 435 and from 380 to 340 million years ago, respectively, relatively small chunks of continental crust collided with the eastern margin of Laurentia. In both cases, the chunks were added, or *sutured*, to Laurentia, but the force of the collision did not reach as far west as West Virginia. However, the compressional forces produced during the Alleghanian Orogeny did extend into the Mountain State.

The Alleghanian event was a collision between two large continents, which shoved the rocks of eastern Laurentia more than 100 miles to the west along compressional fractures: either *thrust faults,* where the fracture plane was at a low angle (less than 30 degrees from horizontal), or more steeply angled *reverse faults.* The compression also squeezed the sedimentary rocks into a series of folds called *anticlines* and *synclines*. In anticlines, the layers are folded into an arch, while within adjacent synclines the rocks resemble the cross section of a bowl.

The Alleghanian Orogeny lasted from about 330 to about 250 million years ago, nearly twice as long as the Taconic and Acadian events. This lengthy event allowed enough time for the formation of the ancestral Appalachian Mountains as well as an associated foreland basin, the accumulation of the Alleghanian clastic wedge, and also the subsequent faulting and folding of the entire sequence of sedimentary rocks that had been forming since the latest Proterozoic Eon. This collision completed the assembly of the supercontinent Pangea that combined the world's continents into one large landmass and simultaneously closed the Iapetus Ocean. The land that became West Virginia was locked in the interior of Pangea until that landmass rifted.

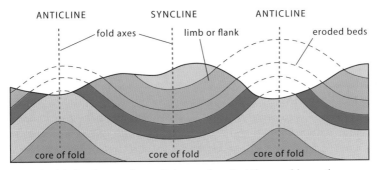

In this book, we often tell the readers that the road is on the limb, or flank, of a fold or that the road crosses a fold axis.
–Adapted from Spencer, C. 2011. *Roadside Geology of Missouri.*

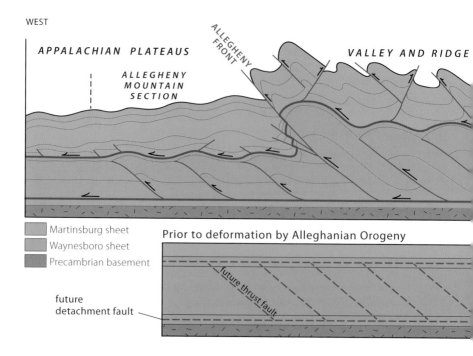

WEST

APPALACHIAN PLATEAUS

ALLEGHENY FRONT

VALLEY AND RIDGE

ALLEGHENY
MOUNTAIN
SECTION

Martinsburg sheet
Waynesboro sheet
Precambrian basement

Prior to deformation by Alleghanian Orogeny

future
detachment fault

future thrust fault

SHAPING THE MODERN LANDSCAPE
250 million years ago to present time

The development of the state's geology and topography began after the Alleghanian Orogeny came to a close some 250 million years ago. The region became an erosional landscape, even as Pangea broke apart about 180 million years ago, and the Atlantic Ocean opened, sending the continents as we know them today toward their current positions. The younger rock layers deposited during the Paleozoic and, possibly, Mesozoic Eras were partially eroded. Their removal had an important side effect. As the mass of the continent was reduced, the lithosphere slowly began to rise, a phenomenon known as *isostatic adjustment.* This elevated the remaining rocks, increased the rate of erosion, and sculpted a new mountain range: the modern Appalachian Mountains.

Although they are often referred to as one of the older mountain ranges on Earth, the Appalachians as a landform are geologically very young, having evolved to their current shape during the shifting climates of the last 10 million years or so. Confusion about their age is certainly understandable and likely exists because the rocks into which these young mountains are carved are rather old, their sediments having been deposited before the end of the Paleozoic Era over 250 million years ago. But the age of the rocks only represents a maximum age for the mountains because they could not have existed before the originally flat-lying rocks were deposited, and much has happened to those rocks since that time. The layers were buried to a depth of thousands of feet, deformed by compression in the Alleghanian Orogeny, and finally uplifted to the surface as the younger rocks above were removed.

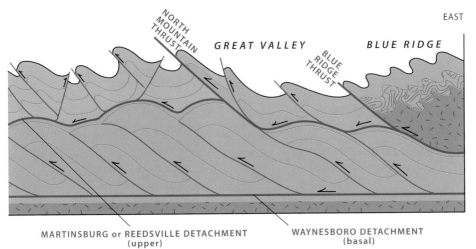

EAST

NORTH MOUNTAIN THRUST

GREAT VALLEY

BLUE RIDGE

BLUE RIDGE THRUST

MARTINSBURG or REEDSVILLE DETACHMENT
(upper)

WAYNESBORO DETACHMENT
(basal)

The force of the collision during the Alleghanian Orogeny caused nearly horizontal thrust faults, or detachments, to propagate through weak rock layers, permitting large slabs of rock to slide upward and to the west. The lower slab, called the Waynesboro sheet, is composed of rigid limestone layers that broke into sections and were stacked like dominos. The upper slab, the Martinsburg sheet, contains mostly soft shales, which were heavily folded and faulted. –Kulander and Dean, 1966

The series of events described above led to the current bedrock geology of West Virginia, which is dominated by a single feature, the Appalachian Basin. The basin, floored by continental crust, contains the sum of rock layers deposited during the Paleozoic Era. These rocks were compressed during the Alleghanian Orogeny into what appears at the surface as an elongated bull's-eye pattern with its center along the northwestern region of the state in the vicinity of the Ohio River. Any cross section of the Appalachian Basin is essentially the same as that of a syncline: the youngest rocks in the middle and the oldest rocks along the edges. As a result, the youngest rocks are exposed in West Virginia extend from about 20 miles north of Wheeling in the northern panhandle to approximately the course of the Kanawha (pronounced "kuh-NAW") River north of Charleston. Moving in any direction away from this center is to move into regions of progressively older rocks.

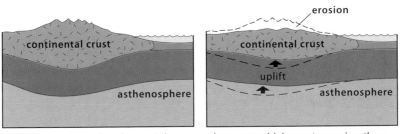

Young compressional mountain ranges have very thick crust, causing them to ride higher on the asthenosphere (left). Over time, erosion reduces the crust's thickness, causing it to bob upward (right).

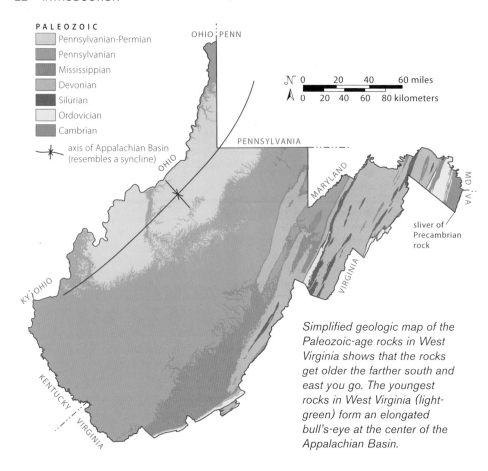

PALEOZOIC
- Pennsylvanian-Permian
- Pennsylvanian
- Mississippian
- Devonian
- Silurian
- Ordovician
- Cambrian

✳ axis of Appalachian Basin (resembles a syncline)

N 0   20   40   60 miles
0   20   40   60   80 kilometers

OHIO ¦ PENN

PENNSYLVANIA

OHIO

MARYLAND

MD ¦ VA

sliver of Precambrian rock

VIRGINIA

KY ¦ OHIO

KENTUCKY ¦ VIRGINIA

Simplified geologic map of the Paleozoic-age rocks in West Virginia shows that the rocks get older the farther south and east you go. The youngest rocks in West Virginia (light-green) form an elongated bull's-eye at the center of the Appalachian Basin.

One final point needs to be made about the geological history not only of West Virginia but of Earth itself: nearly every process that has been described in this introduction is still at work on both the geology and the topography of this state and the larger world and will continue into the future. The planet we inhabit is as much in flux now as it was in the past. Understandably, it may be difficult for some to connect their own lived experience with the developments set forth here, that in the course of several billion years the current shape of the land and the vast array of rocks that compose it developed.

To make such connections requires, first, recognition of the kinds of forces that are in play. For West Virginia, two of the most important are weathering and erosion, which in combination have shaped the state's topography. Water trapped in crevices in rocks can freeze and expand, causing those rocks to break apart in the same way potholes form on roads. The pieces of splintered rock can erode downslope where they may accumulate on the land surface. However, such accumulations are short-lived, as any material above sea level is considered by geologists to be in temporary storage until other processes move it below sea level and out of the reach of water or wind currents that would otherwise continue to redistribute the material. This is apparent after any heavy rainstorm in the state, when most rivers and streams run brown with loose sediments washed off the land adjacent to their courses. Melting snows at the end of winters have a similar impact but over a matter of weeks. However long such runoff lasts, the material it transports downstream alters the local topography, and the elevation of some portion of the land is lowered. On larger time scales, meandering streams widen their valleys or change course altogether and in doing so move still more sediment downstream.

Beyond natural forces, human influence is also observable, though on a much shorter time scale. Buildings, agriculture, coal mines, and roads all generally require modification of the land. Oftentimes, vegetation is stripped and dirt and rock is broken up and moved, which increases the rates of natural weathering and erosion. For example, in many places the highway system within the state has been carved into the sides of valleys and hills. Those roadcuts increase the angle of slopes near the roads and are prone to landslides, another way in which the land is reshaped by erosion. Taken together, and given enough time, these forces can wear mountains away completely, but time is the key.

Indeed, a comprehension of geologic time is essential to linking the past with the present. One must learn to accommodate the idea that geologic history extends back several *billion* years to the formation of the Earth itself (note: "one billion" expressed numerically requires nine zeros to the left of the decimal point and to the right of the number one: 1,000,000,000). While the erosional events just mentioned may seem trivial when viewed in isolation, when placed within this vast expanse of time their power to alter both geology and topography begins to make more sense. Visualizing such a time scale, as well as the types of forces at work within it, can go a long way to helping one make sense of the incredible succession of developments that make up the history of the geology of any region of the planet. Nowhere is this more the case than in the Mountain State.

View to the north of several roadcuts that line US 19 along the north slope of Powell Mountain of the Appalachian Plateaus.

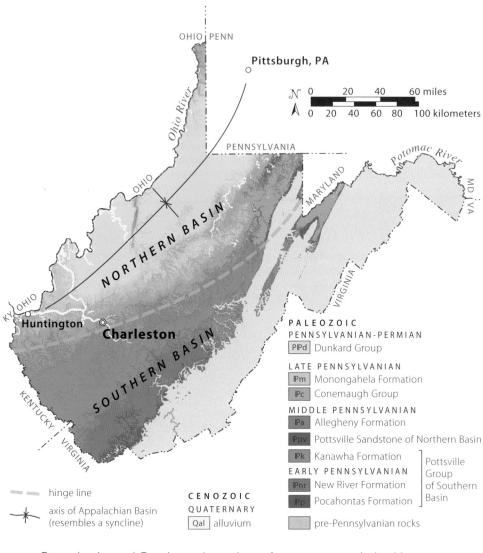

Pennsylvanian and Permian rocks at the surface get progressively older away from the axis of the Appalachian Basin. The youngest rocks are mapped in light green and become darker green the older they are. The hinge line, a coal-poor zone, forms the border between the Northern and Southern Basins. –Modified from Fedorko and Skema, 2011

APPALACHIAN PLATEAUS PROVINCE

More than three-quarters of the Mountain State is located on the westward-tilted landscape of the Appalachian Plateaus Province. The lower western part of the province has developed on the younger, gently folded portion of the Appalachian Basin, where the degree of dip in the rock layers is so low that they often appear to lie horizontally where exposed along the highways. This pattern changes to the east on the Allegheny Mountain Section of the Appalachian Plateaus, where increased stress from the Alleghanian Orogeny folded the layers to a greater degree. There, the dip of the strata is more noticeable and the greater uplift elevated the landscape.

The Appalachian Plateaus Province in West Virginia is further subdivided into two basins, of which the northern one constitutes more than half of the province within the state. While the Northern and Southern Basins do contain some of the same rock formations, there are considerable differences, especially in the oldest and youngest rocks in the sedimentary record of each region, so much so that the Northern Basin can be thought of as the younger and the Southern Basin the older of the two. In fact, almost all of the numerous coal beds mined in the Southern Basin are older than their counterparts to the north. The boundary between the two basins occupies a relatively coal-poor zone that runs through Charleston in a northeasterly direction and extends all the way to western Maryland. It has been historically referred to as the "hinge line."

West Virginia has sixty-two mineable coal beds. The vertical repetition of coal beds brings several inherent and often puzzling aspects of stacked sedimentary rocks to light. The formation of coal, like many other sedimentary rocks, requires that a unique set of environmental conditions be present at the Earth's surface. Thus, the fact that coal appears again and again in the rocks indicates that the same environment appeared over and over again in the past. Geologists have recognized similar repetition of layers in Pennsylvanian rocks in other parts of the world and use the term *cyclothem* to describe packages of repeated layers. The other often puzzling aspect of the coals is how quickly the original peat deposits were buried under younger sediments, preserving them before they could decay or erode away. Gradual subsidence of the landscape during the accumulation of the peat explains the quick burial.

Much of the peat accumulated in low-lying coastal swamps between meandering rivers draining the rising ancestral Appalachian Mountains to the southeast. As the mountains rose during the Alleghanian Orogeny, the crust in this area was forced downward. If the areas had not subsided, the rivers would

Alternating shale and sandstones of the Kanawha Formation along the King Coal Highway southeast of Williamson.

have eventually migrated back and forth across the swamps, carved into the peat deposits, and washed them away. With gradual subsidence, the accumulating river and swamp deposits were buried before the active rivers could shift back across the surface and remove them.

The total amount of subsidence in the Appalachian Basin also needs to be considered here. The coal seams in West Virginia are bituminous, produced when the peat deposits were exposed to increased heat and pressure consistent with a burial depth of 1 to 2 miles below the surface. Subsequently, the rocks were later uplifted by isostatic adjustment when erosion removed most the overlying material.

Cyclothems of the Pennsylvanian Period

A *cyclothem* is a series of beds of sedimentary rock deposited in recurring sequences, or cycles. They are characteristic of Pennsylvanian rocks in many parts of the world. Geologists attribute these cycles to changes in the volume of extensive ice sheets that occupied Gondwanaland, a large landmass in the southern hemisphere during the Late Pennsylvanian Period. As in the current ice age, the extent of glaciers changed periodically in response to changes in climate. When the ice volume increased, the volume of water in the world's oceans would decrease, causing a drop in sea level called a *regression*. As this happened, continental environments such as rivers, floodplains, and lakes followed the retreating shoreline. When the ice volume decreased, the water would return to the world's oceans, causing a sea level rise, or a *transgression*. This would often drown the low-lying coastal environments with saltwater and establish marine environments on top of them.

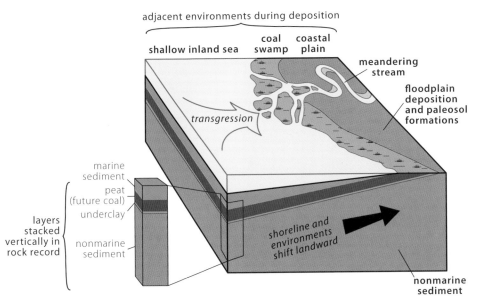

Development of the transgressive, or rising sea level, part of a Pennsylvanian cyclothem showing the application of Walther's Law: adjacent environments during deposition can often be stacked in the rock record.

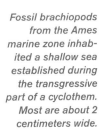

Fossil brachiopods from the Ames marine zone inhabited a shallow sea established during the transgressive part of a cyclothem. Most are about 2 centimeters wide.

The resulting succession of rocks in a cyclothem is a perfect example of Walther's Law, which states that environments that were originally next to each other—nearshore marine and coastal swamps or rivers—are now stacked vertically in the rock record. Within the Conemaugh Group is one of the more well-developed cyclothems in West Virginia. The complete cyclothem includes (from base to top) the Pittsburgh red beds (exposed floodplain deposits), Harlem coal (coastal swamp deposits), and the laterally extensive Ames marine zone (nearshore and offshore marine deposits), the top of which was eroded by a river that deposited the Grafton Sandstone during the next cycle.

NORTHERN BASIN

The oldest rocks in the Northern Basin are assigned to the Pottsville Sandstone, deposited during the Middle Pennsylvanian Period. The Southern Basin also contains this unit, but the characteristics of its rocks are much different. For one, the Pottsville in the Northern Basin is about 200 to 300 feet thick, while in the Southern Basin it is over 3,000 feet thick. In addition, the thinner Pottsville in the Northern Basin is a single, undivided stratigraphic formation, whereas its counterpart in the Southern Basin has been elevated to group status and divided into distinct formations, discussed in detail in the introduction to the Southern Basin.

The youngest rocks in the Northern Basin, and in the state, are assigned to the Dunkard Group, which spans the boundary between the Pennsylvanian and Permian Periods. In fact, geologists often use the term *Dunkard Basin* as a synonym for the Northern Basin. The Dunkard Group and Monongahela

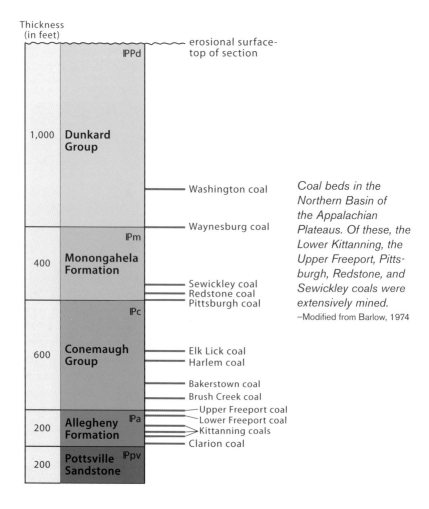

Coal beds in the Northern Basin of the Appalachian Plateaus. Of these, the Lower Kittanning, the Upper Freeport, Pittsburgh, Redstone, and Sewickley coals were extensively mined.
–Modified from Barlow, 1974

Formation are completely absent from the Southern Basin, and the youngest rocks exposed are from the Conemaugh Group of Late Pennsylvanian age.

In Late Pennsylvanian time, West Virginia had been elevated above sea level by the Alleghanian Orogeny. While the mountains lay to the east and southeast, environments in this region were established on a gently sloping, low-relief landscape that drained to the northwest. Thus, the Dunkard Group rocks were deposited during a succession of continental environments in either freshwater or terrestrial settings, including shallow lakes, peat swamps, and meandering streams. The appearance of these environments seems to have been largely controlled by climate, which is one of the most important variables influencing the types of environments that exist on land. During wet, humid times, lakes developed on low areas in the region. These lakes alternated between freshwater peat swamps, which eventually became coal beds, and limy bodies of water when increasing rates of evaporation during dry periods led to calcium carbonate precipitation on the lake bottoms. Periodically draining into these lakes were meandering streams flowing from the highlands to the east. These streams are represented by either sandstones that developed in and around the active stream channels or by shales that developed from mud deposited on the adjacent floodplains.

The Dunkard Group contains, from oldest to youngest, the Waynesburg, the Washington, and (part of the) Greene Formations. Where the precise boundary of the Pennsylvanian and Permian Periods is located in this part of the country remains one of the unsolved mysteries of the geologic record, not only in West Virginia but also in many other parts of the world. The index fossils used to define the Pennsylvanian-Permian boundary are the jaws of ancient marine fish. However, most of the rocks in the Dunkard Group were deposited in continental environments such as rivers, floodplains, and lakes, and no marine index fossils have been found within them. Furthermore, many of the fossils contained in the Dunkard Group lived throughout the period that encompasses the Pennsylvanian-Permian boundary and thus cannot be used to designate it. Although tentative, the consensus among geologists today, based on terrestrial and freshwater fossils, is that the Waynesburg and Washington Formations in the Dunkard Group are Pennsylvanian and that the uppermost rocks in the Greene Formation are Permian.

The rock types within the Dunkard Group include sandstone; siltstone; black, gray, green, and red shale; limestone; and thin, impure coals. Like the older Pennsylvanian units below, these rock types seem to occur in repeating sequences that reflect the cyclic nature of environments that existed at the time. However, unlike the Pennsylvanian cycles that record changes in sea level, the Dunkard cycles are thought to represent shifting climates, with the base of the cycle having been deposited during a wet period and the top of the cycle during a dryer one.

With all the repetition of similar rock types among the Pennsylvanian units, it can be difficult to distinguish the different formations, even for the trained geologist. Fortunately, along with several other units in the rock record, the Conemaugh Group, Monogahela Formation, and Dunkard Group can be identified in part by the presence of red shale and mudstone, termed *red beds*, that were originally floodplain muds accumulating next to rivers at the time. As they were exposed to the atmosphere, the muds weathered and were converted to soils. During this process, oxygen bonded with iron in the sediments, producing hematite, a reddish-brown mineral. In effect, these rocks can be thought of as fossilized soils, and geologists refer to them as *paleosols,* or ancient soils. The presence of hematite indicates that the climate during the Late Pennsylvanian was more arid than that during the Early to Middle Pennsylvanian Period. In a humid climate the iron would have been leached from the sediments, limiting the development of hematite and producing the gray to green shale layers common in formations of the Early and Middle Pennsylvanian Period.

The shape of the land through which roads in the Appalachian Plateaus travel largely reflects the impact of weathering and erosion that has been under way since the land was initially uplifted in the Late Paleozoic. These processes will continue for the foreseeable future. Streams carving the landscape are arranged in a dendritic drainage pattern, a consequence of their flowing over rocks with more or less equal resistance to the forces of erosion. In this case, most of the Appalachian Plateaus is covered by easily eroded shale, and as a consequence streams cut rapidly into the soft rocks, producing rounded hills and steep, narrow valleys. In addition, shale weathers, or breaks down, fairly quickly into mud, which is then transformed by organisms and the atmosphere into soils that provide a suitable substrate for the thick vegetation covering the rocks over most of the lower part of the Appalachian Plateaus Province.

Interstate 64
KENOVA—HUNTINGTON—CHARLESTON
58 miles

The westernmost point of West Virginia lies near the longitude of Detroit, Michigan, quite a ways west for a mid-Atlantic state. I-64 enters the state at that point, passing the town of Kenova, the name's three syllables referencing *Ken*tucky, *O*hio, and (West) *Va*rginia. For 10 miles or so, the interstate parallels the Ohio River, running on the south side of Huntington, the largest city in the state. It is named for Collis Potter Huntington, the financier who built the Chesapeake & Ohio Railway that originally terminated there.

As I-64 crosses the Big Sandy River and enters West Virginia, it passes over rocks of the Conemaugh Group, deposited some 300 million years ago in Late Pennsylvanian time. This unit is fairly common in the low portion of the Appalachian Plateaus, but this region contains a fairly complete section, including the Ames marine zone, a marine shale and limestone unit separating the Glenshaw and the Casselman Formations. You can see large exposures of the Casselman Formation around exit 11 and in many places in the Huntington area. The Casselman, unlike the Glenshaw Formation below, does not contain any marine units in this area and is largely composed of river channel sandstones, floodplain shales, and red beds, along with an occasional thin coal bed.

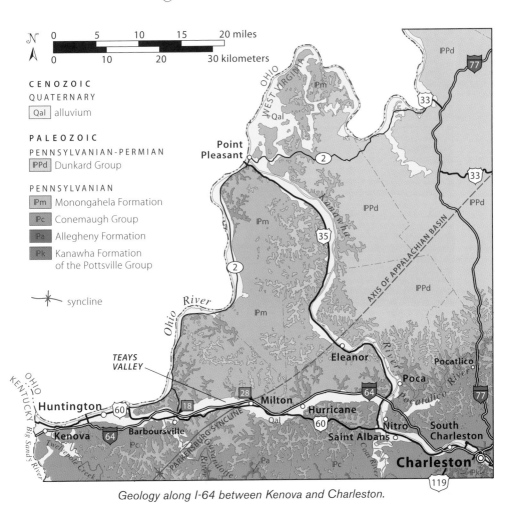

Geology along I-64 between Kenova and Charleston.

The rocks here are nearly horizontal, with only a slight dip to the southeast toward the axis of the Parkersburg Syncline near mile marker 25. At this point, the base of the overlying Monongahela Formation, marked by the Pittsburgh coal, occurs at road level. East of mile marker 25, exposures of the Monongahela Formation, which look much like the Casselman Formation with sandstone, shale, and red beds, continues until Charleston.

The bedrock, however, is not the highlight of this route. The main attraction is the valley the highway enters east of Huntington and follows all the way to Charleston. Known as the Teays Valley, named for an early white settler, it is a paleovalley with a long history pre-dating the glacial advances of the Pleistocene Epoch. I-64 runs along the north wall of the Teays Valley for much of the route between mile marker 18 and Charleston, and here and there are exposures of rocks deposited in Late Pennsylvanian time. At exit 18 for Barboursville, you can see sandstones of the Conemaugh Group.

Rivers often produce a characteristic lens-shaped body of sandstone similar to this one in the Conemaugh Group at exit 18 in Barboursville. The curved lower contact was produced by river currents eroding the older underlying shales.

Teays Valley

The Teays Valley is no ordinary valley. For one thing, it runs in a relatively straight line east to west. Most of the major rivers in this part of the Mountain State drain to the northwest, perpendicular to the Ohio River. For another, no single river occupies the valley. An examination of the succession of US Geological Survey topographic maps of the Teays Valley shows that here and there small rivers and streams flow across it from one side to the other, but that is all. None could be said to flow along it. The Teays Valley was carved before Pleistocene time by a river flowing west across what is now Ohio, Indiana, and Illinois.

Why is there no Teays River today? Because it was captured by another river system west of Charleston at the point where I-64 crosses the Kanawha River. In effect, the water that flowed westward through the ancient Teays Valley now flows to the northwest in the Kanawha River valley, terminating at the Ohio River near Point Pleasant, West Virginia. The event that caused this is termed a *stream capture*.

The capture of the ancient Teays River involved the advance of large ice sheets through central Ohio during the Pleistocene Epoch. The leading edge of one of the earliest blocked the westward flow of the Teays, creating a large glacial lake called Lake Teays or Lake Tight, named after William G. Tight, the

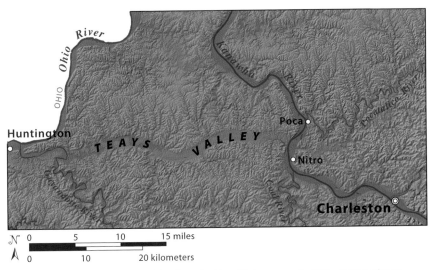

The shaded relief map of the Appalachian Plateaus west of Charleston shows the wide Teays Valley, comparable in size to the valley of the Kanawha River but lacking a significant stream.

Glacial advances during the Pleistocene led to the abandonment of the Teays Valley, which set the Kanawha River in its present, postglacial course, flowing north-northwest to join the Ohio River at Point Pleasant.

geologist who first recognized its former existence. As the Teays River flowed into the lake from the east, its current slowed, allowing up to 140 feet of fine silts and clays to settle to the bottom, a lake bed that now forms the valley floor from Huntington to Nitro. The accumulation of silt and clay increased the elevation of the valley, making the postglacial river easy prey for capture by an adjacent river system of lower elevation. One scenario involves the nearby Pocatalico River, which was lower in elevation and did not receive the silt and clay that settled in Lake Teays at the time. After the ice retreated and the lake drained, a tributary of the Pocatalico River carved through the divide that had separated it from the Teays, captured that river, and established the modern course of the Kanawha River.

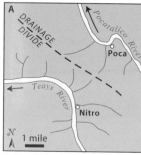  

A. Preglacial Teays River drainage map near Nitro, WV.

B. Thick silts deposited in Lake Teays to west slow Teays River and encourage meandering to northeast.

C. Tributary near Poca erodes into divide and captures the Teays tributary and river itself; modern, north-flowing course of the Kanawha River is established.

One possible scenario for the capture of the ancient Teays River and the establishment of the modern course of the Kanawha River to the Ohio River. —Modified from Welker, 1982

Interbedded river sandstones and floodplain shales in the Monongahela Formation at exit 28.

At exit 28 for Milton, exposures of younger rocks of the Monongahela Formation appear. On the west side of Charleston, particularly east of the highway crossing of the Kanawha River and west of its merger with I-77, you can see massive sandstones and thin shales of the Allegheny Formation, the presence of which signals that the highway is located on the hinge line separating the Northern and Southern Basins of the Appalachian Plateaus.

Interstate 70/Interstate 470
Pennsylvania State Line—Wheeling
13 miles

A major route from the central Midwest to the mid-Atlantic region of the East Coast, I-70 crosses the northern panhandle of the Mountain State. For many, this may be their first encounter with West Virginia, and if so, it is a brief one. Like many interstate highways, this one represents an "upgrade" from a previously constructed federal highway, in this instance US 40. That highway incorporated much of the route of the National Road, the country's first federally funded highway, constructed between 1811 and 1821. It linked Cumberland, Maryland, at the head of navigation on the Potomac River, with Wheeling, Virginia (as it then was known) on the Ohio. The National Road would later be extended across Ohio, Indiana, and Illinois, eventually reaching St. Louis on the Mississippi.

That Wheeling lay on its route probably had as much to do with the local terrain as any other consideration. On both sides of the valley are small streams that had cut their own valleys into this part of the Appalachian Plateaus at more or less right angles to the Ohio River. Both are named Wheeling Creek and flow into the Ohio opposite one another. Their valleys facilitated the construction of a highway having comparatively easy grades that afforded travelers, be they using horse- or ox-drawn wagons or automobiles and trucks, a relatively gradual descent into and ascent out of the Ohio River valley.

At the boundary separating Pennsylvania from West Virginia, just west of the town of West Alexandria, the elevation is 1,300 feet above sea level. At the point where I-70 crosses the Ohio River, it is 700 feet. That drop was made easier by the presence of one tributary of West Virginia's Wheeling Creek, known as Middle Wheeling Creek, a small stream that had carved a narrow valley dropping 500 feet in elevation in approximately 3 miles. Parallel to this route and no more than 1 mile to the north, US 40 and the original route of the Baltimore & Ohio Railroad made a similar descent down Little Wheeling Creek. The two streams merge near the town of Triadelphia, a few miles east of Wheeling.

Although the rocks along the route appear horizontal, they are tilted slightly to the southeast along the northwest limb of the Loudenville Syncline. The slight tilt exposes more units along the route than if the rocks were horizontal. Although the difference in elevation along the route is only 600 feet, the outcrops reveal nearly 900 feet of alternating, or *interbedded*, sandstone, siltstone, shale, limestone, and coal of the uppermost Conemaugh, all of the

Monongahela, and the lower part of the Dunkard Group, all of Late Pennsylvanian age.

For the first 5 miles west of the Pennsylvania state line, I-70 passes by vegetated outcrops of the Greene Formation of the Dunkard Group. As the road descends the steep gradient to the west, exposures of the Washington Formation, another component of the Dunkard Group, can be seen at mile markers 8.6 and 7. Limestone beds are visible among the shale and sandstone layers of the Washington Formation and tend to be light gray or tan and fracture in a brick-like pattern. Near the top of these exposures lies the Washington coal, the youngest coal bed mined in the Appalachian Basin, although it is no longer

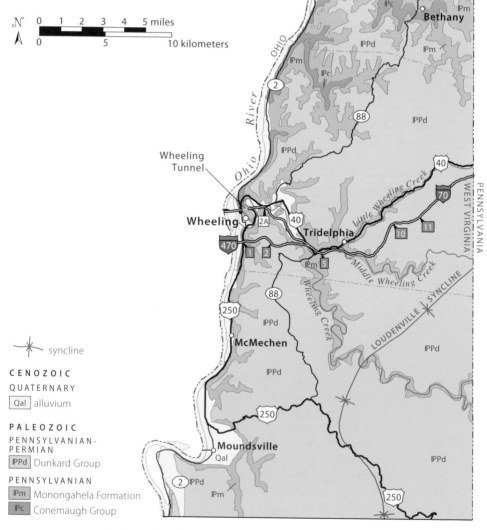

Geology along I-70 between Pennsylvania and Wheeling.

considered productive to mine. At the junction with the I-470 bypass, rocks of the underlying Monongahela Formation are visible.

While there is no noticeable difference between the rocks of the Dunkard Group and Monongahela Formation, mineable coals are more common in the Monongahela Formation, and they include the famous Pittsburgh coal that accounts for a significant proportion of the coal production in the Appalachian Basin. Abandoned mines in the Pittsburgh are located near the bridge over Wheeling Creek at mile marker 3.5, and the coal itself is exposed near mile marker 3. Half a mile east of the Ohio River, I-70 passes through the Wheeling Tunnel, which lies under a ridge located between Wheeling Creek and the river. The tunnel was bored into the base of the lower Pittsburgh Sandstone, and about 15 feet above the tunnel roof are abandoned mines of the Pittsburgh coal. On the west side of the bridge over the Ohio lies the boundary between Ohio and West Virginia.

The I-470 portion of this route ascends and descends through a similar sequence of rocks. After diverging from I-70 the route passes an old quarry, now a baseball field, where green shales in the Monongahela Formation are exposed. At the top of the hill near exit 2, beds of the Greene Formation mark the youngest rocks along this road. As I-470 descends, it drops back into the Monongahela Formation and, just east of where it crosses over WV 2, passes an exposure that includes several coal beds and the distinctive tan to yellow Benwood Limestone, which formed in one of the many ancient freshwater lakes in the region. Fossils of freshwater clams, snails, and fish are common in this unit.

Interstate 77
WILLIAMSTOWN—PARKERSBURG—CHARLESTON
86 miles

Interstate 77 enters West Virginia where it crosses the Ohio River just south of Marietta, Ohio. Because the rolling topography has few dramatic contrasts in elevation, there are few exposures to be seen. The rocks that do appear along the highway are of the Dunkard Group of Late Pennsylvanian to Permian age, mostly river-deposited sandstones with a few gray and red shales at mile markers 161, 150, and 120. These rivers are thought to have been established during the transitions from wet to dry climates as vegetation on land became scarce, and the rivers were able to erode and transport the sediment elsewhere. South of mile marker 120, the road descends from the Dunkard Group through rocks of the Monongahela Formation and Conemaugh Group, also of Late Pennsylvanian age, although the change is quite subtle as the rocks appear rather similar. Exposures of the Conemaugh Group become increasingly common as the route approaches Charleston, with a well-exposed section of sandstone and shale at mile marker 103.5.

Approximately 1 mile farther south, I-77 and I-79 merge in the valley of the Elk River, where rocks of the Conemaugh Group and the underlying

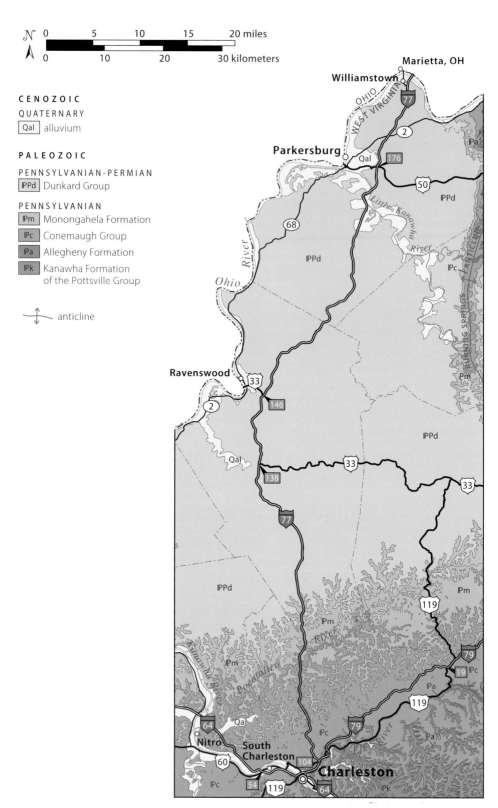

Geology along I-77 between Williamstown and Charleston.

One of the few exposures of river sandstones and the characteristic red mudstones of the Conemaugh Group on this stretch of I-77 is just north of the I-79 junction. The loose blocks of sandstone fell as the softer underlying mudstones and shales were eroded.

Middle Pennsylvanian Allegheny Formation are exposed along both sides of the highway. The two units contain massive sandstone beds and thick shale layers. The units can be distinguished from one another by the presence of red shale and mudstone, termed *red beds*, in the Conemaugh Group. The red beds were originally floodplain muds that accumulated next to rivers in Late Pennsylvanian time. As they were exposed to the atmosphere, the muds weathered and were converted to soils, and oxygen combined with iron to form the mineral hematite. Red beds are absent in the Allegheny Formation because a wetter climate in Middle Pennsylvanian time leached the iron from its sediments. Both the Allegheny Formation and Conemaugh Group are to be seen in several exposures as I-77 merges with I-64 and heads east and south through Charleston and up the valley of the Kanawha River, with tall cliffs of the massive Allegheny Formation sandstones becoming more common.

Interstate 79
PENNSYLVANIA STATE LINE—
MORGANTOWN—CHARLESTON
161 miles

This section of I-79 traverses the Northern Basin of the Appalachian Plateaus. Between the Pennsylvania border and exit 79 at Burnsville, I-79 crosses the northern West Virginia coalfield, which is an extension of that located in southwestern Pennsylvania. The first rocks to be seen are those of the Dunkard Group, which contain several coal beds, but they only hint at the extensive mining operations in this area. The principal target was and still is the Pittsburgh coal, which can be up to 10 or more feet thick. Between the state line and Morgantown, the route travels over a vast underground network of both active and former mines in the Pittsburgh and Sewickley coal beds of the Monongahela Formation, which lies just below the Dunkard and was deposited in Late Pennsylvanian time. Much of the region along the route has also been surface mined, creating oddly sculpted and often treeless hills.

On the east side of I-79, where it enters West Virginia at mile marker 160.5, appears an exposure of Waynesburg coal, which was surface mined west of the highway at mile marker 157.5. Note the grass-covered, stepped terrain of the former surface mine. This coal also marks the boundary between the Monongahela Formation and the overlying Dunkard Group. The peat that eventually became coal accumulated in poorly drained swamps near rivers. These swamps would have also served as the floodplains for the rivers, receiving mud and sand during floods. Thus, most of the coals, shales, and thin (less than 1 to 2 feet) sandstone beds with a flat base represent the floodplain portion of the river

Thick, multistory sandstone layers like this one in the Dunkard Group can be formed by the stacking of several river channels, which are outlined by a curved lower surface formed during erosion by the river's current.

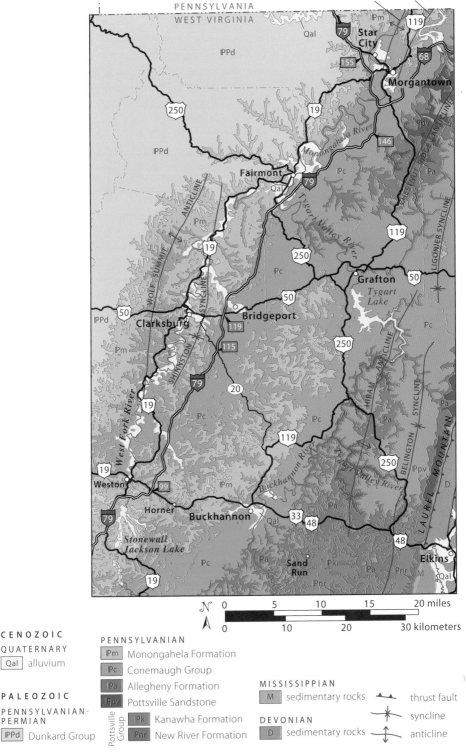

Geology along I-79 between Pennsylvania state line and Weston.
See map on page 47 for southern end of route.

CENOZOIC

QUATERNARY

Qal alluvium

PALEOZOIC

PENNSYLVANIAN-
PERMIAN

IPPd Dunkard Group

PENNSYLVANIAN

IPm Monongahela Formation

IPc Conemaugh Group

IPa Allegheny Formation

IPpv Pottsville Sandstone

IPk Kanawha Formation

IPnr New River Formation

Pottsville Group

MISSISSIPPIAN

M sedimentary rocks

DEVONIAN

D sedimentary rocks

▲▲ thrust fault

✳ syncline

↕ anticline

system. The river channels themselves are represented by thick (often tens of feet), cross-bedded sandstones that have an uneven, convex base produced by river currents scouring some of the older underlying floodplain sediments and peat. Many of these channel sandstones also have low-angle surfaces cutting diagonally across them that record the migration of point bars located on the inside curve of the ancient rivers' meander bends.

In addition to the mineral quartz that makes up the majority of the sand grains, feldspar grains are also common in many of these sandstones. Unlike quartz, feldspar chemically breaks down in water, and its presence indicates that the sand grains had not traveled very far from their source in the mountains before being deposited. Had they traveled farther to the shoreline and been part of an ancient beach at the edge of a continent, or even a barrier beach just offshore, little to no feldspar would remain.

As the interstate climbs hills between the Pennsylvania border and Morgantown, look east to see Chestnut Ridge on the eastern horizon. The ridge is the surface expression of the Chestnut Ridge Anticline, the westernmost fold of the Allegheny Mountain Section, which extends east to the Allegheny Front and the western edge of the Valley and Ridge Province.

On the north side of Morgantown, I-79 descends through the Dunkard and Monongahela rocks to the elevation of the Sewickley and Pittsburgh coals near exit 155. Both coals are between 5 and 10 feet thick here, which required an accumulation of peat that was at least ten times as thick! Although the rocks appear nearly horizontal, an exposure of the Monongahela's Benwood Limestone on the east side of the highway is dipping noticeably to the northwest on the west limb of the Fayette Anticline. Below the Benwood, both the Sewickley and Pittsburgh coal beds were extensively mined on both sides of the highway. Just south of exit 155, the route passes a reclaimed mine portal on the east side that led to underground mines in the Sewickley that extended nearly 1 mile to the east, almost reaching the Monongahela River.

Near exit 152, the highway crosses south into older rocks of the Conemaugh Group and follows these rocks around the southern edge of the Dunkard Basin en route to Charleston. By following the Conemaugh Group, the highway is routed through soft shales that form a landscape of comparatively low relief. In addition, this routing also avoids most of the underground Pittsburgh coal mining operations. South of its climb over Price Hill, the road crosses the Monongahela River south of Morgantown between mile markers 149 and 148. The river, a major tributary of the Ohio River, flows north to its confluence with the Allegheny River at Pittsburgh.

Most of the Conemaugh Group, like the younger Monongahela and Dunkard, was deposited in a series of river environments, and most of the exposures are either thick cross-bedded channel sandstones or floodplain shales, coals, and thin sandstones. Many of the floodplain shales, especially in the Conemaugh, have a distinctive red color from iron oxides that developed in soil, reflecting the change to a predominantly semiarid climate in the Late Pennsylvanian Period. However, the lower part of the Conemaugh Group, unlike the younger units, contains seven laterally extensive marine units. One of these, the Ames

A nearly complete cyclothem in the Conemaugh Group on the north side of exit 146. The dark-gray layer is the Ames marine zone, deposited during one of several episodes of sea level rise. It is sandwiched between the thin Harlem coal and the tan Grafton Sandstone at the top of the outcrop, both of which were deposited on land when sea level was lower. The gray to light-tan layer below the Harlem coal is a thick paleosol that also formed during low sea level.

marine zone, marks the boundary between the Glenshaw and Casselman Formations in the Conemaugh and is exposed on the north side of exit 146 for Goshen Road. The Ames is part of one of the more well-developed examples of a cyclothem in West Virginia. See the sidebar on cyclothems on pages 26 to 27.

Rocks in the Ames cyclothem stay near the elevation of the highway and are present in many of the exposures. The Grafton Sandstone is exposed on the south side of the highway between mile markers 145 and 144. At mile marker 139.5, the complete cyclothem is again well exposed.

While passing the city of Fairmont, to the west at mile marker 136, the highway is at the elevation of the Pittsburgh coal at the base of the Monongahela. The coal has been mined here. Two thinner coals below the Pittsburgh, the Little Clarksburg and the Little Pittsburgh, are exposed, separated by the Connellsville Sandstone, all part of the Casselman Formation of the Conemaugh Group.

At mile marker 133, the interstate crosses the Tygart Valley River, which flows from the southeast. Three miles farther downstream to the north, the Tygart Valley River joins the West Fork River to form the Monongahela.

Between Fairmont and US 50 at Bridgeport, I-79 runs parallel to the axes of several small folds. While the dip of the rocks is too gentle to be noticed at the surface, it effectively increases the width of the Monongahela outcrop belt at

The characteristic orange iron residue of acid mine drainage, formed when water reacts with pyrite in coal, has stained the underclay of one of the coal beds below the Pittsburgh coal along I-79 at exit 136. Pyrite is also known as fool's gold.

A dark layer of shale and coal separates river channel sandstones of the Conemaugh Group at exit 136.

the surface, which also widens the mineable extent of the Pittsburgh coal. The impact on the land can be seen south of mile marker 127, where the presence of treeless, flat surfaces hint at the extensive surface mining in the past. At exit 121 near the Meadowbrook Mall, the highway tracks just east of abandoned surface and underground mines in the Pittsburgh coal.

On the north side of exit 119, where the interstate intersects US 50, exposures of Conemaugh and Monongahela rocks, mostly river sandstones and shales, are frequent. The Pittsburgh and Redstone coals around the junction have been extensively mined. The large shopping plaza on the southeast side of the intersection was built on a large reclaimed surface mine. South of US 50, the highway dips below the level of the Pittsburgh coal and the Ames marine zone is once again exposed at exit 115 and again near mile marker 113, although the Grafton Sandstone dominates the latter exposure. Here the Grafton Sandstone contains coal and shale fragments, commonly called *rip-up clasts,* which were scoured from the floodplain by the river flow and incorporated into the sand.

These 1-to-2-centimeter-wide, oddly shaped voids in the Grafton Sandstone were formed by the weathering out of shale and coal fragments that were originally incorporated into the sandstone after the river ripped them from the banks of an ancient river channel.

Between exit 110 for Lost Creek and exit 105 for Jane Lew, the interstate begins to negotiate a series of hills, typical of the lower portion of the Appalachian Plateaus, by following valleys of small streams that enable the interstate to avoid steep grades. In Lewis County, I-79 is south of the region of extensive Pittsburgh coal mining, but the Redstone coal, which lies just above the Pittsburgh, was mined here. Even though the wide, flat-bottomed valley at exit 105 may seem typical of reclaimed surface mining, it is actually the work of two meandering streams, Jesse Run and Lifes Run, that merge here, forming a broad floodplain.

Conemaugh rocks continue to be exposed between exit 99 for Weston and the southern end of I-79, just north of Charleston. Along this stretch, iron oxide from the ubiquitous red beds has mixed with water and stained red the surface of many of the sandstones, while others have retained their original tan or gray color. Some of the concrete drainage ditches have also been stained red. Look to the east at exit 99. Here open terrain reflects the work of two meandering streams, the larger being Stonecoal Creek, the smaller Mud Lick. The Redstone coal was extensively surface mined from these valley walls. Climbing southwest out of the valley, I-79 follows smaller creek valleys, crosses the West Fork River at exit 96, and proceeds up the valley of Rushs Run to exit 91.

The highway's relationship to the surrounding terrain changes between exit 91 and 3 miles south of the Tully Ridge Rest Area. Rather than following valleys and, where necessary, cutting through the ridges separating them, it climbs up onto Tully Ridge, which conveniently runs in a south-southwesterly direction and has an elevation between 1,100 and 1,200 feet above sea level. By comparison, the elevation at exit 99 was approximately 1,060 feet. To maintain a comparatively level grade on a ridgetop that varies in elevation required road builders to fill in the terrain where the ridge dropped away. Along the 5 or so miles atop Tully Ridge you can see in all directions the undulating landscape of the Appalachian Plateaus.

The highway descends the valley of Dumpling Creek to Burnsville at exit 79, where it crosses the Little Kanawha River. From there, it travels up Saltlick Creek and then Burns Run as far as practical and then travels along another ridge before descending once again, this time by way of Cedar Creek, to exit 67 for Flatwoods. Near mile marker 70, note the small exposures of red beds peeking through vegetation, which along with the soil cover have slid downslope.

South of exit 67, there are repeated exposures of Conemaugh channel sand-stones, some with obvious cross beds and point bar surfaces, legacies of ancient river currents. Just north of the Elk River crossing at mile marker 63, an expo-sure includes distinctive soil features, called *glaebules,* common in the red beds. These are small calcium carbonate nodules, many having a diameter roughly equal to that of a quarter, that formed as the original floodplain muds were converted into soils. Like the red color of these paleosols, the glaebules indicate a predominately semiarid climate was present at the time of their formation. South of mile marker 58 is a comparatively high exposure consisting of red to gray Conemaugh sandstones and paleosols, and another is visible at the junc-tion of I-79 and US 19 at exit 57.

Between exit 57 and mile marker 43, I-79 turns almost due west and, as a consequence, follows the outcrop belt of the Conemaugh Group. While rocks are not as well exposed in this region as they are farther north, the telltale red color appears again and again in various roadcuts and other exposures. The highway crosses the Elk River again near exit 51. Both the interstate and river are headed for the Kanawha River at Charleston.

The countryside is more open around and west of mile marker 43; slopes are comparatively gentle and the hills rounded. The difference in elevation between the highway and the ridges and hills on either side is about 300 feet. The route

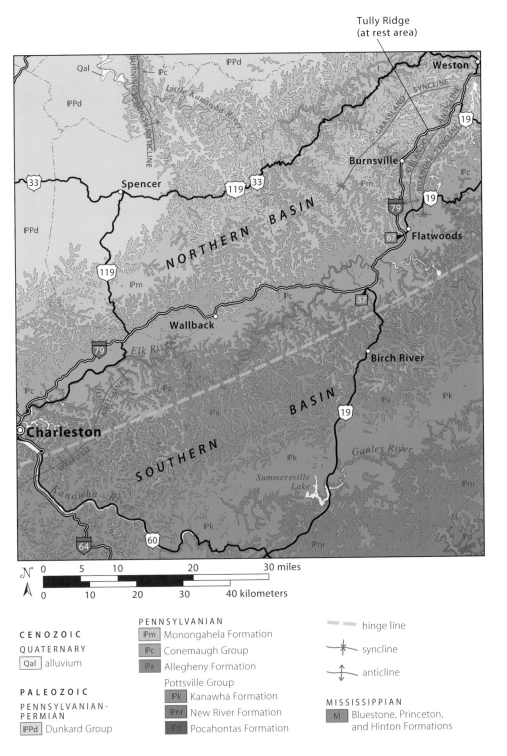

Geology along I-79 between Weston and Charleston.

takes advantage of the presence of small stream valleys that lie roughly 800 feet above sea level. The slopes become steeper between exit 40 for Big Otter and exit 34 for Wallback. The elevation of I-79 remains relatively constant, but the ridges top out at 1,300 feet for a number of miles with many of the surrounding hills capped by the younger Monongahela Formation. The difference in topography is likely due to the numerous gentle folds in the rocks along this portion

Glaebules form in soil as water evaporates and calcium carbonate is left behind. They are a common feature in red beds of the Conemaugh Group.

Large exposure of gray river sandstones and red mudstones in the Conemaugh Group north of the Elk River at mile marker 63.

Near exit 57, diagonal lines running down and to the right in this Conemaugh Group sandstone record the deposition of a point bar on the inside of a meander bend in an ancient river. As the channel shifts, the construction of a point bar is accompanied by erosion on the opposite side of the channel, forming a cutbank.

of the interstate. While the folds are too gentle to discern in the exposures, they effectively thicken the underlying rocks and thus may be increasing the relief of the landscape.

Around mile marker 7.5, the ubiquitous Conemaugh rocks to the east give way to the underlying Middle Pennsylvanian Allegheny Formation to the west. Although the two units contain mostly shale and sandstone, the Allegheny Formation has more thick sandstones and does not contain the red beds so common in the Conemaugh Group. It is also important to note that the outcrop belt of the Allegheny Formation generally serves as the dividing line between the Northern and Southern Basins, the latter beginning just a few miles to the south. Around mile marker 1, I-79 drops once again into the Elk River Valley. A few final and comparatively thick exposures that include the Allegheny-Conemaugh contact can be seen along the interstate as it merges with I-77 at mile marker 0.

US 50
Grafton—Clarksburg—Parkersburg
95 miles

US 50 is the oldest highway to traverse the central Appalachians through West Virginia and was originally known as the Northwestern Virginia Turnpike when chartered in 1827 by Virginia's General Assembly. The turnpike originated in Winchester, Virginia, and ended in Parkersburg on the Ohio River when completed in 1840. Its route took it through what were then the most populous counties of western Virginia, and as a consequence it was a financial

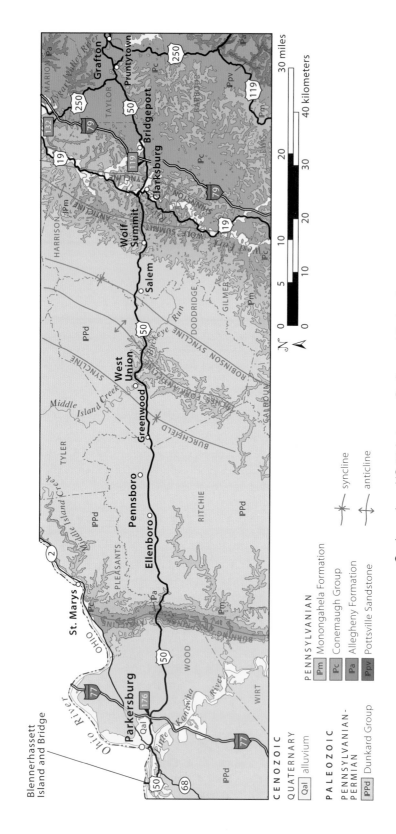

Geology along US 50 between Grafton and Parkersburg.

CENOZOIC

QUATERNARY

Qal alluvium

PALEOZOIC

PENNSYLVANIAN

IPm Monongahela Formation

IPc Conemaugh Group

IPa Allegheny Formation

IPpv Pottsville Sandstone

PENNSYLVANIAN-
PERMIAN

IPPd Dunkard Group

syncline

anticline

success. The original route of the Baltimore & Ohio Railroad (B&O) from Cumberland, Maryland, to Cincinnati, Ohio, now a rail trail, at times parallels the highway through the Allegheny Mountain Section of the Appalachian Plateaus, as well as across the lower portion of the plateau to Parkersburg.

At the western end of Grafton, US 50 crosses the Tygart Valley River, which flows north and west toward Fairmont, where it joins West Run to form the Monongahela River. Between Grafton and Clarksburg, the route crosses the southern portion of West Virginia's northern coalfields. Fifty years ago the area was dotted with coal operations, both underground and surface. The B&O had branch lines running in various directions to service the mines. All of that rural industrial activity is now a thing of the past, and without consulting documents from the time or hearing the memories of longtime residents along the highway, it would be impossible to imagine that it happened at all, given the placid, rural scenery today.

The main target of many of the mining operations was the Pittsburgh coal, the thickest and most productive bed in the Appalachian Basin and the boundary between rocks of the Conemaugh Group and those of the overlying Monongahela Formation. At Pruntytown, the valley bottoms are Conemaugh and the hilltops are Monongahela Formation, with the Pittsburgh seam located about halfway up most of the hills to the south of US 50. North of the highway, the elevation of the Pittsburgh coal is higher as it approaches the axis of an unnamed anticline and does not intersect the surface.

Looking at the hills, you may notice odd breaks in the vegetation and topography, a consequence of the reclaiming of Pittsburgh surface mines. After the end of operations, the contour of the land was restored, the topsoil was replaced, and the ground was revegetated. The graded, grassy slopes also hide numerous mine entrances, or *adits*, leading into the hills where the coal companies followed the beds underground. A great example of reclaimed mining operations lies about 10 miles west of Grafton. Here, US 50 descends into a valley running north-south at right angles to the road and intersects Buck Run Road. To the south and along both sides of the valley you can see reclaimed mines, now rolling hills covered with hay.

Near the Taylor-Harrison county line, east of Bridgeport, the route crosses the axis of the unnamed anticline, and the Pittsburgh coal, along with the evidence of mining, temporarily disappears. Climbing west out of Bridgeport, the highway passes exposures of Conemaugh sandstone but soon reaches the level of the Pittsburgh coal as US 50 crosses over I-79 en route to Clarksburg. This area was the site of intense surface and underground mining. Between I-79 and Clarksburg, US 50 passes over at least two different underground mining operations. Unfortunately, Clarksburg and many of the smaller communities in this area have withered since the end of active mining.

West of Clarksburg, US 50 cuts through red and green shales and sandstones of the Monongahela Formation. The rocks have a slight northwest dip that takes the Pittsburgh coal and most of the abandoned mining operations well below road level. Exposures of the Monongahela Formation continue near Wolf Summit, where there are prominent exposures of red shale and gray to tan

Rounded, treeless hills cover the remains of abandoned Pittsburgh coal surface mines along US 50 near Buck Run Road.

sandstone. Look for a lens-shaped channel sandstone in the exposures; most of the rocks seen along the route were deposited by streams that flowed through this area during the Late Pennsylvanian. About 1.5 miles west of Wolf Summit, the intersection with Jarvisville-Makin Road marks the approximate westward extent of abandoned underground coal mining operations.

West of the Jarvisville-Makin Road, the highway drops into the valley of Salem Fork and crosses onto rocks of the Dunkard Group. The boundary between the Monongahela Formation to the east and the younger Dunkard Group to the west is hardly noticeable in this area because the rocks look very similar. Between Salem and Parkersburg, most of the route will remain in the Dunkard Group, with the uppermost Monongahela Formation making an occasional appearance near the hinges of several gentle anticlines; an example of which lies west of Salem near the Harrison-Doddridge county line between mile markers 59 and 60. Here, the Washington and Waynesburg coals are exposed, the latter of which marks the boundary between the Dunkard and Monongahela rocks. West of the county line, the route descends into the long, narrow valley of Buckeye Run and passes two massive, cross-bedded channel sandstone exposures in the Monongahela Formation, the first to the south, the second on the north just west of the intersection with Antioch Road.

Between the intersection with Antioch Road and the exit for West Union, the highway passes exposures of the Benwood Limestone and red beds, both of the Monongahela Formation. The Benwood, an important indicator of the Monongahela, was deposited in freshwater lakes. On the east side of

A thick, river channel sandstone in the Monongahela Formation west of Antioch Road. The irregular base of the sandstone was formed as rivers carved into older shales below. Metal oxides carried by water flowing over the sandstone produced the dark gray streaks.

Greenwood, exposures of Dunkard Group channel sandstones are easy to see and continue periodically to the west, with tall cliffs of the Marietta Sandstone member of the Dunkard's Washington Formation near Ellenboro. In the vicinity of Greenwood, the highest terrain averages about 1,000 feet above sea level. In Grafton, at the east end of this road guide, elevations reach 1,300 to 1,400 feet. Gradually, as the highway proceeds west, the elevation of the plateau drops. At Parkersburg, where US 50 crosses the Ohio River, the elevation of US 50 is about 800 feet.

Oil and Gas in the Burning Springs Anticline

Most of the Appalachian Plateaus countryside is shaped almost exclusively by the twin forces of weathering and erosion. The results of these forces are hills and ridges that are quite distinctive, in some cases having steep cliffs, and in others striking contours that suggest they resulted from some dramatic geological developments. Not so. In truth, though West Virginia is known as the Mountain State, which would imply that forces lifted up its features, from a geological perspective it might be described more accurately as the Valley State, since weathering and erosion have been cutting into an uplifted region over millions of years.

So persistent has been the work of these forces that exposures of rock become increasingly rare the farther west you are in West Virginia. Topsoil and attendant vegetation cover so much of the land that for miles at a time there is nothing to see that would exemplify the geological history of the region. That is until US 50 crosses to the west side of the Ritchie-Wood county line and encounters the Burning Springs Anticline.

Folds are one by-product of the collision of tectonic plates. During the Alleghanian Orogeny, the African Plate pushed into the North American Plate, forcing its eastern margin more than 100 miles to the west. Because the center of the North American Plate was stable and therefore largely immune to the pressures of this collision, the land to the east compressed into a series of anticlines and synclines that resemble waves. Such structures greatly influence the topography in both the Valley and Ridge Province and the Allegheny Mountain Section of the Appalachian Plateaus. The folds continue farther west into the lower part of the plateaus, but here the anticlines and synclines have very gentle dips of less than 5 degrees and for the most part have left no impression on the landscape. To use a geologist's term, they have no *topographical expression*. In the 65 miles between Grafton and Ellenboro, US 50 traverses a total of four anticlines and six synclines, none of which affect the topography of the route. But the Burning Springs Anticline presents as a north-south-oriented ridge with elevations approximately 400 feet above that of the surrounding landscape, requiring the highway to climb more than 200 feet to traverse it.

This anticline is anomalous for more than its mere presence this far west. First, it runs in a north-south direction, virtually at right angles to the highway. Most of the folds caused by the Alleghanian Orogeny run northeast-southwest

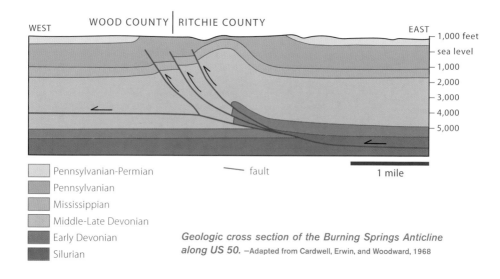

WEST   WOOD COUNTY | RITCHIE COUNTY   EAST

1,000 feet
sea level
1,000
2,000
3,000
4,000
5,000

☐ Pennsylvanian-Permian
☐ Pennsylvanian
☐ Mississippian
☐ Middle-Late Devonian
■ Early Devonian
■ Silurian

— fault

1 mile

Geologic cross section of the Burning Springs Anticline along US 50. –Adapted from Cardwell, Erwin, and Woodward, 1968

or approximately at right angles to the direction from which the African Plate collided with the North American Plate. Second, the limbs of the anticline have a maximum dip of about 70 degrees. Although most of the layers are covered with vegetation, red and green shales of the Conemaugh Group (on the south side of the road at mile marker 24.5) have a noticeable dip of approximately 50 degrees to the east. On the north side of the road, the contact between the Conemaugh and underlying Allegheny Formation is poorly exposed but shows the dip, dropping to about 30 degrees as the road climbs west toward the axis.

Conemaugh Group sandstone beds on the east limb of the Burning Springs Anticline dip away from the fold hinge.

More exposures are at the top of the ridge near the fold hinge. Here, Allegheny Formation sandstones are nearly horizontal as the dip changes from east to west. Just west of the Ritchie-Wood county line, the Homewood Sandstone member of the Pottsville Sandstone, making a rare appearance in the Northern Basin of West Virginia, can be seen on the south side of the road. The west limb of the fold is very poorly exposed, but rocks of the younger Conemaugh Group are steeper here, making the anticline asymmetrical.

The uniqueness of the Burning Springs Anticline has long been recognized, but not until 1955 did geologists drill the Sandhill Deep Well on the crest of the fold just to the north of US 50 in an attempt to determine the origins of this structure. It turns out that the compression caused by the Alleghanian Orogeny was transmitted along a type of subsurface fault called a *detachment*. These are horizontal thrust faults in which one rock layer slides, or is thrust, over another. Typically, in between these two layers is a third consisting of softer rock that acts almost like a lubricant between the two harder rock layers. These are usually shales, but in this instance they are salt layers from the Silurian Period.

Movement along the detachement fault transmitted the compression that would have otherwise crumpled the layers above the detachment until the western end of the salt layer was reached. Unable to continue forward, the stress was directed upward, forming a series of subsurface thrust faults that sliced and stacked rocks of Early and Middle Devonian time more than 1 mile below the surface. This, in effect, increased the thickness of the Devonian section below the anticline until the faults died out in softer rocks of Late Devonian age. Even though the faults likely never reached the surface, the thicker section pushed up and bent the Mississippian and Pennsylvanian rocks above, thus forming the Burning Springs Anticline.

Of particular interest is that trapped within this structural formation are hydrocarbons, crude oil and natural gas that formed hundreds of millions of years ago when marine plankton and algae inhabiting a shallow inland sea were covered by sand and mud. Lacking sufficient oxygen to decompose completely, they were then subjected to elevated temperatures and increasing pressure from layer upon layer of sediment deposited above them. These two forces caused chemical reactions that transformed this material into petroleum, which migrated upward into nearby sandstones and other porous rocks. Migration continued until the petroleum encountered impermeable layers above that served to trap it in place. When folded within an anticline like the Burning Springs, these layers become an effective anticlinal trap, concentrating the gas and oil in specific locations.

As unique as this feature may be in geological terms, it had a far greater impact on industry in the United States. The subsurface faults were a conduit for brines that flowed to the surface, the first commodity extracted from the anticline. It was also into this structure in nearby Wirt Country that the first oil well was drilled in West Virginia. It was second only to the first commercial oil

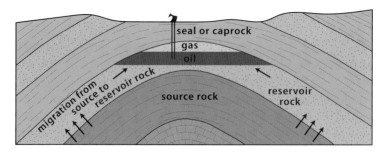

Cross section of an anticlinal oil and natural gas trap. Once the oil and gas seep into the reservoir rock, they migrate upward until they are blocked by the seal, or caprock, and separate by density. Drill down through the overlying layers and you strike petroleum!

well drilled in the United States by Edwin Drake near Titusville, Pennsylvania, in 1859, also located in the Appalachian Plateaus about 160 miles north-north-east. In fact, at the onset of the Civil War, the Burning Springs and Titusville fields were the only producing oil fields in the world! In addition to being among the first known anticlinal traps, the Burning Springs Anticline was well suited to early drilling techniques. Drillers located their wells on competent sandstones that would not cave in or collapse into the drill hole. These techniques were not effective when drilling into soft shales.

Between the Burning Springs Anticline and Parkersburg, US 50 returns to the typical topography of the western Appalachian Plateaus, at around 800 feet above sea level, and travels over rock of the Pennsylvanian-Permian Dunkard Group. Just west of I-77, rocks of the Dunkard Group are exposed in a series of fairly recent roadcuts created when US 50 was rerouted around Parkersburg on its way to the Blennerhassett Bridge, which crosses the Ohio River. Numerous red beds of the Washington Formation are exposed, along with tan to gray sandstones deposited by rivers draining the region right about the time the Pennsylvanian Period ended and the Permian Period began, about 299 million years ago. Exposures can be seen near the exit for Staunton Avenue on the south side of the road and again as the highway ducks under the overpass for County Road 9, near the Ohio River. More exposures can be seen as the highway swings to the north and descends toward the Blennerhassett Bridge.

WV 2
CHESTER—WEIRTON—PARKERSBURG
131 miles

The Ohio River valley is heavily vegetated, and for most of this route the rocks are not well exposed. Fortunately, because they are fairly horizontal and extend west into Ohio, recent construction across the river has created excellent outcrops that we have photographed and used in the text to supplement our discussion of exposures on the West Virginia side.

WV 2 runs along flat river terraces, former floodplains of the Ohio River, for much of its length through the northern panhandle. An alternating pattern of flat land and steep cliffs, termed *cutbanks*, characterize the route. The elevations of terraces along the northern portion of the route can be over 100 feet above the river, while those near the southern end of the route descend to a few tens of feet above the river. The difference in elevation reflects the steep stream gradient

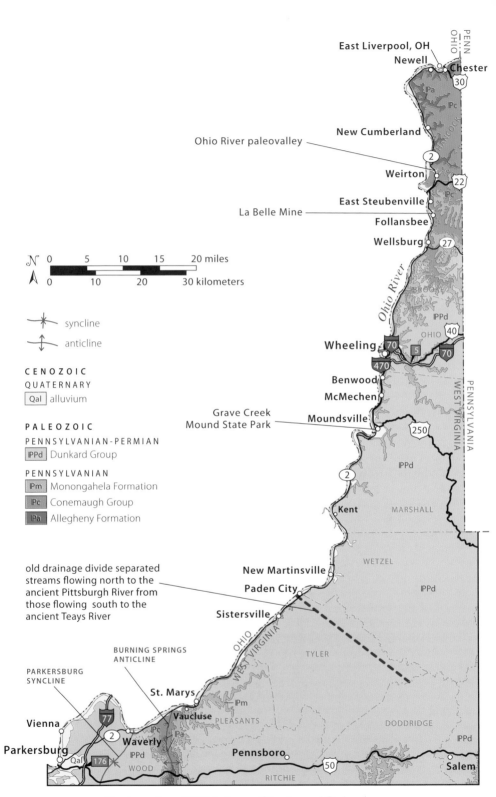

Geology along WV 2 between Chester and Parkersburg.

Tall cliffs of Allegheny Formation sandstones were formed as the Ohio River cut into the landscape on the Ohio side of the river north of Newell.

present at the end of the Pleistocene ice age, when braided streams of glacial melt-water deposited outwash (see sidebar about the Ohio River on page 60).

Chester is situated on a terrace, where the Ohio River has cut through the glacial outwash, splitting the floodplain between West Virginia and Ohio. West of Chester, WV 2 is pressed up against a steep cliff of the Middle Pennsylvanian Allegheny Formation. At Newell, the Ohio River bends to the southwest, and almost predictably the valley floor widens on the inside of the meander bend that provided the flat ground for the town. Across the river on the Ohio (or cutbank) side, roadcuts expose a thick section of rocks in the Middle Penn-sylvanian Allegheny Formation, the oldest rocks at the surface in the northern panhandle. The rocks get progressively younger to the south toward the center of the Appalachian Basin.

The town of Newell, and Hancock County in general, were home to the largest fire and paving brick industry in the United States. The raw clay used in this industry comes from layers called *underclays*, which get their name from their typical location under coal beds. Underclays are paleosols and often contain fossil roots from the plants that formed the coals above. These clays are sometimes referred to as *fireclays* when they are pure enough to be used in industries that fire their products during the manufacturing process. The Lower Kittanning coal and its associated underclay were heavily mined along this portion of WV 2 and provided both the raw materials and fuel for the clay products industry. Newell's location along the banks of the Ohio

Ohio River

The Ohio River's location today is ultimately a consequence of developments during the current ice age, in which the advance of major ice sheets from the north dictated many aspects of the landscape. Prior to the onset of the ice age around 2.5 million years ago, the Ohio, for all practical purposes, did not exist. Instead, the present-day upper Ohio River valley was drained by the north-flowing Steubenville River, a tributary of the larger Pittsburgh River system that flowed into ancestral Lake Erie and ultimately into the Atlantic Ocean. Today, smaller tributaries of the Ohio in the northern West Virginia panhandle still flow toward it in a northwesterly direction, just as they did prior to the advance of those glacial ice sheets.

The southern limit of the ancient Pittsburgh River watershed, an example of an old divide separating two ancient river systems, lies just south of Paden City,

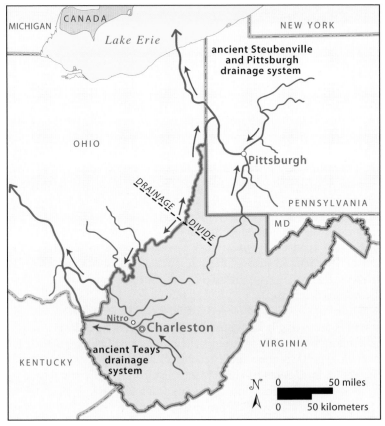

Pleistocene preglacial drainage of the Pittsburgh-Steubenville drainage system to Lake Erie and the ancient Teays drainage system to the west. –Adapted from Teller and Goldthwait, 1991; Welker, 1982

West Virginia, along the Ohio River. South of the divide, streams drained to the southwest as part of the extensive Teays River system that ultimately flowed to the west, joining the ancestral Mississippi River in central Illinois.

During the earliest advance of major ice sheets in the Pleistocene Epoch, ice, along with *outwash* (coarse gravels deposited by glacial meltwater streams), blocked both the north-flowing Pittsburgh River system, north of East Liverpool, Ohio, and the west-flowing Teays River system, northwest of Chillicothe, Ohio. Among the results of the blockage was the formation of Glacial Lake Teays and another lake, Glacial Lake Monongahela, in the north-central part of the state. After the last major ice sheets retreated some 10,000 years ago, the rivers were unable to resume their preglacial courses. The gravels that had partially blocked their path did not disappear with the ice, and the rivers assumed a course that took them to the west around the southern extent of the ice to join with the Mississippi River at Cairo, Illinois. Thus, the Ohio River system as we know it was established.

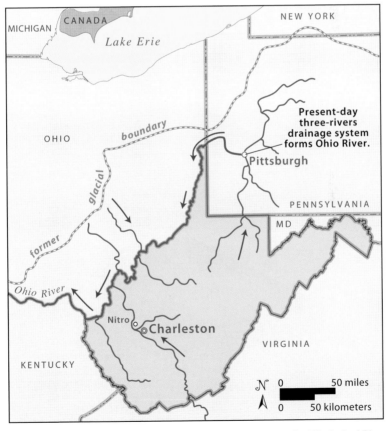

Present-day postglacial Ohio River drainage flowing west to the Mississippi River system at Cairo, Illinois. –Glacial boundary from Teller and Goldthwait, 1991

Today, the Ohio begins in Pittsburgh, Pennsylvania, at the confluence of the Allegheny and Monongahela Rivers, the former coming down from the north, the latter up from West Virginia to the south. From Pittsburgh, the Ohio River flows in a northwesterly direction and eventually turns west-southwest at the town of East Rochester, Pennsylvania, approximately 30 miles downstream from Pittsburgh. The Ohio holds that course, with some minor bends, for another 25 miles or so to where, southwest of Newell, West Virginia, it turns south. Except for a couple of wide turns, one temporarily reversing the river's flow direction, it follows a southwesterly course until it reaches Huntington. Just west of the city it turns northwest and becomes the boundary between Ohio and Kentucky.

The Ohio River gently meanders within its valley, so wide expanses of what many call *bottomland* appear on one side or the other. For the geologist, the term is not always satisfactory because it does not describe the origin of this flat terrain that dates back to the ice age. As the glaciers receded, huge volumes of meltwater, choked with sediment eroded by the glaciers, formed a braided stream system in the Ohio River valley that drained to the south. The braided streams deposited coarse outwash in the channels as well as on the floodplains. Today, these outwash deposits are quarried for gravel on the ancient floodplains or dredged from the riverbed.

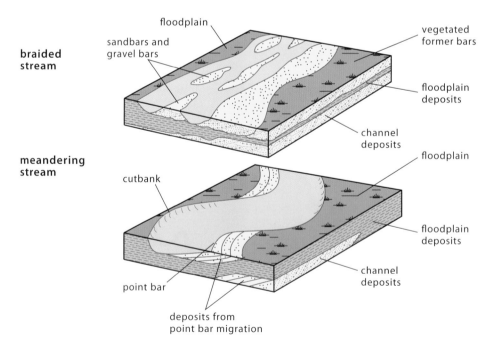

During the retreat of Pleistocene ice sheets, the Ohio River was filled with glacial meltwater choked with coarse sand and gravel and became a braided stream (top). Once the ice sheets were gone, it became a meandering stream (bottom).

Once the glaciers completely retreated from this area, the Ohio River changed to a meandering stream system in which a single channel flows through the valley. The present-day river has cut down through the deposits of glacial outwash on the ancient floodplains, producing a generally alternating pattern of bottomlands at a somewhat higher elevation than the river's surface. These flat surfaces, called *terraces*, were prized by early settlers because they allowed for conventional agriculture, unlike the narrow V-shaped valleys formed by smaller tributary streams that enter both sides of the river. Towns were sited on these bottomlands as well, though as their populations grew, they reached up the sides of the valleys.

An example of the soft, gray underclay that was the raw material used by the many brick and paving industries that once operated in the northern panhandle. The underclays are a type of paleosol that formed as minerals were leached from the clay soils in more humid climates.

River was ideal, providing an easy route of transportation for the finished products. To this day, the Homer Laughlin China Company maintains an active factory in Newell.

About 2 miles west of Newell is a bend in the Ohio River that sets it on the southerly course it largely follows to Huntington. On the Ohio side of this bend, a tall outcrop exposes both the Allegheny Formation and the overlying Conemaugh Group. The two units can be easily distinguished by numerous red beds in the younger Conemaugh Group, which are absent in the Allegheny.

View across the Ohio River at a roadcut along OH 7. The dark stripe near the middle of the exposure is the Upper Freeport coal, the boundary between gray sandstones of the Allegheny Formation below and red beds in the Conemaugh Group above.

A few exposures of Allegheny Formation coals and sandstones can be seen around the town of New Cumberland.

Just north of Weirton, WV 2 follows Kings Creek for several miles. Like many of the streams in the area, Kings Creek is an example of *barbed drainage*, where tributaries join a larger stream in the opposite direction of its flow. In this case, Kings Creek's barbed confluence with the Ohio is an artifact of the postglacial drainage reversal—the ancient river in the Ohio River valley flowed north prior to the Pleistocene ices ages.

Part of Weirton is situated in a broad valley of which the northern half contains no modern streams. The floor of this valley is covered by ancient river deposits, indicating it was the site of a former channel of the Ohio River and is thus a paleochannel. At some point in the past, conditions caused the river to abandon this route and assume its present course.

Because the rocks become younger to the south, the Allegheny Formation is now belowground, and rocks of the Conemaugh Group of Late Pennsylvanian age are exposed on both sides of the modern Ohio River valley. South of Weirton, cross-bedded sandstones and red shales of the Conemaugh Group form high cliffs that continue south to Wheeling. Sandstones similar to these provided essential material for the glass industry in the state. From the vicinity of Wellsburg, you can see more cliffs of Conemaugh rock across the river in Ohio, and others appear on the West Virginia side of the river south of town.

At the north end of East Steubenville, WV 2 crosses over the northern limit of the La Belle Mine. No evidence of this coal mine is visible. It is an

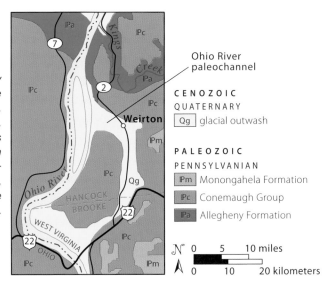

WV 2 temporarily follows the course of Kings Creek, which is barbed, meaning it joins the Ohio River in the upstream direction. Farther south, WV 2 follows the paleochannel.

underground mine, opened in 1909, that targeted the Lower Freeport coal bed, located nearly 200 feet below the surface in rocks of the Allegheny Formation. The mine not only extends for 1.5 miles south along the path of WV 2 to the town of Follansbee, but it has also been dug 175 feet below the surface of the Ohio River and continues into parts of Ohio.

Wheeling, the state's first capital, is where the National Road, the nation's first public works project, crossed the Ohio River (the road later became US 40 and most recently was superseded by I-70). At Wheeling gently sloping valleys on both sides of the river enabled travelers of the original National Road and its successors to take advantage of comparatively easy grades as they traversed the valley. Both of the streams that created those valleys—one in Ohio, the other in West Virginia—bear the same name: Wheeling Creek.

A point of interest is the Wheeling Suspension Bridge, which dates from 1849 and, at the time, was the longest bridge of this design in the world at 1,010 feet. Now on the National Registry of Historic Places, the bridge carried the National Road over the Ohio River to Wheeling Island, on the other side of which flows a shallow back channel of the river easily bridged by what was then a more conventional structure. The historic bridge currently serves local traffic.

In Wheeling, WV 2 passes under I-70 just west of the Wheeling Tunnel. The tunnel is bored into rocks of the uppermost Conemaugh Group about 15 feet below the Pittsburgh coal, at the base of the overlying Monongahela Formation. South of the US 250 merger with WV 2, the highway passes under I-470 close to the level of the Pittsburgh coal. To the south, the Conemaugh Group disappears below road level, giving way to rocks of the Monongahela.

South of Wheeling is the town of Benwood, the type locality for the Benwood Limestone, an important indicator of the Monongahela Formation.

A *type locality* is the location where a given rock unit was first described or best exposed. This limestone was deposited in a series of shallow, freshwater lakes and is typically white, tan, or gray. It erodes in a blocky pattern that visually distinguishes it from the shales common in the Monongahela Formation. Look for good exposures of the limestone in and around Benwood. This community and its neighbor McMechen are both situated on a contiguous terrace composed of glacial outwash, separated only by a small stream: McMechens Run. South of McMechen, the Ohio River turns briefly southwest, and the valley closes in, leaving just enough room for the highway and the single-track line of the CSX Railroad, which parallels WV 2 for almost its entire length.

North of Moundsville, US 250 heads to the east, while WV 2 continues down the river valley. Moundsville takes its name from the presence of the Grave Creek Mound, which archeologists believe was completed around 200 BCE by members of the Adena people, who constructed numerous mounds in the Ohio River valley. Grave Creek Mound, the largest conical mound known, is 62 feet high, 240 feet in diameter at the base, and estimated to contain 57,000 tons of earth. It is located in Grave Creek Mound State Park two blocks east of WV 2 between 8th and 10th Streets.

South of Moundsville, across the river you can see a large exposure of light-colored shales, thin layers of sandstone, and limestones of the Monongahela Formation and the Dunkard Group, which contains the Pennsylvanian-Permian boundary. Near the village of Kent, rocks of the Dunkard Group, the youngest rocks along WV 2, occur at road level.

Mannington Sandstone

View of rocks of the Monongahela Formation and Dunkard Group across the Ohio River. The thick, light-colored band in the middle of the exposure is the Mannington Sandstone, located near the base of the Dunkard Group.

South of Kent, the Ohio River bends to the southeast for a few miles before turning first southwest and then south. Just north of that meander, WV 2 crosses the line separating Marshall and Wetzel Counties, a line that represented the westward extension of the Mason-Dixon Line surveyed in the late 1700s. The point where the Mason-Dixon Line ended, 5 degrees west of the mouth of the Delaware River, determined the western boundary of Pennsylvania, and this extension in effect marks the southern boundary of the Mountain State's northern panhandle.

Between the county line and Paden City, West Virginia gets the vast majority of the bottomland of the river valley. As a point of information, the boundary between the states lies close to the bank on the Ohio side of the river; the Ohio River is mostly part of the Mountain State.

Just north of Paden City, the river takes a turn to the southwest and will hold this course, with the exception of two major meanders, all the way to Point Pleasant. By doing so, the river is in effect moving farther west in the Appalachian Plateaus, which means that elevations of the surrounding country become progressively lower the farther west and south it flows. At the southern edge of Paden City, WV 2 crosses the paleodivide that separated the ancient Steubenville River draining to the north from the ancient southerly flowing Marietta River that joined the Teays River system (see sidebar about the Ohio River). South of Paden City, the smaller tributaries are not barbed and flow into the Ohio River in a southwesterly direction consistent with a southerly flowing drainage system that persisted through the Pleistocene ice age to the

Sandstones of the Monongahela Formation dipping away from the hinge on the east limb of the Burning Springs Anticline.

modern day. South of Sistersville, the river enters what boatmen in the nineteenth century termed the Long Reach, flowing southwest with little deviation. In this stretch of water boatmen need not navigae around shallow water and other hazards along the inside of meanders because the river is straight.

South of St. Marys, WV 2 intersects the Burning Springs Anticline, a north-south-oriented fold structure. (See the sidebar in the US 50 road guide.) South of the St. Marys Bridge over the Ohio River, WV 2 turns west and approaches older rocks in the core of the anticline. Sandstones of the Monongahela Formation on the east limb of the anticline near Vaucluse can be seen dipping at about 20 degrees to the east. To the west, the road crosses into rocks of the Conemaugh Group and then back through younger rocks of the Monongahela Formation and Dunkard Group.

At Waverly, WV 2 turns south to Parkersburg, away from the river, cutting off the large meander that carries the river to Williamstown, West Virginia, across the Ohio from Marietta, Ohio.

SOUTHERN BASIN

The rocks in the Southern Basin of the Appalachian Plateaus are thicker and contain a more complete record of deposition during Late Paleozoic time than do those in the Northern Basin. The Southern Basin was closer to the collision zone between North America and northwest Africa during the Alleghanian Orogeny. As the orogeny proceeded, huge slabs of the North American crust were shoved to the northwest over 100 miles along low-angle thrust faults as the continental margin crumpled. The enormous weight of these slabs caused the crust in the Southern Basin to subside earlier and to a much greater depth than in the Northern Basin. Vast amounts of sediment, carried by streams from the rising ancestral Appalachian Mountains, accumulated in the deepening basin.

Even though subsidence was greater in the south, the foreland basin was situated on thick continental crust formed by the overlap of the North American and African continents. This kept the region just above sea level for most of the Pennsylvanian and Permian Periods. River and swamp environments were widespread, leading to the deposition of thousands of feet of sediment and plant matter that was transformed into the shale, sandstone, and coal layers that make up the vast majority of the rocks. Only for brief periods of time was the land below sea level. When sea level rose, it drowned the terrestrial landscape with marine waters. These times are recorded as thin marine units that occur periodically in an otherwise vast terrestrial sequence.

The differences between the same rock units that were deposited in both the Northern and Southern Basins relate to subsidence. Here, the Mauch Chunk Group is 3,000 to 3,700 feet thick, compared to a maximum of about 350 feet in the Northern Basin of the Appalachian Plateaus. The Pottsville Group in the Southern Basin is more than ten times the thickness of its counterpart to the

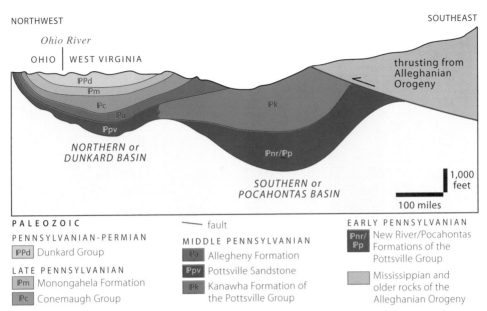

NORTHWEST

Ohio River

OHIO | WEST VIRGINIA

thrusting from Alleghanian Orogeny

SOUTHEAST

PPd
Pm
Pc
Pa
Ppv

Pk

NORTHERN or DUNKARD BASIN

Pnr/Pp

SOUTHERN or POCAHONTAS BASIN

1,000 feet

100 miles

PALEOZOIC

PENNSYLVANIAN-PERMIAN

PPd Dunkard Group

LATE PENNSYLVANIAN

Pm Monongahela Formation

Pc Conemaugh Group

fault

MIDDLE PENNSYLVANIAN

Pa Allegheny Formation

Ppv Pottsville Sandstone

Pk Kanawha Formation of the Pottsville Group

EARLY PENNSYLVANIAN

Pnr/Pp New River/Pocahontas Formations of the Pottsville Group

Mississippian and older rocks of the Alleghanian Orogeny

Earlier and greater subsidence in the Southern Basin compared to that in the Northern Basin during the Alleghanian Orogeny caused differences in the thickness and age range of the Pennsylvanian and Pennsylvanian-Permian rocks. –Modified from Nadon and others, 1998

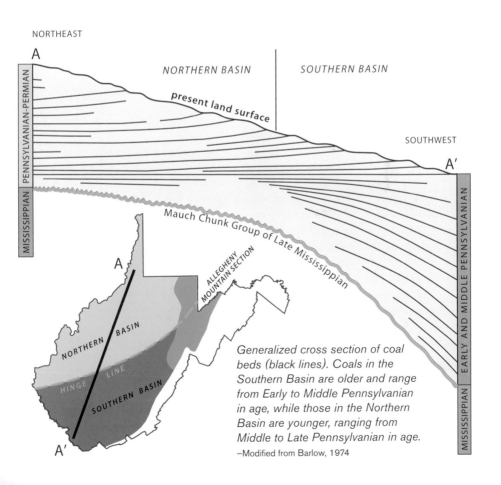

NORTHEAST

A

NORTHERN BASIN

SOUTHERN BASIN

present land surface

SOUTHWEST

A′

Mauch Chunk Group of Late Mississippian

PENNSYLVANIAN-PERMIAN

MISSISSIPPIAN

EARLY AND MIDDLE PENNSYLVANIAN

MISSISSIPPIAN

A

ALLEGHENY MOUNTAIN SECTION

NORTHERN BASIN

HINGE LINE

SOUTHERN BASIN

A′

Generalized cross section of coal beds (black lines). Coals in the Southern Basin are older and range from Early to Middle Pennsylvanian in age, while those in the Northern Basin are younger, ranging from Middle to Late Pennsylvanian in age. –Modified from Barlow, 1974

SOUTHERN BASIN

AGE	GROUPS		FORMATIONS
PENNSYLVANIAN	Pottsville Group	Pk	Kanawha Formation
		Pnr	New River Formation
		Pp	Pocahontas Formation
MISSISSIPPIAN	Mauch Chunk Group	Mbp	Bluestone Formation
			Princeton Sandstone
		Mh	Hinton Formation
		Mbf	Bluefield Formation
	Greenbrier Group	Mg	Greenbrier Limestone

NORTHERN BASIN

Pottsville Sandstone

Mauch Chunk Formation

Greenbrier Limestone

Scaled thickness of Mississippian and Pennsylvanian rocks in the Southern Basin compared to the same rocks scaled to the thicknesses found in the Northern Basin. –Data from Patchen and others, 1985

north (the Pottsville Sandstone) and contains a more continuous and complete record of deposition during the Pennsylvanian Period.

Both the Mauch Chunk and the Pottsville Groups are divided into recognizable formations in the Southern Basin. The Mauch Chunk contains, from oldest to youngest, the Bluefield, Hinton, Princeton, and Bluestone Formations. The Pottsville Group is also subdivided, again from oldest to youngest, into the Pocahontas, New River, and Kanawha Formations. In fact, the Southern Basin is often referred to as the Pocahontas Basin for the unique occurrence of this formation south of the hinge line.

The Kanawha Formation has a maximum thickness of over 2,000 feet in the southern part of the state and is the thickest of the formations within the Pottsville Group. The unit consists predominantly of shale and sandstone with smaller amounts of coal, limestone, and iron-bearing beds. Sandstones are more frequent in the upper part of the Kanawha as it grades into the overlying Allegheny Formation. The Kanawha contains twenty-six of the state's sixty-two mineable coal beds, and before the close of the twentieth century it accounted for over 40 percent of the state's coal production.

Most of the Kanawha Formation was deposited in a low-lying coastal plain near the shore of a large inland sea that periodically occupied portions of the eastern part of ancient North America through much of the Pennsylvanian Period. Changes in the volume of ice sheets on Gondwanaland, a large landmass in the southern hemisphere, caused numerous transgressions that drowned the coastal plain with seawater. This would have cut off the production of peat accumulating in coastal swamps and established a variety of marine environments above them. As transgression slowed and regression began, river systems draining the ancestral Appalachian Mountains to the southeast became increasingly active, delivering clastic sediments to the region. The resulting rock record is a stacked series of river sandstones and shales, along with coastal coals, marine shales, and limestones.

Most of the New River Formation was deposited by a network of streams draining the ancestral Appalachian Mountains to the east and flowing to the edge of the inland sea. However, near the top of the New River Formation lies the Nuttall Sandstone. Unlike many of the sandstones from Pennsylvanian time that contain feldspar and other mineral grains, the Nuttall is predominantly composed of durable quartz grains, suggesting that the grains in the Nuttall traveled farther than those sourced from the mountains to the east. Several Pennsylvanian sandstones, including the Nuttall, have been traced westward across the Appalachian Basin where the quartz was derived from the granites and granite-like rocks that composed the stable interior, or *craton*, of the North American continent.

Interstate 64
Beckley—White Sulphur Springs—Virginia State Line
64 miles

Beckley, the most populous town in West Virginia south of Charleston, represents the gateway to the state's southern coal mining operations. It was named after General Alfred Beckley, who served as clerk of Congress during the Washington, Adams, and Jefferson administrations. The region at one time accounted for about 60 percent of the state's total coal production, principally exploiting the Sewell coal in the New River Formation, which constitutes most of the outcrops near Beckley.

For a little more than 8 miles from the point where I-64 separates from I-77 to mile marker 128.5, I-64 passes through thick sandstones, thin-bedded shales, siltstones, and coals of the New River Formation, deposited in streams draining the ancestral Appalachian Mountains in Early Pennsylvanian time. With its high quartz content the Nuttall Sandstone, near the top of the New River Formation, resists weathering and erosion and therefore is responsible for the plateau-like landscape that dominates the region. Lying pretty much at road level, this typically white to tan sandstone forms steep cliffs along this portion of the route. The effect of the Nuttall, as well as other resistant New River sandstones, can be seen at mile marker 129 where the interstate

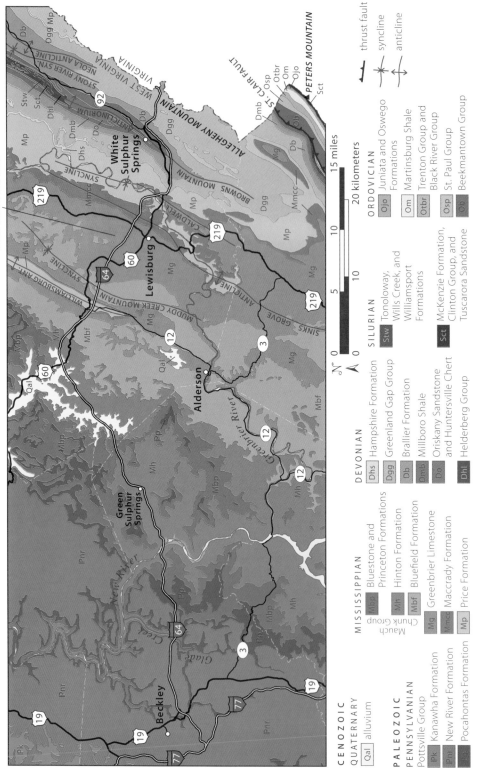

Geology along I-64 between Beckley and the Virginia state line.

Lost World Caverns

CENOZOIC

QUATERNARY

Qal alluvium

PALEOZOIC

PENNSYLVANIAN
Pottsville Group
Pk Kanawha Formation
Pnr New River Formation
Ppa Pocahontas Formation

MISSISSIPPIAN
Mbp Bluestone and Princeton Formations
Mh Hinton Formation
Mbf Bluefield Formation
Mauch Chunk Group
Mg Greenbrier Limestone
Mmcc Maccrady Formation
Mp Price Formation

DEVONIAN
Dhs Hampshire Formation
Dgg Greenland Gap Group
Db Brallier Formation
Dmb Millboro Shale
Do Oriskany Sandstone and Huntersville Chert
Dhl Helderberg Group

SILURIAN
Stw Tonoloway, Wills Creek, and Williamsport Formations
Sct McKenzie Formation, Clinton Group, and Tuscarora Sandstone

ORDOVICIAN
Ojo Juniata and Oswego Formations
Om Martinsburg Shale
Otbr Trenton Group and Black River Group
Osp St. Paul Group
Ob Beekmantown Group

thrust fault
syncline
anticline

0   5   10   15 miles
0   10   20 kilometers

crosses Glade Creek, a north-flowing tributary of the New River. The creek has managed to cut a narrow, V-shaped valley into the hard sandstones and the less resistant rocks below. The narrow, 600-foot-deep chasm is visible north of the highway, a break in the otherwise broad, flat landscape, which has an elevation of 2,600 feet above sea level. At mile marker 132.5 lies another outcrop of New River sandstones and shales that contains plant fossils, some of which are preserved as sand-filled casts of tree stumps visible from the road.

The highway descends the valley of Earleys Creek as it approaches the New River. From elevations around 2,600 feet, the highway drops to 1,320 feet at the

The fossil seed fern Neuropteris *from the New River Formation of Early Pennsylvanian age. Length of frond is 4 inches.*

Cast of a fossil tree trunk segment from the New River Formation.

bridge. As the road begins to descend, it crosses the boundary separating the Pennsylvanian from the older Mississippian Period, as evidenced between mile markers 135 and 137 by exposures of sandstone and red beds characteristic of the Mauch Chunk Group of Late Mississippian age. Like the Pennsylvanian units above, much of the Mauch Chunk was deposited on a low-relief coastal plain by streams draining mountains to the east. Deposition by streams was interrupted only occasionally by a few transgressions that established near-shore, shallow marine conditions atop the plain. A tall cliff of the Stony Gap Sandstone, deposited during one of the marine transgressions, can be seen to the south as the interstate crosses the New River.

The appearance of the Mauch Chunk Group is the first signal of a pattern that began at Beckley and will continue with a few exceptions until the highway reaches the Virginia state line. Essentially, as the highway continues east, you will encounter progressively older rocks as you move away from those of the Pennsylvanian and Permian Periods in the center of the Appalachian Basin. A few small folds and changes in elevation will briefly interrupt the pattern, but in effect the interstate is traveling back in time nearly 70 million years, from the Early Pennsylvanian to the Middle of the Devonian Period. Numerous additional exposures of Mauch Chunk rocks, principally the red beds, can be seen on the east side of the New River valley, and outcrops of these rocks continue as the highway reaches exit 143 for Green Sulphur Springs.

While readers may have heard of White Sulphur Springs and the famous Greenbrier Resort that is its principal business (farther east on I-64), Green Sulphur Springs is little known. It is the site of another of the numerous springs in West Virginia whose promoters, before the Civil War, promised treatments or even cures for various ailments, including rheumatism, if sufferers would only come to their spring to bathe in or drink its water. These waters percolated principally through Devonian Oriskany Sandstone and Helderberg Group limestones at depth before coming to the surface through porous Mississippian units. What makes the water sulfurous is the presence of hydrogen sulfide, which, whatever its alleged health benefits, smells like rotten eggs.

As eastbound travelers approach mile marker 150, a long view to the east reveals Peters Mountain, the boundary separating the Appalachian Plateaus Province from the Valley and Ridge. Whereas farther south this ridge doubles as the state line with Virginia, along I-64 that boundary shifts farther west to Allegheny Mountain.

Between mile markers 152 and 160, more red beds and sandstones of the Hinton and Bluefield Formations of the lower Mauch Chunk Group appear. The highway then crosses a small valley developed on the Greenbrier Limestone. A limestone quarry can be seen in the valley north of the highway at exit 161. Just east of exit 161 at mile marker 162, an outcrop of medium to thickly bedded sandstones and shales of the older Price Formation of Early Mississippian age lies along both sides of the highway. The Price Formation makes up the core of the Williamsburg Anticline, and its shales and sandstones gently curve, following the contour of the hilltop. They drop below the surface just to the east of the fold.

Gently folded interbedded sandstones and shales of the Early Mississippian Price Formation at the hinge of the Williamsburg Anticline.

Ripple marks in the Price Formation were produced by the back and forth currents of waves sweeping sand along the seafloor.

Near the base of the outcrop, the Price Formation contains marine fossils, as well as trace fossils, that indicate this rock was deposited below sea level. In addition, the numerous sandstone beds have wave ripples and flat bases, a more common feature when sand is deposited on an offshore shelf, unlike the curved, scoured bases usually found in stream-channel sandstones. East-dipping gray shales of the Price Formation signal that the highway has crossed to the east side of the axis of the Williamsburg Anticline, and as it leaves this structural formation in the course of crossing over the Muddy Creek Mountain Syncline, I-64 moves into an entirely different terrain.

At and east of mile marker 164, I-64 is suddenly in open country locally known as "the big levels." Trees are few and widely scattered, and the land appears bumpy with depressions of various diameters and depths that are seemingly scattered randomly in the fields. West of this point, where it was advantageous for construction, I-64 stuck close to streams and their valleys; now streams are not easily seen, primarily because most are flowing underground. These features are typical in areas of limestone bedrock, and east of mile marker 164 the Middle Mississippian Greenbrier Limestone is exposed on both sides of the highway.

Karst of the Appalachian Plateaus

German geologists first observed bumpy landscapes in limestone bedrock in what is now Slovenia, close to its border with Italy. The region was known as *Karst*, ("Kras" in Slovene) and that has become the term used to describe topographies resulting from the subterranean erosion of thick limestone formations. Where it can be seen, the soil of karst regions is of a reddish hue. It's called *terra rossa* and is the product of iron-rich clays that weather from the underlying limestone.

To understand the evolution of this unique landscape requires a synopsis of the developments from the Middle Mississippian Period to the present-day. About 350 million years ago, what became West Virginia lay at the bottom of a large shallow sea that had been established when the volume of glacial ice on Earth was low, causing sea level to rise above the land surface of many continents. On ancestral North America, it extended from what is now Virginia all the way to its then western border of Arizona, Utah, and Idaho. The water in that sea was warm because it was situated near the equator, and it teemed with marine organisms similar to those living near the modern Bahamas off the southeast coast of Florida.

Many of the organisms that flourished in this sea secreted hard parts made of calcium carbonate. As they died their shells and skeletons accumulated on the seafloor in great thickness and became the raw materials for limestone. This extensive tropical sea changed drastically as large ice sheets formed on Gondwanaland in the southern hemisphere, and the land rose to the east during the initial stages of the Alleghanian Orogeny. The Appalachian Mountains that formed became a vast source of mud, sand, and gravel, effectively ending widespread calcium carbonate production. Under the weight of that sediment, the calcium carbonate was lithified, resulting in up to 1,200 feet of Greenbrier Limestone. Subsequently, millions of years of uplift, weathering, and erosion brought the limestone to the surface, where it is readily dissolved in naturally acidic water, unlike the clastic materials above and below it.

Now lying at or just below the surface, the limestone began to dissolve as water, made acidic by carbon dioxide found both in the atmosphere and in plants and other organisms in the topsoil, percolated into the bedrock. Small natural fractures in the rock became progressively larger, gradually linking up to form still larger passages. Streams that had flowed on the surface disappeared into the formation, only to reappear hundreds if not thousands of feet away. So large did many of the openings in the limestone become that they formed caves running for dozens of miles underground. Where the roofs of these caves are near the surface, they are prone to collapse, creating depressions on the landscape called sinkholes.

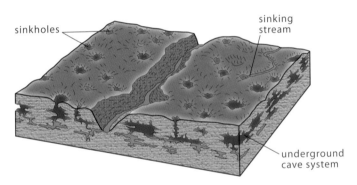

Natural, slightly acidic groundwater dissolves carbonate rocks such as limestone and dolostone to produce the distinctive underground cave systems and karst topography.

At mile marker 167, the eastbound and westbound lanes of the highway split apart for a couple of miles. Approximately 1 mile farther east, the westbound lanes cross over one of these caves that is part of Lost World Caverns. In the vicinity of Lewisburg, the seat of Greenbrier County, there are several caves that have been commercially developed. Those wishing to see how water over millions of years has transformed the subsurface of this region are encouraged to visit one of them. As you enter the cave and stand, perhaps in a large room with a ceiling 20 feet or more overhead, bear in mind that at one time that open space was solid limestone.

Lost World Caverns

To reach Lost World Caverns from I-64, take exit 169 to Lewisburg and head south into town. North of the downtown business district of Lewisburg, turn northwest on Arbuckle Lane, then right onto North Court Street, following the brown signs for Lost World Caverns. North Court Street becomes Country Road 32 and crosses over I-64. Continue on CR 32 until you see the signs for Lost World Caverns and turn left onto Lost World Road. Follow the long gravel driveway, around a sinkhole on the left, to the main building.

Lost World Caverns constitutes an extensive cave system dissolved into the Greenbrier Limestone. Cave tours lead through a large, well-lit cavern containing numerous stalactites, stalagmites, columns, and flowstone collectively known as *cave formations* or *speleothems*. The same water that dissolves limestone under pressure in the tight confines of fractures also delivers the calcium carbonate that makes up these formations, once the pressure is released in the cave. One may also embark upon a professionally guided "wild cave" tour that explores unlit and relatively unmodified passages. One of the passages in the wild cave tour extends under the westbound lane of I-64, approximately one-third mile south of the cave's entrance. The wild cave tour can be a rather strenuous adventure and is not for the faint of heart.

One mile east of exit 169 are bright-red exposures of the Maccrady Formation of Early Mississippian age, which lie below the Greenbrier Limestone. The rocks have a slight westward dip because they are located on the west limb of the Sinks Grove Anticline. The Maccrady Formation is a transitional unit between the Greenbrier Limestone above and the Price Formation below, and it contains numerous red bed paleosols, thin limestones, and sandstones of both marine and continental origins.

The highway turns south and shortly thereafter crosses the Greenbrier River, a south-flowing tributary of the New River. Just north of the bridge there are exposures of Price Formation rocks. Just to the south on the east side of the river is White Rock Mountain. At mile marker 173, on the east side of the river, the contact point between the Maccrady and Price Formations can be easily spotted as the gray sandstones of the Price give way to red beds of the Maccrady above.

It will not have escaped the reader's attention that folds seem to be coming in rapid succession at this point, although the degree of dip in the rocks is rather subtle east of mile marker 176, as evidenced by the nearly horizontal beds at the exposure at mile marker 173. Between mile markers 176 and 177 things change dramatically for eastbound travelers. Here, on both sides of the highway, the gently dipping layers give way to steeply dipping and then to nearly vertical

Laminations in limestone are often formed by bacterial mats that cover tidal flats and trap fine muds. This specimen is from the Maccrady Formation.

Red bed paleosols and sandstones of the Maccrady Formation of Early Mississippian age formed in a predominately arid climate.

Exposure of the contact between the dark-gray Price Formation of Early Mississippian age and the overlying red Maccrady Formation.

Steeply dipping beds of the Price Formation on the western limb of the Browns Mountain Anticlinorium were deformed by compression during the Alleghanian Orogeny.

beds of the Price Formation. The change occurs on the west limb of the severely deformed Browns Mountain Anticlinorium. The term *anticlinorium* is used to indicate more complex folding and faulting within an overall anticlinal structure. In crossing to the east side of the Greenbrier River, I-64 enters the Valley and Ridge Province.

I-64 swings around the southern end of the Browns Mountain Anticlinorium, which extends for at least 100 miles to the northeast and is the westernmost large fold structure in this part of the Valley and Ridge. The severity of folding in this structure, with its numerous thrust faults and tight folds exposed at the surface, is typical of the Valley and Ridge Province. As the highway continues east, it passes several outcrops of tightly folded rocks of Middle and Late Devonian age. (For more information about this major structure, see the side trip to Devils Backbone in the guide to US 460 and US 219: Bluefield—Lewisburg—Marlinton, in the Valley and Ridge chapter.)

At mile marker 179, on the south side of White Sulphur Springs, I-64 crosses the main line of the CSX Railroad just before the railroad enters a short tunnel as it snakes its way east into the heart of the Valley and Ridge. The railroad passes through three lengthy tunnels and numerous shorter ones, all constructed by hand in the nineteenth century. One of the longer ones is Lewis Mountain Tunnel, located about 10 miles to the east in Virginia where, according to the most recent scholarship, the historical John Henry worked and died, possibly "with a hammer in his hands."

West Portal of the CSX Railroad tunnel at White Sulphur Springs. The tunnel was bored into steeply dipping beds of the Brallier Formation.

A syncline in the Brallier Formation of Late Devonian age is exposed on the north side of I-64, west of exit 183.

The bumps on the upper surfaces of these thin sandstone beds in the Foreknobs Formation are ripple marks formed by wave currents that swept sand across a Late Devonian seafloor.

East of White Sulphur Springs, the interstate turns southeast, ascending the valley of Wades Creek to the crest of Allegheny Mountain, on the Virginia border. Brown, thin-bedded layers of the Brallier and Foreknobs Formations of Late Devonian time are periodically exposed on the east limb of the Browns Mountain Anticlinorium. Many of the outcrops contain a variety of folds easily seen from the road. One prominent example in the Brallier lies just west of exit 183, where a syncline is exposed on the north side of the highway.

Just west of the Virginia border at mile marker 184, several exposures of the Foreknobs rocks present themselves. The last of the exposures, just west of the state line, is an excellent example of a *dip slope*, where the dip of a rock layer is roughly the same as the angle of the slope. The tops of the beds constitute the slope of the land, resembling big sheets of rock leaning against the surface. The tops of the Foreknobs sheets in this case are covered by ripple marks that were created by currents of water flowing over the sand and mud where it had come to rest on an offshore shelf. They are hard to see by travelers heading east. We recommend you continue to the first exit in Virginia, Jerry's Run Trail, turn around, and head west. The shoulder is wide enough for safely exiting a car, and the exposures are well worth the time.

Interstate 77/Interstate 64
CHARLESTON—BECKLEY
61 miles

Traveling southeast, the combined I-77/I-64 highway begins at exit 59 for I-64 and exit 101 for I-77 in downtown Charleston. Thereafter, the mile markers and exit numbers are those of I-77. The combined highway is the West Virginia Turnpike, which dates originally from the 1950s and was completely upgraded to interstate standards only in 1986. The turnpike was not constructed to supersede a federal or state highway as so many interstate highways were. Rather, it represented an entirely new route intended to link the southeastern counties of the state with the central and western regions while cutting in half the driving time between them.

As with many highways constructed in the Mountain State, the West Virginia Turnpike's architects sought to make use of whatever valleys ran in the right directions to reduce costs. Those valleys are narrow because they were created by creeks, not by rivers. To create an adequate right-of-way often required dynamiting the valley walls and moving millions of cubic yards of rocks and earth. The resultant exposures provide excellent views of the underlying geology of the Southern Basin.

The farther south and east you travel on this highway the greater the terrain's relief, with significant contrasts in elevation as it approaches the eastern edge of the Appalachian Plateaus Province. If you are traveling from south to north, there will be an obvious opening up of the terrain as the Appalachian Plateaus levels off at progressively lower elevations.

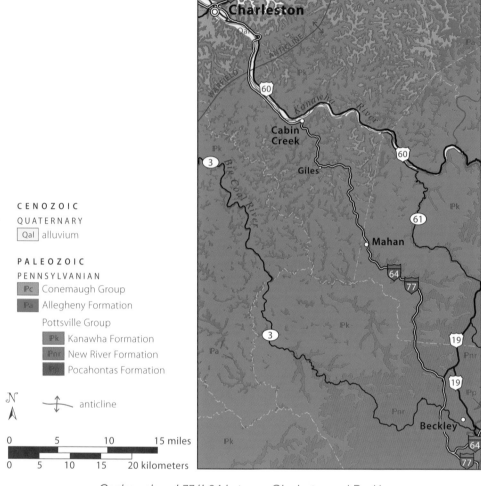

CENOZOIC
QUATERNARY
Qal alluvium

PALEOZOIC
PENNSYLVANIAN
IPc Conemaugh Group
IPa Allegheny Formation
      Pottsville Group
      IPk Kanawha Formation
      IPnr New River Formation
      IPp Pocahontas Formation

N

⤙ anticline

0   5   10   15 miles
0   5   10   15   20 kilometers

Geology along I-77/I-64 between Charleston and Beckley.

Between downtown Charleston and the community of Cabin Creek, the interstate follows the Kanawha River valley floored by Quaternary-age stream deposits. The West Virginia Turnpike begins at exit 96, and just south of that the interstate crosses to the south side of the Kanawha, and for the next 10 miles or so, it closely parallels the CSX Railroad's main line. Initially, the valley walls include exposures of Middle Pennsylvanian Allegheny Formation sandstones. But as the highway approaches the axis of the Warfield Anticline that runs nearly perpendicular to the river, older Middle Pennsylvanian rocks, the Kanawha Formation, line the valley, though extensive vegetation hides them from view. The upper half of the Kanawha contains several thick sandstones, named the Salt Sands by drillers for the salty groundwater, or brines, within these layers. These brines were heavily used by industries in the Kanawha

Valley. Several coals from the upper part of the Kanawha Formation were surface mined from the hilltops surrounding the valley, and the No. 2 Gas coal in the middle Kanawha was mined from the valley walls.

At Cabin Creek, the turnpike leaves the Kanawha Valley and heads up Cabin Creek. The valley walls are lined with tall exposures of the Kanawha Formation. The Kanawha contains a lot of coal, and the region between Cabin Creek and Paint Creek to the south is one of the most extensively mined areas along the route.

Several miles to the south, at the town of Giles, the turnpike turns east into a small valley created by Greens Brook. It then punches through a ridge by means of an enormous roadcut and enters the Paint Creek Valley, along which it will run for about 15 miles. The roadcut bypasses a tunnel, originally constructed for the turnpike. The tunnel is now used as a site for antiterrorism exercises by various government agencies. Among the rocks found in the Kanawha, the cut exposes the Fire Clay coal, which contains a *tonstien*, or ancient ash layer, ejected by volcanoes to the east during the Alleghanian Orogeny. The ash accumulated in the quiet water of peat swamps and is now preserved between layers of the Fire Clay coal. The distinctive ash layer serves as an important correlation tool in the Kanawha Formation and, as measured by the decay of radioactive isotopes, has been dated to between 315 and 310 million years old. The cut also reveals beds of a variety of Kanawha Formation units: sandstones, coals, and dark shales more than 100 feet thick.

At exit 66, near Mahan, the route crosses the contact between the Kanawha Formation and the next oldest formation of the Pottsville Group: the New River Formation of Early Pennsylvanian age. Unlike the lower part of the Kanawha, the New River Formation contains a greater proportion of sandstones, some

Outcrop of the Nuttall Sandstone along the southbound on-ramp. The Nuttall is the uppermost sandstone in the New River Formation, and its high quartz content makes it a predominant cliff former in the region.

of which were deposited by rivers draining the North American continental interior to the west. This is rather unusual in that most of the Pennsylvanian strata are comprised of sediments shed from the rising Appalachian Mountains to the east. The sandstones derived from the western source tend to be very quartz rich and are resistant cliff formers in this region. The Nuttall Sandstone at the top of the New River Formation is one example. It is exposed between exits 63 and 60. From mile marker 56 south to the point where I-64 and I-77 divide, southeast of Beckley at mile marker 40, more or less continuous exposures of the cross-bedded Nuttall Sandstone and other members of the New River Formation are easily visible until just south of the toll plaza.

I-77

Beckley—Princeton—
East River Mountain Tunnel
31 miles

The stretch of I-77 between Beckley and Virginia, which is also the West Virginia Turnpike, travels more or less due south and crosses over a major landform known as Flat Top Mountain. Unlike the route from Charleston to Beckley, which struck out cross-country, so to speak, south of Beckley I-77 parallels US 19, thus conforming to the more common practice wherein an interstate highway supersedes a federal highway.

The route crosses some of the most intensely mined territory in the state. In the course of the 1870s, as Collis P. Huntington was completing the Chesapeake & Ohio Railway across the northern edge of the state's southern coalfield counties, financier Frederick J. Kimball made a trip to the southeastern edge of the same region with his wife and another couple. Reportedly, their exploration of the Flat Top Mountain area, which revealed a number of easily spotted coal beds, first led Kimball to realize the enormous coal reserves waiting to be exploited, then to order his business associates to acquire the right to mine that coal from as many local residents as possible, and finally to construct what would become the Norfolk & Western Railway to transport that coal to the East Coast.

This stretch of the highway does not pass any active mining operations, but those travelers who exit the interstate and travel the two-lane country roads will soon come upon signs announcing one or another unincorporated village that had at one time been a coal company town housing miners and their families. In most cases, these mines ceased operations decades ago, the structures were dismantled, and the railroad tracks were taken up as well. If you look carefully along the side of any one of these roads, you may detect the location of a railroad right-of-way, but it will have returned to a state of nature.

South of the point where I-64 splits off and heads east, I-77 continues to travel over members of the New River Formation, as can be seen in an exposure at the point where Raleigh County Route 25 crosses over the interstate. At mile marker 36.5 gray shales appear, underlain by channel sandstones with the telltale concave lower surface made by ancient streams. Four miles farther

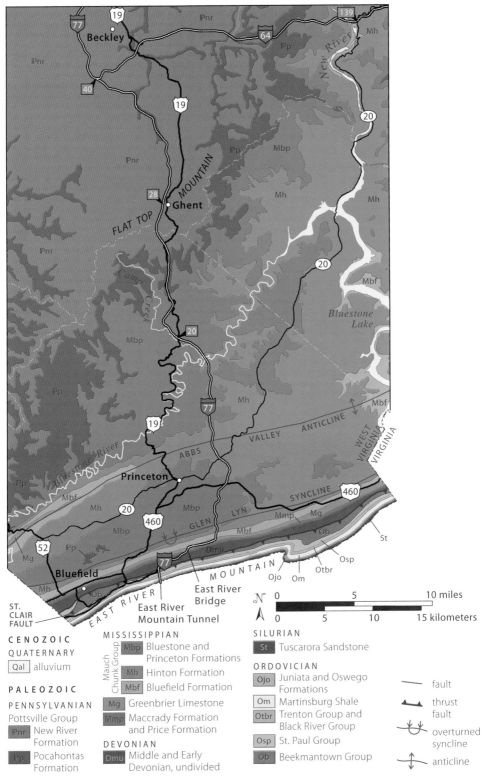

CENOZOIC

QUATERNARY

Qal alluvium

PALEOZOIC

PENNSYLVANIAN

Pottsville Group

Pnr New River Formation

Pp Pocahontas Formation

MISSISSIPPIAN

Mauch Chunk Group

Mbp Bluestone and Princeton Formations

Mh Hinton Formation

Mbf Bluefield Formation

Mg Greenbrier Limestone

Mmp Maccrady Formation and Price Formation

DEVONIAN

Dmu Middle and Early Devonian, undivided

SILURIAN

St Tuscarora Sandstone

ORDOVICIAN

Ojo Juniata and Oswego Formations

Om Martinsburg Shale

Otbr Trenton Group and Black River Group

Osp St. Paul Group

Ob Beekmantown Group

— fault

▲ thrust fault

⧫ overturned syncline

↕ anticline

Geology along I-77 between Beckley and the East River Mountain Tunnel.

south, at mile marker 32.5, evidence of these former rivers continues with excellent exposures of coarse, cross-bedded channel-fill sandstones and point bar surfaces produced by the meandering of the streams. Exposures of these sandstones continue as the highway heads south.

Between exit 40 and Ghent, I-77 ascends the northern slope of Flat Top Mountain. At the highest point, the highway reaches an elevation of more than 3,200 feet, which is at the level of the Sewell coal in the middle part of the New River Formation. For purposes of comparison, in the vicinity of Charleston the highway elevation is around 800 feet. Just south of the toll plaza at Ghent is an exposure of New River sandstones, shales, and thin coal beds.

South of exit 28, the route begins to descend the southern slope of Flat Top Mountain, dropping more than 1,000 feet in elevation in a couple of miles. As that happens, a view opens up to the south that is breathtaking. In the middle distance, you see the terrain typical of the Appalachian Plateaus: hills and ridges seemingly running in all directions—the product of the arbitrary processes of weathering and erosion. On the horizon, however, slightly more than 20 miles away, appears something altogether different: a more or less continuous ridge running at what may seem to be right angles to the interstate. That ridge is known as East River Mountain where I-77 encounters it; farther to the north, it is called Peters Mountain. This ridge is the westernmost landform of the Valley and Ridge Province.

At mile marker 23 the highway passes the Mississippian-Pennsylvanian boundary. Unlike the occurrence of this boundary in the Northern Basin along I-68, where the Middle Kanawha equivalent—the Lower Connoquenessing Sandstone—is just above the Mississippian Mauch Chunk Group, here the Pennsylvanian Pocahontas Formation is in contact with the Mauch Chunk. This suggests that several thousand feet of rock comprising the Pocahontas, New River, and lower Kanawha Formations were never deposited in the north and illustrates the tremendous difference in the subsidence of the basins.

The transition from the Mauch Chunk Group to the Pocahontas Formation represents a dramatic shift in environments across the Mississippian-Pennsyl-vanian boundary. Dry climates of the Mississippian Period gave way to tropical conditions during the Early and Middle Pennsylvanian Period. Much of the Pocahontas was deposited on low-lying coastal plain environments dotted by coal swamps that flourished in the wet, humid climate. Plant fossils, including seeds of the fern *Neuropteris,* are common at the Mississippian-Pennsylvanian boundary at mile marker 23.

North of exit 20 (Camp Creek) lie exposures of sandstones and the Pride Shale, a nearly 100-foot-thick, dark-gray shale deposited in marine environ-ments of Late Mississippian time. The Pride, part of the Bluestone Formation of the Mauch Chunk Group, serves as a regionally extensive marker bed and has yielded a variety of fossils, including fish from limestone nodules near its base. As the highway continues south it passes a tall cliff of the Princeton Sandstone and continues to older limestones of the Hinton Formation by mile marker 10. Other units of that formation, specifically gray and tan sandstones as well as marine shales, are exposed at exit 9, Princeton.

Seeds from the fern Neuropteris *in the Pocahontas Formation of Early Pennsylvanian age. They vary from 1 to 2 centimeters in length.*

The Pride Shale, deposited near active deltas during a regional transgression in Late Mississippian time, is exposed along the northbound lanes north of the Camp Creek exit along I-77.

Just south of exit 9, the highway begins to descend a long grade. Rocks of the Mauch Chunk Group are nearly horizontal until south of mile marker 6, where the highway passes through a water gap created by Twelve Mile Creek. This gap passes through the first of the northeast-southwest-trending ridges that characterize the Valley and Ridge Province to the south. Although not well exposed, the rocks that form the ridge are from the lower part of the Mauch Chunk Group and have been folded so severely that they are now overturned, dipping steeply to the southeast on the east limb of the Glen Lyn Syncline. The highway turns in a west-southwesterly direction and travels along the Spangler Valley for several miles. Where it turns briefly south, overturned light-gray beds of the Middle Mississippian Greenbrier Limestone are exposed on the east side of the highway just north of the bridge across East River.

South of East River, I-77 turns west once again and follows Big Spring Brook for another mile. Overturned beds of thin sandstone and shale of the Brallier Formation, deposited in Late Devonian time, dip steeply toward the highway near mile marker 3.5. At exit 1 for US 52 are carbonates of the Early Ordovician Beekmantown Group dipping to the southeast. Unlike the Brallier rocks, these are right-side up. This unusual juxtaposition is the work of the St. Clair Fault, a major thrust fault that formed during the Alleghanian Orogeny. The Ordovician carbonates are in the headwall block above the fault, which was uplifted nearly 6,000 feet and shoved tens of miles to the west. As the block slid, friction along the fault bent the rocks of the footwall up and over, resulting in the series of overturned beds to the north on the east limb of the Glen Lyn Syncline.

The Beekmantown Group of Early Ordovician age at exit 1 on I-77. The dolomite beds on the left can be seen dipping to the southeast, while those on the right are more deformed above the St. Clair Fault and are not easily distinguished.

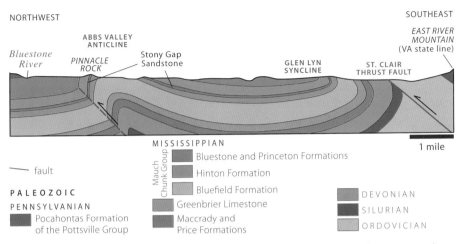

Movement along the St. Clair thrust fault shoved older rocks on top of younger rocks in and east of Bluefield. The force also folded and faulted the rocks to the northwest of the fault. –Modified from Whisonant and Schultz, 1986; Reger and Price, 1926

In this part of the state, the St. Clair Fault also marks the western edge of the Valley and Ridge Province, a region of regularly repeating northeast-southwest-trending ridges. The Beekmantown carbonates make one last appearance in the Mountain State, this time with distinctive black chert nodules. Look quickly because shortly thereafter I-77 enters East River Mountain Tunnel, which takes it into Virginia.

Nodules of black chert define southeast-dipping bedding in the Beekmantown Group. Most nodules are about 2 to 4 inches in length.

US 19
Exit 57 of I-79—Summersville—Beckley
67 miles

The stretch of US 19 between I-79 and Beckley, known as Corridor L of the Appalachian Corridor highway system, is also called the Mountaineer Expressway. South of I-79, the highway immediately crosses the hinge line and enters the Southern Basin of the Appalachian Plateaus. Here, the thickness of Pennsylvanian and Mississippian units increases dramatically compared to those in the Northern Basin, and the route remains within Pennsylvanian rocks all the way to Beckley.

The rocks along the highway are nearly horizontal with a slight regional northwest dip of about 1.5 degrees. As such, the units along the entire route get progressively older to the south. The high relief of the landscape in this area, combined with the low dip, produces a distinct relationship between elevation and rock type. Older rocks are exposed in the deep valleys while younger rocks cap the various mountains and knobs.

For example, at its junction with I-79, US 19 is 1,400 feet above sea level and surrounded by the characteristic red beds and sandstones of the Conemaugh Group of Late Pennsylvanian age. Within 5 miles the highway begins to descend a small valley carved by Bear Run, dropping 400 feet by the time it crosses the Little Birch River. As it does so, Conemaugh rocks give way to those of the older Middle Pennsylvanian Allegheny Formation.

While both the Conemaugh and Allegheny are composed primarily of sandstones and shales deposited in ancient river channels and on their floodplains,

Stacked meandering stream channels of the Middle Pennsylvanian Allegheny Formation are separated by thin shales and coal beds. The long, low-angle surfaces resulted from point bar sands deposited as the river cut across its floodplain.

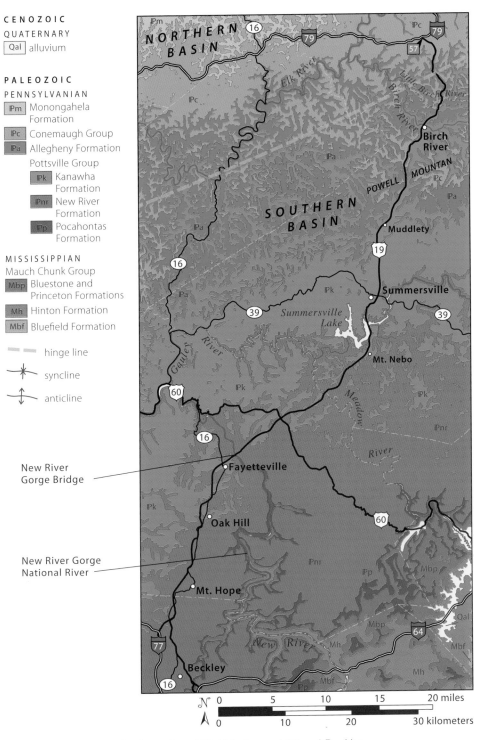

CENOZOIC
QUATERNARY
Qal alluvium

PALEOZOIC
PENNSYLVANIAN
Pm Monongahela
Formation
Pc Conemaugh Group
Pa Allegheny Formation
Pottsville Group
Pk Kanawha
Formation
Pnr New River
Formation
Pp Pocahontas
Formation

MISSISSIPPIAN
Mauch Chunk Group
Mbp Bluestone and
Princeton Formations
Mh Hinton Formation
Mbf Bluefield Formation

— — — hinge line

⚹ syncline

⇕ anticline

New River
Gorge Bridge

New River Gorge
National River

NORTHERN BASIN

SOUTHERN BASIN

Birch River

POWELL MOUNTAIN

Muddlety

Summersville

Summersville Lake

Mt. Nebo

Meadow River

Elk River

Little Birch River

Birch River

Gauley River

Fayetteville

Oak Hill

Mt. Hope

Beckley

New River

N
0   5   10   15   20 miles
0   10   20   30 kilometers

Geology along US 19 between I-79 and Beckley.

the Allegheny can be distinguished from the Conemaugh by the presence of thick sequences of stacked river channel sandstones and a lack of red bed paleosols. The thick, tan to white sandstones, along with the thin, tan shales and coals squeezed between them, produce several striking outcrops along both sides of the road. Cross beds and low-angle point bar surfaces are common, products of the river currents that transported the sand.

South of the Little Birch River, US 19 follows another of that stream's tributaries, Laurel Run, and long outcrops of the Allegheny Formation continue. US 19 climbs to 1,600 feet before descending the Mill Creek valley, and sandstones of the Allegheny Formation give way to the Middle Pennsylvanian Kanawha Formation of the Pottsville Group. The location of the contact is close to the intersection with Davis Street and a group of large buildings on the east side of the highway. South of here, the next outcrops, on the east side near the bottom of the valley, are Kanawha Formation. Mill Creek valley quickly bottoms out near its confluence with the Birch Rive, at the village of the same name, at 1,140 feet above sea level.

South of Birch River, US 19 begins to climb the shoulder of Powell Mountain and, in doing so, ascends more than 1,000 feet. The right-of-way was constructed by blasting a shelf from the side of the mountain wide enough to permit not only two lanes in each direction, with a median strip in between, but a third climbing lane for slow-moving vehicles. That work revealed a nearly continuous and complete section of the Kanawha Formation exposed in several spectacular roadcuts along the way to the top of Powell Mountain.

Sandstones are more frequent in the Allegheny Formation than they are in the overlying Conemaugh Group rocks to the north. Photo taken south of mile marker 65.

At mile marker 58, south of the Birch River exit, you can see one of several dark, silty shale units in the Kanawha that were deposited in a nearshore marine environment. The large tan ovals are limestone concretions that formed after the muds were deposited.

On the north side of Powell Mountain, US 19 passes about 500 feet of stacked coals, shales, siltstones, and sandstones. Although much of the unit was deposited on land in stream channels and on floodplains, dark shales containing marine fossils occur periodically throughout the unit and represent at least ten transgressions of an inland sea that flooded the low-lying coastal plain. Here, the thickness of the Kanawha Formation represents a middle ground between that of the Northern and Southern Basins. To the north, it thins to less than 200 feet, and to the south it thickens to around 2,000 feet. The thickness trend corresponds to increased subsidence in the Southern Basin, which provided more room for sediment to accumulate from source areas to the east.

Sandstone beds become more frequent in the upper part of the Kanawha Formation. The top of the unit is marked by the Kanawha Black Flint marine zone, deposited during one of the many transgressions that occurred during the Middle Pennsylvanian. Thick sandstones of the Allegheny Formation dominate the section above the Kanawha and are exposed on the west side of the highway across from a scenic overlook, where the highway reaches its highest point at around 2,200 feet (the top of this mountain is 160 feet higher still). Coals of the Allegheny Formation, including the economically important No. 5 Block coal, are also exposed at this elevation.

As the highway crosses Powell Mountain there are dramatic views of the high hills and deep valleys that lie to the east and south. Many of the surrounding

Stacked river channel sandstones of the Allegheny Formation separated by thin shale and coal beds near the summit of Powell Mountain.

hills have been mined for coals, both on the surface and underground. The coals are in the upper half of the Kanawha Formation. As US 19 descends the valley of Brushy Fork, look up to the south to see the edge of a former surface mine that created a distinctive flat area, which contrasts with the rounded hills in the vicinity. This location is an early example of the practice of mountaintop mining/valley fill dating back to the 1980s.

In mountaintop mining/valley fill operations, numerous coal beds are targeted simultaneously. Usually there is a lower, thick main bed and several smaller ones located above. While the process removes coal more efficiently than smaller operations, it creates tremendous volumes of undesirable waste rock, called *overburden*, which is pushed into nearby stream valleys (the valley fill) and sculpted into what resembles a large, stepped upside-down triangle. A little farther to the south near the exit for Muddlety, the tops of several mountains on the east side of the highway contain both former and active surface mines, as well as slurry impoundments, which hold small bits of coal and rock washed from mined coals before they are shipped to customers.

Why is there such a dramatic high-relief landscape in this location as compared to the low relief common in the Northern Basin? The answer in part has to do with the abundance of sandstone of the Middle Pennsylvanian Allegheny and upper Kanawha Formations. Unlike the easily weathered, shale-dominated Conemaugh, Monongahela, and Dunkard units that cover most of the Northern Basin, the Allegheny and upper Kanawha Formations, which cover large portions of the Southern Basin, contain more resistant sandstones. Certainly, streams have been able to carve deep valleys into these rocks, but erosion outside of the channels themselves has been much slower. Otherwise the great contrasts in elevation between the summits of the hills and the bottoms of adjacent valleys would not be present.

Near Summersville, exposures of the lower half of the Kanawha Formation can be seen periodically along both sides of the road. Underground and surface mining of coals from the middle portion of the Kanawha has occurred in the region. (Note to travelers: This section of highway is notorious for speed traps. Please be mindful of your speed as you pass by the town.)

The highway crosses a bridge over Summersville Lake, a reservoir that snakes through the hills east of town and was created by the damming of the Gauley River. The Summersville Dam, west of the highway, was constructed between 1960 and 1966 and is the second largest earthen dam in the eastern United States. During the fall when the lake levels are high, scheduled releases of water from the lake race down the Gauley River and provide world-class whitewater conditions that attract paddlers from far and wide.

Below the bridge, tall cliffs of the Nuttall Sandstone rise from the lake surface and signal the top of the New River Formation. This sandstone composes roughly the uppermost 200 feet of the New River Formation and is generally light colored and quartz rich, with coarse conglomeratic bases. Unlike most of the Pennsylvanian sandstones, the Nuttall Sandstone was deposited by rivers draining the craton of the North American continent to the west. Because the sands had to travel much farther than those sourced from the ancestral Appalachian Mountains to the east, most of the feldspars and other minerals were weathered away, concentrating the quartz. The high-quartz content also makes the Nuttall beds very resistant and therefore a prominent cliff-forming layer in the area.

View of Nuttall Sandstone cliffs on Long Point in Summersville Lake. Photo was taken when the lake level was low, and normally submerged blocks of fallen sandstone are visible along the base of the cliff.

To better view Summersville Lake and the Nuttall Sandstone turn right, or west, on WV 129, across from the town of Mt. Nebo, and head 1.2 miles to Long Point Overlook. Erosion of the Long Point cliffs occurred when the Gauley River was untamed, producing sculpted cliffs of resistant cross-bedded sandstone. A short walk from the overlook along a trail to the east will take you to a large block of the Nuttall along the trail, offering an up-close view of the sandstone's characteristic quartz grains and cross beds. For travelers interested in viewing the Summersville Lake Dam, WV 129 continues west and crosses the dam about 2.5 miles from US 19.

South of Summersville Lake, exposures of both the lower Kanawha and uppermost New River Formations can be seen. On the east side of US 19 at mile marker 34.5, exposures contain *cut-and-fill* structures, which were produced by the erosion (cut) and subsequent deposition (fill) of sand by ancient rivers. An excellent exposure of the Nuttall Sandstone with prominent cross bedding appears on the east side of US 19 as the route approaches the bridge over Meadow River, at the Nicholas-Fayette county line. Looking out near the top of the valley, you can see a break in the slope that marks the continuation of this Nuttall Sandstone.

As the highway approaches the New River from the north, it begins to descend onto a broad, flat landscape that has developed on the Nuttall Sandstone. The drop is not precipitous, but it does place you a couple of hundred feet lower than you were at Summersville. Just northeast of the bridge, at mile marker 20, is the Canyon Rim Visitor Center, operated by the National

New River Gorge

At mile marker 20, US 19 crosses the New River Gorge on one of the highest single-span bridges in the western hemisphere. The New River flows 876 feet below the bridge. Prior to its construction, crossing the New River valley took about one hour; now it just takes a minute or so. To commemorate its construction, the bridge is closed to all vehicular traffic and open only to pedestrians on the third Saturday of every October (known as Bridge Day).

The New River's ability to create such a deep valley suggests that it took advantage of fractures in the Nuttall Sandstone. Here, the river's general northwest course runs perpendicular to the regional trend of folds. However, one set of joints, or fractures, in the underlying bedrock trends northwest. The fractures, produced by the same compressional forces as the folds, enables the river to cut down through the hard sandstone and through many older layers in the New River valley as well.

The New River cuts across many prominent topographic features in the Appalachian Mountains, including the imposing Allegheny Front to the south, at the town of Rich Creek. The New River is a *superimposed stream*, a stream that existed before the most recent uplift, and it has been actively cutting down through layers of younger rock, superimposing its original course on the modern landscape. The New River would have had to cut down not only through the rocks in the gorge but at least 1 to 1.5 miles of younger Pennsylvanian and possibly Permian rocks above them.

One puzzling aspect of the New River that geologists have pondered is its age. However, there is no definitive method for determining the age of a river.

The New River Gorge Bridge as seen from river level.

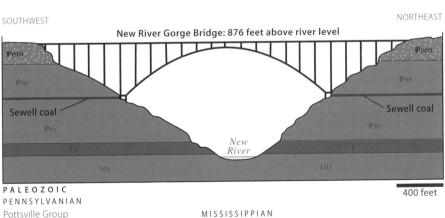

Rock layers in the vicinity of the US 19 bridge over the New River Gorge. The hard Nuttall Sandstone is the rimrock for the gorge and provides a strong foundation for the bridge.
—Modified from Cecil and others, 1989

One possibility, based on cross-cutting relationships, suggests that it may be as old as 320 million years, the age of the youngest rocks in the gorge. Another possibility is that it is as young as 65 million years, presumably the age of the last major uplift in the area. Other ideas about the New River's age are based on observed rates of stream erosion in modern rivers of North America and yield much younger ages in millions of years, but they do not take into account erosion of the younger rocks that once existed above the modern rocks but have been eroded away. The quest for the New River's age continues.

The New River Gorge National River is overseen by the National Park Service and is dedicated to preserving the natural beauty of both the river and the gorge along a 53-mile stretch, from the New River Gorge Bridge upstream to the town of Hinton, West Virginia. The river was one of the first sites of coal mining in the state, which began in the early 1870s when the Chesapeake & Ohio Railway was constructed along the gorge.

The mining operations targeted the famous Sewell coal, which is located about halfway down the walls of the gorge near the lower abutments of the New River Gorge Bridge. In fact, the lower abutments of the bridge are set within an abandoned underground Sewell mine. The Sewell was often referred to as one of the "smokeless coals" for its low ash and sulfur content, at least compared to coals in the Northern Basin, and was used primarily in steel furnaces. US 19 crosses over many abandoned underground mining operations from just east of the New River Gorge all the way to Beckley, which lies about 25 miles to the south.

Park Service. In addition to information about the bridge and local geology, the center has a short trail leading to a spectacular overlook of the New River Gorge Bridge. Stairs along the walkway wind around large blocks of the Nuttall Sandstone. From this vantage point, it is clear why this region is called the Appalachian Plateaus: the area around the gorge is a low-relief, elevated landscape made of rocks resistant to the forces of weathering and erosion, though not entirely so.

South of the New River and the town of Fayetteville are repeated exposures of the New River Formation, which are still visible even as the highway crosses back into Kanawha Formation rocks from time to time. The upper part of the New River Formation is exposed at the exit for Mt. Hope. Here the Nuttall is well above the road level, and the highway passes by shales, thin sandstones, and coals deposited in coastal plain and shallow marine environments along the margins of an inland sea that, during Early Pennsylvanian time, was located to the south. Exposures of sandstone, shale, and coal in the New River Formation continue as US 19 makes its way to the West Virginia Turnpike (I-77/I-64) north of Beckley.

US 52
Huntington—Williamson—
Virginia State Line
171 miles

Prior to the construction of I-64 and I-77, east-west travel across the southern half of the state was essentially limited to two federal highways: US 60, known as the Midland Trail, and US 52. US 60 runs along the northern edge of the southern coalfields, the largest deposits of this resource in the Mountain State, while US 52 traverses the heart of this region. Paralleling much of its route is the Norfolk Southern Railway, formerly the Norfolk & Western Railway, most of which was constructed during the 1870s and 1880s. It mainly transported coal, produced by the rapidly expanding mining operations, to Chesapeake Bay for distribution along the East Coast for various industrial uses, as well as for export. By the time of its completion in the 1890s, the N&W had become a trunk line linking the Atlantic Coast to the Midwest, and as a consequence coal moved both east and west.

Like the railroad, US 52 provided passage through the mountains, and after World War II, when the mining industry rapidly mechanized its operations, slashing thousands of jobs in the process, this highway provided many displaced miners and their families the route to midwestern cities, where they sought employment in heavy industries fueled, in many instances, by the very coal they were formerly employed to mine. So great was the reduction in force in the mines that the southern coalfields region had lost almost half of its former population by the 1960 census.

The western half of the highway's route passes through that part of southwestern West Virginia where the principal resource is not coal but rather timber. Expect to encounter logging trucks along the way. Only from the vicinity of Williamson south will the highway pass through the coalfields.

Huntington to Williamson

US 52 enters the state from Ohio through downtown Huntington, and after 2 miles, it heads west, joining with I-64 at exit 6. Sandstones and shales of the Conemaugh Group, deposited in Late Pennsylvanian time, are easily seen along the highway. At mile marker 4.5 the Ames marine zone, deposited during the most extensive of the marine transgressions during Late Pennsylvanian time, is exposed along the south side of the interstate.

Leaving I-64 at exit 1, US 52, now joined by WV 75, turns southwest and then south to enter the valley of the north-flowing Big Sandy River, which it follows until south of Hubbardstown. More or less continuous exposures of Conemaugh sandstone and shale lie east of the highway. The Conemaugh is easy to distinguish from older rocks to the south because it contains red bed paleosols that are absent in the older formations. These red beds are predominantly floodplain deposits that accumulated next to the rivers. As they were exposed to the atmosphere, oxygen bonded with iron in the sediments, converting them

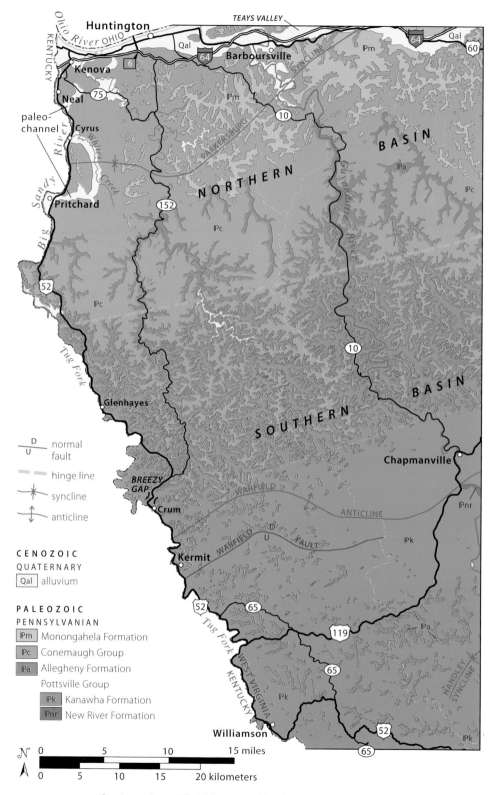

Geology along US 52 between Huntington and Williamson.

The distinctive red beds of the Conemaugh Group near Pritchard. Note the large, lens-shaped river channel sandstone in the middle of the outcrop.

to hematite, a reddish-brown mineral. The presence of hematite indicates that the climate during the Late Pennsylvanian Period was more arid than that during the Early to Middle Pennsylvanian Period. Humid climates would have leached the iron from the sediments, limiting the development of hematite and producing the gray and green shale layers common in the older formations.

WV 75 heads southeast from US 52, following a side valley that is a paleochannel of the Big Sandy, a wide meander that rejoins the present-day valley south of Neal. Miller Creek now flows through the upper part of this valley, Dock Creek the lower. A few miles south of Neal lies the northern end of another paleochannel in which the settlement of Cyrus is located. Where once the Big Sandy flowed, Whites Creek now runs northwest to the river. The paleochannel heads in a southeasterly direction for a few miles and then due south for a comparable distance, turning west to rejoin the current course of the river at Prichard.

It bears repeating that the bottomland of the Big Sandy, like that of many other rivers in the state, consists of alluvium: a mixture of sands and gravels deposited by the river. In a way, the location of this alluvium appears to contradict the geological principle of superposition, which states that older formations lie below younger ones. The formations along the valley walls are considerably older than the material at the bottom of the river. In the present example, and this applies to almost every river valley, weathering and erosion created the valley by removing the older rock and left behind the recently deposited alluvium.

South of Prichard, only a few small, isolated rock exposures can be observed along US 52. At Fort Gay is the confluence of the Tug Fork and the Levisa Fork. South of Glenhayes, the road continues along the Tug Fork River valley for several miles and then goes overland, first up Drag Creek and then, south of the junction with WV 152, down the valley of Bull Creek and through Breezy Gap before returning to the Tug Fork at Crum. At Breezy Gap, excavation for a portion of what will become the King Coal Highway has exposed a thick sequence of the upper portion of the Kanawha Formation of the Pottsville Group. The outcrop contains several gray river-channel sandstones, 10 to 12 feet thick, with thinner coal and shale layers in between. Plant fossils of Pennsylvanian age are common. The shales are gray to tan and do not contain the distinctive red beds common in the younger Conemaugh Group.

The fossil tree root Stigmaria *at Breezy Gap. The rootlets emanating from the thick main root helped anchor the trees* Lepidodendron *and* Sigillaria *in the waterlogged coal swamps.*

The Kanawha Formation was deposited in a rapidly subsiding foreland basin produced by the collision of North America and northwest Africa during the Alleghanian Orogeny. A range of environments is preserved in this 2,000-foot-thick package of rock dominated by thick sandstones and shales, former river and floodplain deposits; coastal swamps are preserved as coal. Periodically, the sea would cover the low-lying coastal regions, thus dark-gray to black shales and limestones that contain marine fossils are found within the unit. The sea's transgressions were caused by the melting of large continental ice sheets on Gondwanaland, in the southern hemisphere, during the Late Paleozoic ice age.

South of Crum, US 52 crosses the axis of the Warfield Anticline. This fold is the most prominent structure in the Southern Basin. The effect of this fold on the distribution of the rocks at the surface far surpasses that of the more subtle folds that characterize this lower portion of the Appalachian Plateaus Province. The fold places the Kanawha Formation at the surface over a larger area than if the formation had not been folded. This effect is evident on the state geologic map

Outcrop of the Kanawha Formation along the tracks that follow the Tug Fork River at Crum. The lower dark shales were deposited in a marine zone during one of the many transgressions that inundated low-lying coastal areas.

where the outcrop belt of the Kanawha widens to the south into a broad wedge shape.

South of the fold axis, and south of Kermit, lies the Warfield Fault, which at the surface extends for 17 miles. The trace of the fault closely parallels the axis of the Warfield Anticline, as they both run northeast, bend to the east, and bend back to the northeast. The plane of the fault dips approximately 45 degrees to the north and has displaced the rocks downward between 100 and 240 feet to the north. Unfortunately, erosion and vegetation have concealed the fault's presence.

Coal mining operations have been adversely influenced by the fault presence. Mines that target the Coalburg coal in the upper part of the Kanawha Formation are split by the fault, requiring separate portals and operations on each side. Whereas the vast majority of faults in West Virginia are either thrust or reverse faults formed by compressional forces associated with Alleghanian mountain building, the Warfield Fault is an extensional, or normal fault. This extension is thought to have followed the compression and folding of the rocks in the region, as they essentially relaxed and stretched after the compressional forces waned.

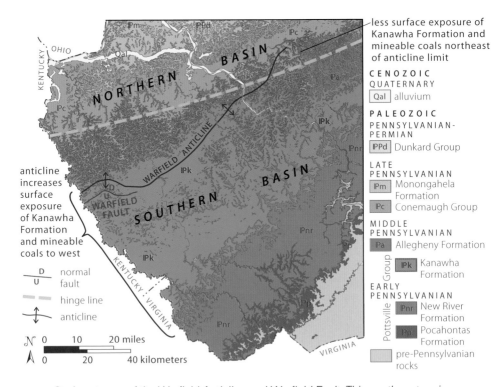

Surface traces of the Warfield Anticline and Warfield Fault. This gentle, yet regionally extensive anticline greatly widened the outcrop belt of the Kanawha Formation at the surface and increased the area available for mining its many valuable coal beds. –Modified from Coolen, 2003

Southeast of the junction of US 52 and US 119, the Robert C. Byrd Freeway (Corridor G), you can see exposures of the Kanawha Formation along the road, some of which are quite tall. Along this stretch, US 52 hopscotches back and forth across the Tug Fork, meaning travelers are momentarily in Kentucky in several places. Close to Williamson, US 52 returns once and for all to West Virginia, where it remains until east of Bluefield, where it crosses into Virginia.

As you travel from Ohio to Virginia on US 52, the higher the elevations of the surrounding terrain become. Heading south from Kenova, the Big Sandy River was approximately 580 feet above sea level, and the surrounding hills topped out at slightly more than 800 feet, a difference of roughly 220 feet. In the vicinity of Williamson, some of the highest ridges have elevations above 1,400 feet, while the Tug Fork lies at 720 feet, almost 700 feet below.

Two sites in Williamson serve as reminders of the impact of geology and topography upon this part of the state. The first is a high flood-control wall intended to protect the town from the ravages of the Tug Fork in times of flooding. The flooding is most often due to intense, prolonged rainstorms, including, on occasion, those associated with hurricanes that make their way over the central Appalachians even as they weaken in force. Over the years a number of devastating floods have affected communities along the Tug Fork, including Williamson. In the deep, narrow V-shaped valleys that characterize the topography of much of the Southern Basin, excess water floods the channels and bottomland, inundating everything in its path. This flood-control wall has significantly moderated the impact of major floods on Williamson.

The second site is the large sorting yard of the Norfolk Southern Railway, which runs east of downtown Williamson for several miles. Numerous parallel

The flood-control wall protects the town of Williamson within the narrow valley of the Tug Fork. Large flood gates on the routes into town can be closed during flood events.

strings of coal hoppers fill the yard. Some are loaded, ready to be assembled into coal trains of a hundred cars or more. Others are empty, waiting to be taken to nearby coal mines to be loaded. At the eastern edge of the coalfields, the railroad built a comparable yard in Bluefield for trains heading to the Atlantic seaboard.

Williamson to Bluefield

Near the eastern end of the railroad yard in Williamson, US 52 climbs out of the Tug Fork valley following Sycamore Creek, a tributary. For the next 46 miles the highway traverses the southern coalfield, alternately following ridge lines and descending into deep valleys in order to follow the courses of other tributaries of the Tug Fork. Grades are steep, posted speed limits are high, and the road makes S-curves. Along the way, loaded coal trucks are frequently encountered. Cautious driving is strongly recommended.

Here and there along the sides of the valley, rocks of the Kanawha Formation are exposed along the road. The Kanawha contains twenty-six of the sixty-two mineable coal beds in the Mountain State, and the landscape around the route has been and continues to be extensively mined. The method used by companies to mine the coal has a lot to do with its relationship to the surface. Coals in the middle of the Kanawha Formation, including the Eagle, No. 2 Gas, and Peerless, outcrop in the valley walls and have been extensively mined underground. Coals near the top of the Kanawha, such as the Coalburg and Stockton, lie near the tops of the valleys and are surface mined, in some cases as part of large mountaintop mining/valley fill operations.

US 52 descends into the valley of Pigeon Creek at Delbarton, where it joins WV 65. These roads share the highway to Taylorsville where the old US 52 turns east toward Varney and Mountain View.

South of Taylorsville, US 52/WV 65 turns to the east and begins to climb. As the highway ascends a long grade, note the large outcrop to the east. Continuous exposures like this are rare in this heavily vegetated region, but travelers here are rewarded with an extensive outcrop of the Kanawha Formation that includes thick gray to tan sandstones, gray to black shales, and numerous thin coal beds. This outcrop continues uphill almost to the entrance to the King Coal Highway, indicated by a sign for US 52 pointing to the left. WV 65 continues south away from the highway.

Those wanting to get a good look at the scale of mountaintop mining/valley fill operations should take the King Coal Highway. This new highway is intended to replace US 52 as the principal east-west route along West Virginia's southern border. When completed, it will run from Williamson to Bluefield and become part of I-73. At the present time, the right-of-way and two lanes running for approximately 10 miles have been completed and travel past extraordinary exposures of the Kanawha Formation.

The landscape surrounding the new route is very different from that passed by on old sections of US 52. Note the absence of trees and the abundance of bare rock. Immediately, the road begins to climb through deep cuts exposing the upper part of the Kanawha Formation. As the road levels off, it offers views

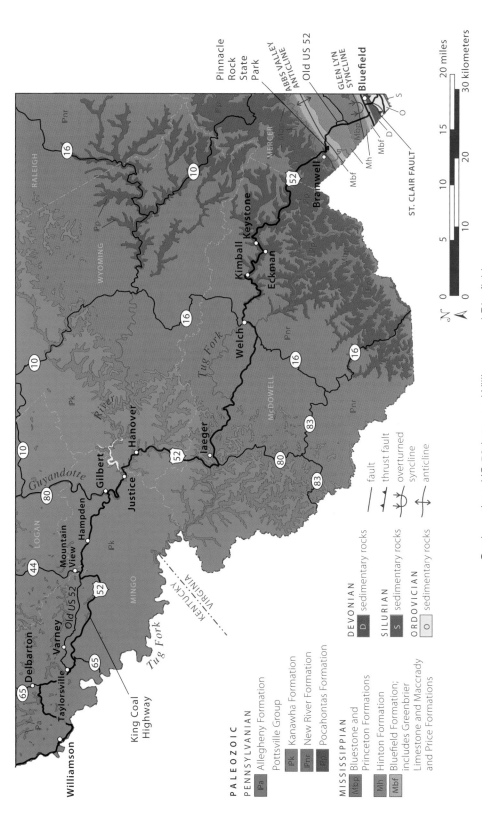

Geology along US 52 between Williamson and Bluefield.

PALEOZOIC

PENNSYLVANIAN

IPa Allegheny Formation

Pottsville Group

IPk Kanawha Formation
IPnr New River Formation
IPp Pocahontas Formation

MISSISSIPPIAN

Mbp Bluestone and
     Princeton Formations
Mh Hinton Formation
Mbf Bluefield Formation;
     includes Greenbrier
     Limestone and Maccrady
     and Price Formations

DEVONIAN

D sedimentary rocks

SILURIAN

S sedimentary rocks

ORDOVICIAN

O sedimentary rocks

——— fault

⊢⊢⊢ thrust fault

⟊ overturned
   syncline

↕ anticline

King Coal
Highway

Old US 52

ST. CLAIR FAULT

Pinnacle
Rock
State
Park

ABBS VALLEY ANTICLINE

Old US 52

GLEN LYN
SYNCLINE

Bluefield

N

0   5   10   15   20 miles

0   10   20   30 kilometers

On the ascent to the King Coal Highway, you can see one of several black shales sandwiched between sandstones in the Kanawha Formation, deposited in Early to Middle Pennsylvanian time when sea level rose and flooded a low-lying coastal plain.

The slope in the foreground is valley fill along the King Coal Highway, with exposures of the Kanawha Formation in the background. Note the rock-lined channels used to direct drainage down the valley fill.

of the surrounding hilltops, many of which have been modified by mountaintop mining/valley fill operations.

At the conclusion of active mining here, the exposed land was graded to create the comparatively flat terrain over which the highway now runs. Valley fills along the route can be seen by pulling off the road where it appears that the flat ground ends abruptly, resembling the edge of a cliff. There are many of these valley fills that resemble stepped inverted triangles, especially along the south side of the road.

These fills are not entirely stable. In more than one place there are short stretches of asphalt on what is otherwise a concrete road. In all likelihood these patches were used where the roadbed settled because the loose fill material compacted under the weight of vehicles and the road itself. Exposures of the Kanawha continue to the east, with several spectacular cuts lining the road as it begins its descent toward Mountain View.

Whether or not you followed the King Coal Highway or continued on old US 52, just south of the junction with WV 44, at Mountain View, US 52 passes through another thick cut of the Kanawha Formation. Here, nestled among the ubiquitous sandstones, shales, and coals lies the Fire Clay coal, which contains ancient ash ejected from volcanoes that were erupting to the east during the Alleghanian Orogeny. The ash is 315 to 310 million years old. US 52 makes a brief visit to Logan County but returns to Mingo County as the road descends

A series of outcrops of the Kanawha Formation line the road near the present-day eastern terminus of the King Coal Highway.

into the Guyandotte River valley. Along the way, travelers frequently are faced with what might be best described as a wall of trees covering the sides of the numerous high and steep valleys. Active mountaintop mining/valley fill operations to the east, along which the King Coal Highway will be extended, continue on the ridge just south of Hampden. Valley fills can occasionally be spotted on the road east of town.

US 52 and WV 80 merge in Gilbert. Along the Guyandotte River, which flows north to Huntington, are tall exposures of the Gilbert Sandstone, marine zone rocks, and coal, all of the same name. These rocks lie in the lower part of the Kanawha Formation, indicating that the road, as it heads southeast, is approaching the base of the Kanawha and the top of the New River Formation of Early Pennsylvanian age.

The town of Justice lies close to the Mingo-Wyoming county line, and there the Gilbert Sandstone is again exposed in cliffs along the road. Here and there you can see cross bedding produced by the currents of ancient streams. East of Justice, US 52/WV 80 follows Little Huff Creek and then Muzzle Creek south to Iaeger. Between Hanover and Iaeger lies the settlement of Ikes Fork, just north of a small anticline exposed in a bend along the north side of the road.

Several miles south of Ikes Fork, the road climbs to a high ridge that crosses the Wyoming-McDowell county line and passes an exposure the Kanawha Formation, making its southernmost appearance along this route. Two miles northwest of Iaeger, at the village of Johnny Cake, the highway reenters the valley of the Tug Fork. The Norfolk Southern Railway, which follows the river, once again parallels the highway. At Iaeger the elevation of the river is approximately 1,000 feet above sea level. In Williamson, its elevation is a little over 700 feet. The Appalachian Plateaus are rising in elevation as you proceed east along the highway.

US 52 follows the Tug Fork east of Iaeger (pronounced *Yay-ger*) for about 5 miles and then continues up Spice Creek, crosses over a drainage divide, and descends Little Indian Creek to the Tug Fork once again. Exposures of the New River Formation now line the road. Welch, the seat of McDowell County, is situated at the point where Elkhorn Creek enters the Tug Fork. As the highway moves up the gentle valley of Elkhorn Creek, the road enters the Pocahontas Formation of Early Pennsylvanian age. The Pocahontas Formation contains several mineable coal beds, the most productive of which is the Pocahontas No. 3 coal, which has been extensively mined in the area. Between Welch and Kimball, the road passes over a network of underground mines that targeted that coal, and current mines operate in coals higher in the formation on either side of the highway.

Like Welch and several other towns in the region, Kimball was not undermined. It was named for Frederick J. Kimball, founder and first president of the Norfolk & Western Railway, the predecessor of the Norfolk Southern, the right-of-way of which runs very close to the highway at a slightly higher elevation. Where Elkhorn Creek created a tight meander, the railroad tunnels through the adjacent ridge. The east portal of that short tunnel is situated in the midst of Kimball.

A coal bed in the upper part of the Pocahontas Formation in Kimball. The curved base of the overlying sandstone formed due to the weight of the sand pushing into the underlying muds above the coal.

In terms of the extent and exploitation of its coal deposits, McDowell was once the principal county of the southern coalfields. At one time, it was the most populous of West Virginia's fifty-five counties because of the enormous size of the workforce that labored in the hundreds of mines that dotted the landscape. Times have changed, and many mines now operate with a handful of employees, but some evidence of the former size of many operations can be observed at regular intervals along the highway: signs identifying the name of a community, including the term *unincorporated*. These communities were the coal company towns of the past—"coal camps" was the local term—in which hundreds of miners and their families lived. Along stretches of US 52 these communities were almost continuous, so intense was the mining of coal; the edge of one company town was simultaneously the boundary of the next one. Today, little is to be seen of many of these towns, apart from the signs themselves, but before and during World War II, they were thriving.

East of Kimball the Pocahontas No. 3 coal was extensively mined from the valley walls at a level higher than the road. These mines line the valley almost continuously until just west of the Bluestone River in Mercer County, about 15 miles to the east. In the communities of Eckman and Keystone, both company towns at one time, active mining operations are visible from the highway. In Keystone, the highway also passes another sorting yard of the Norfolk Southern, though it's considerably smaller than those in Williamson and Blue-field. Along this part of the route, thick layers of sandstone and coal seams of the Pocahontas Formation are clearly visible. East of Ennis, the highway leaves the valley of Elkhorn Creek for that of the Little Fork, one of its tributaries, and shortly thereafter it heads out of the valley and over a ridge en route to the valley of Simmons Creek. In the course of doing so, it passes by coal beds near which the aptly named town of Coaldale is located. Simmons Creek flows into the Bluestone River, which the highway crosses at Bramwell.

North of the bridge over the Bluestone River, the highway passes an exposure of grayish-brown and red shale. Although its appearance is subtle, it marks an important transition in geologic time. These shales are from Late Mississippian time and part of the Bluestone Formation in the Mauch Chunk Group, and their appearance indicates that the highway has crossed the boundary between the Mississippian and Pennsylvanian Periods.

Probably the most significant change affecting the appearance of the rocks across the boundary is climate, one of the most important variables affecting continental environments. The Late Mississippian climate has been interpreted as having been semiarid to seasonally wet and dry, which limited the development of coals and led to the formation of the red beds that characterize the Mauch Chunk. In contrast, the climate during the Early Pennsylvanian Period is thought to have been tropical. Coals of mineable extent are common in this period's rocks, and red beds are absent.

The boundary here has been extensively studied, with geologists now suggesting that part of the rock record across the boundary is missing. Geologists call a gap in the rock record an *unconformity*. The gap in the record was likely due to the onset of the Late Paleozoic ice age, when the expansion of glaciers produced a drop in sea level, exposing the Late Mississippian rocks to erosion prior to the deposition of the Pocahontas Formation in Pennsylvanian time.

The Late Mississippian rocks along the road also underwent another significant change. Unlike the majority of the rocks on the Appalachian Plateaus to the west, these rocks are tilted at a noticeable angle. In fact, as the road starts to climb the steep grade just east of Bramwell, an exposure reveals several vertical sandstone beds. The change in dip marks an increase in the compressional stress that was applied to the rocks and signals that we are approaching the highly deformed Valley and Ridge Province.

The ridge at Pinnacle Rock State Park lies near the boundary between the Appalachian Plateaus and the Valley and Ridge Provinces. The landscape between Pinnacle Rock and East River Mountain can be thought of as a transition zone between the provinces. In this zone, the erosion of two folds, the Abbs Valley Anticline and the Glen Lyn Syncline, has created a pattern of northeast-southwest-trending ridges that are commonplace in the Valley and Ridge Province. In the Appalachian Plateaus Province, topography is largely determined by the weathering and erosion of nearly horizontal rock layers. The topography is thus a function of the different rates of weathering of the hard sandstones and soft shales found in the Pennsylvanian rocks, and ridges and valleys run in all directions, which explains the often circuitous route taken by US 52. But the ridges to the east of Pinnacle Rock are unvarying in their direction and are divided only by gaps created by rivers that pre-dated their formation. These rivers cut down through the rocks even as they were being squeezed upward from the east during the Alleghanian Orogeny.

Pinnacle Rock State Park

Southeast of Bramwell and just east of County Road 52/4 is Pinnacle Rock State Park. The centerpiece of the park is a large outcrop of white to gray sandstone just to the east of the parking lot. The rock contains numerous horizontal lines that, at first glance, resemble bedding planes, possibly leading an observer to conclude that Pinnacle Rock is a tall outcrop of stacked horizontal beds. However, these lines are joint planes that formed as the rocks were tightly folded, and the sandstone beds here, like those observed along the roads, are nearly vertical. Think of them as the Seneca Rocks of Mercer County.

Pinnacle Rock is composed of the Stony Gap Sandstone of the Hinton Formation, which lies just below the Bluestone Formation shales, exposed near Bramwell. These beds are part of the Abbs Valley Anticline, an asymmetrical fold near the eastern edge of the Appalachian Plateaus Province. Pinnacle Rock is an eroded remnant of the steep western limb of that anticline. (See the cross section on page 91.) Close inspection of the surface of the sandstone reveals it is composed almost exclusively of sand and pebble-sized quartz

Pinnacle Rock is composed of nearly vertical beds of the Mississippian-age Stony Gap Sandstone.

East River Mountain, the border between West Virginia and Virginia, constitutes the horizon, as seen from atop Pinnacle Rock.

grains, which accumulated during a marine transgression in the Late Mississippian Period. The quartz also makes the sandstone very resistant, and the rock remains standing tall while the softer rocks around it have eroded away. Follow signs and climb to the overlook, which faces east-southeast. On the overlook, the horizon to the east is dominated by East River Mountain, along the top of which runs the boundary between West Virginia and Virginia.

As the highway descends to the southeast, it crosses the axis of the Abbs Valley Anticline and encounters the east limb of the fold where the dip of the rocks is much less than that on the western limb. The gently dipping rocks near the sign for Bluefield, just west of the town limits, are on the western limb of the adjacent Glen Lyn Syncline.

As US 52 descends into Bluefield from the north, the highway passes an exposure of thinly bedded sandstones and shales of the Bluefield Formation, the lowermost unit in the Mauch Chunk Group. The rocks appear to be dipping about 60 degrees east, but this is deceiving. The road has crossed the axis of the Glen Lyn Syncline, and the eastern limb is folded so severely that these rocks are actually upside down, which makes this an overturned syncline. This pattern continues, although no exposures can be seen, as the road crosses the Norfolk Southern tracks, turns left, merges with US 19, parallels the railroad for several blocks, and then turns south onto Bland Street. As the road climbs south, thin-bedded shale and sandstone of the Brallier Formation of Late Devonian age are also upside down on the east limb of the Glen Lyn Syncline.

An important structure lies hidden underneath the town of Bluefield, but its impact represents one of the most significant changes in the rocks and landscape of southern West Virginia. Bland Street passes over the St. Clair Fault, a major thrust fault that formed during the Alleghanian Orogeny and lies below a huge block of crust that was shoved to the northwest for several tens of miles and uplifted nearly 6,000 feet. Friction between the two blocks along the fault was responsible for bending the rocks of the Glen Lyn Syncline into their now overturned position, placing rocks of very different ages next to each other at the surface. An example lies about 1 mile south of the railroad tracks as US 52 veers to the east and then makes a sharp right-hand bend to the south around a church. Exposed between the church and its parking lot is a small, light-gray outcrop of the Beekmantown Group of Early Ordovician age. These carbonate rocks are about 100 million years older than those of the Brallier Formation on the west side of the fault. The St. Clair Fault also marks the western edge of the Valley and Ridge Province, and thus to the east begins the regular repetition of northeast-southwest-trending ridges described earlier.

Bland Avenue turns east and becomes Cumberland Avenue. US 52 joins US 460 for several miles, and when that highway turns to the north it continues to I-77 along the western slope of East River Mountain. Exposures of Ordovician rocks line I-77 as it enters the East River Mountain Tunnel and Virginia.

Overturned (upside down) beds of the Bluefield Formation in the Glen Lyn Syncline, on the north side of Bluefield. The beds were rotated into this position by drag from the overlying St. Clair Fault.

Near a church is a small outcrop of carbonates in the Ordovician-age Beekmantown Group that were shoved westward and upward along the St. Clair Fault and now lie above younger rocks in the area.

US 119
South Charleston—Kentucky State Line
70 miles

From the state capital, US 119 heads southwest across the Southern Basin of the Appalachian Plateaus to the Tug Fork River, the boundary between West Virginia and Kentucky. Its route takes it from Kanawha through Lincoln, Boone, and Logan Counties before crossing Mingo County to merge with US 52 northwest of Williamson, the county seat. In doing so, it passes some of the most spectacular exposures of rock along any highway in the state.

As in other parts of the state with steep, chaotic terrain, creating a four-lane highway with a median required blasting and removing millions of cubic feet of rock. The construction not only resulted in a relatively safe high-speed highway, it also provided travelers multiple opportunities to in effect look inside the Appalachian Plateaus at three of its principal rock units. From youngest to oldest, they are the Conemaugh Group of Late Pennsylvanian age and the Middle Pennsylvanian Allegheny and Kanawha Formations. In general, the rocks are older to the south as the highway enters the state's southern coalfields.

It will not escape travelers' attention that US 119 is known as the Robert C. Byrd Freeway because numerous road signs attest to that fact. Byrd (1917–2010)

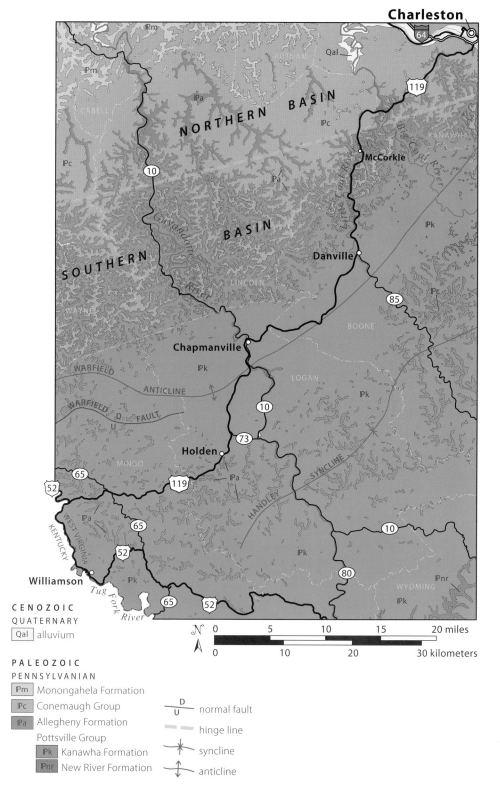

CENOZOIC
QUATERNARY
Qal alluvium

PALEOZOIC
PENNSYLVANIAN
IPm Monongahela Formation

IPc Conemaugh Group

IPa Allegheny Formation

Pottsville Group

IPk Kanawha Formation

IPnr New River Formation

$\dfrac{D}{U}$ normal fault

- - - hinge line

✳ syncline

↕ anticline

Geology along US 119 between South Charleston and the Kentucky State line.

served in the United States Senate from 1950 until he died sixty years later. He is the longest-serving senator in American history. Early on, he was determined to make use of his gradually increasing seniority and political influence to bring federal dollars to the Mountain State. Among his most successful legislative initiatives were those to fund construction of corridor highways through the central Appalachians, highways having many of the characteristics of interstate highways.

Often criticized as pork barrel spending, Byrd's appropriations created an enduring highway infrastructure that has made possible increased economic development within the Mountain State while significantly shortening the time required to cross it in almost any direction. For instance, to drive from Morgantown, just 7 miles south of the Pennsylvania state line, to Williamson on the Tug Fork River, the boundary between West Virginia and Kentucky, once might have taken as many as fourteen hours; now, it takes less than five. For the traveler interested in the state's geology, the exposures created by the construction of these corridor highways provide countless opportunities to see both the materials out of which the land was formed and evidence of the processes that have led to its current topography.

Two miles south of I-64 in Charleston, US 119 passes the first of many exposures of sandstones of the Allegheny Formation. These sandstones were deposited by meandering rivers flowing to the northwest from the ancestral Appalachian highlands. Shale separating the sandstone bodies represent fine-grained mud deposition on the adjacent floodplains. Individual channel sandstones are usually 20 to 30 feet thick, but some outcrops may be 100 feet thick because they are stacked. As the land subsided successive channels were deposited. More of the channels can be seen at the intersection with WV 601, as the route crosses Davis Creek. Farther south, a quarry lies west of the highway offering additional exposures of these sandstones.

Between mile markers 76 and 69 appear numerous exposures of massive sandstone beds. At mile marker 76 look to the north to see stacked river channels on both sides of the highway with cross beds formed by the movement of sand along the ancient streambeds. The exposure enables one to look at a Pennsylvanian-age river in cross section. As the highway climbs and crests, it passes by an outcrop of red beds to the west, indicating that it has crossed the Allegheny-Conemaugh contact and therefore has begun to traverse rocks of Late Pennsylvanian time. The red beds, a characteristic feature of the Conemaugh Group, developed after a shift from a more humid climate in the Middle Pennsylvanian (red beds are absent in the Allegheny Formation) to an arid climate, as iron in the muds was oxidized to hematite during Late Pennsylvanian time. At mile marker 75, the highway passes reddish beds of Conemaugh Group sandstones stained by the hematite in the red beds that overlie them. A comparable exposure may be seen at mile marker 72.

At mile marker 69, a coarse cross-bedded sandstone bed lies under a thin layer of coal, part of the No. 5 Block coal. The term *block* is intended to reflect the blocky nature of the coal when it breaks. This exposure enables one to view two stages of geological history, the first a time in which erosion was distributing sand

View to the southeast of river channel sandstones of the Allegheny Formation on the south side of Davis Creek.

A sandstone in the Conemaugh Group at mile marker 72. It is stained by hematite from the red beds above that are common in this unit.

from higher elevations to the east across this region, the second when extensive tropical vegetation had established itself, later to be covered over, compressed, and transformed into coal, though here that coal layer is too thin to mine.

The dramatic exposures seen thus far invite reflection on the processes by which massive beds of rock, in this case primarily sandstones and shales, formed in the first place. As noted above, the sand was transported here from higher elevations. What also should be borne in mind is that once these sediments were deposited their transformation into rock required the subsequent accumulation of 8,000 to 12,000 feet of material above. However, the landscape of West Virginia was probably not much higher in elevation than it is today. It may seem puzzling that so much rock could be removed without lowering the elevation, but as the rock above was slowly eroded, the mass of the continent was reduced, and the lithosphere slowly began to rise. This isostatic adjustment can happen continuously over long periods of time, and essentially thousands of feet of rock can be removed with no major net change in surface elevation.

As with most routes in the Mountain State, US 119 follows the courses of rivers and streams as much as possible, cutting through intervening ridges when necessary to cross from one valley to the next one. It heads southwest along the valleys of Trace Fork and Alum Creek, crosses the valleys of the Big and Little Coal Rivers, turns south and traverses those of Fuquay and Road Creeks, and subsequently reenters the Little Coal River valley, which it follows for a number of miles. North of mile marker 64, as it crosses the Little Coal River at the northernmost place, you can see exposures of shale, sandstone, and the ubiquitous red beds of the Conemaugh Group. They continue to be visible at the Kanawha-Lincoln county line, along with the No. 6 Block coal in the underlying Allegheny Formation. Near the town of McCorkle, the route reaches the upper part of the older Middle Pennsylvanian Kanawha Formation. These rocks, along with those of the lower part of the Allegheny Formation, are exposed along the east side of the highway in an extensive outcrop. Several thick sandstone beds belonging to both formations dominate the exposure. Between the sands lie several beds of the Stockton coal and the Kanawha Black Flint. The latter marks the top of the Kanawha Formation and is one of several zones in this formation that contains marine fossils.

The marine zones in the Kanawha record times of transgression, as the seas flooded the low-lying coastal plain and swamps. During the turnaround between transgression and regression, rivers became increasingly active, delivering sand and other sediment to the shoreline that would become thick sandstones and shales. At least ten episodes of transgression and regression produced alternating marine and nonmarine intervals in the Kanawha.

The highway continues to follow the valley of the Little Coal River, which is flowing along the west side of US 119. Near the exit for Big Pinnacle Branch Road, the road crosses over the river two times in rapid succession. This may seem a bit odd, but the highway has crossed the neck of a tight meander loop in the river, which swings to the east and then back under the road to its west side. Possibly at some point in the distant future (not within the reader's lifetime in all likelihood), erosional forces, most likely repeated instances of high volumes of water from rainstorms, will cause the river to carve into its banks, making the neck narrower and narrower over time. Eventually, the river may abandon the meander loop, though the old loop may live on as an oxbow lake as long as there is a natural water supply to refresh it.

South of the loop, the highway passes several more exposures of the Kanawha Formation. Although these rocks are older than those seen near McCorkle, they are typical of the upper and middle Kanawha, which contain more sandstone than the lower part. At the intersection of Brown Branch and Shaffer Roads, the highway passes the Hobet Mine to the west, at one time the largest surface mine in the state. Its principal purpose was to extract coal from the numerous beds near the top of the Kanawha Formation. At the time this book was written, this mine still supplied coal to power plants in Michigan, Ohio, Maryland, and Florida.

Just south of the intersection with WV 85, the highway crosses the Little Coal River at Danville. Exposures of the Kanawha Formation appear here and there southwest of Danville. The rocks along the route appear nearly horizontal because US 119 has been following the axis of the Warfield Anticline, which lies to the east. Although not noticeable, the highway intersects the axis north of where it enters Logan County.

The highway crosses the Guyandotte River valley at Chapmanville, where the river has cut down into a more shaley part of the Kanawha Formation. Several mineable coals, including the Peerless, No. 2 Gas, and Eagle, outcrop along the valley walls. A mile south of Chapmanville, the highway

Sandstones and dark shales in the Kanawha Formation record changes in sea level that periodically drowned the low-lying coastal plain. This roadcut is just south of the intersection with Cabin Ridge and Rocky Branch Roads, south of Chapmanville.

Cylindrical burrows and circular resting traces of marine organisms are common in the dark shales of the Kanawha.

leaves the valley and heads overland, where just south of the intersection of Cabin Ridge and Rocky Branch Roads it passes an outcrop that contains the Betsie Shale marine zone, exposed under the Eagle coal near road level. Although body fossils can be hard to find here, numerous burrows, or *trace fossils,* made by marine organisms are common.

As the highway continues to climb and level out, it travels over the Eagle coal and passes numerous underground mining operations that target it and other Kanawha Formation coals. Along the highway lie several dramatic exposures, mostly of sandstones in the middle Kanawha Formation. Tall outcrops of Kanawha rocks are exposed at mile marker 28. You can also see them behind a shopping plaza located at the intersection with WV 73, the area around which was heavily mined with surface and underground operations exploiting several Kanawha coals.

South of the WV 73 intersection, US 119 continues through a region of heavy mining operations, and more often than not passes over underground mines. At mile marker 26 is the northern end of another tall exposure of Kanawha sandstone. South of Holden, you can see at least two large mountaintop surface mines from the highway, although many more dot the landscape just out of sight. Most of the mines are removing several coals that range from the upper part of the Kanawha Formation to the lower part of the Allegheny Formation. Exposures diminish because vegetation covers the rock units more completely until south of the intersection with WV 65 at Belo. Surface operations continue farther south in Mingo County. An excellent example of valley fill from mining lies south of mile marker 9 on the south side of the road. Be sure to look down Deskins Drive to see the base of a large valley fill leading up to an abandoned mountaintop operation. Exposures of the middle part of the Kanawha, near the Williamson and No. 2 Gas coals, can be seen as US 119 merges with US 52 in the Tug Fork River valley.

ALLEGHENY MOUNTAIN SECTION

The Allegheny Mountain Section of the Appalachian Plateaus is an elevated landscape characterized by long ridges and broad valleys. Although this province covers a relatively small part of West Virginia, it presents travelers with some of the most spectacular views and landscapes in the state. These are the high mountains of West Virginia, with many places having elevations in excess of 4,000 feet. Along its eastern edge, the imposing Allegheny Front is home to Spruce Knob, West Virginia's highest elevation at 4,863 feet. As a major landform, the Allegheny Front has presented an obstacle to many who have traveled this region. In places, the change in elevation from the top of the Allegheny Front to the valleys to the east can reach upward of 1,500 feet. With the exception of interstate highways, the many paved roads that cross the Front contain numerous switchbacks that force travelers to make sharp turns while ascending or descending its steep face.

The magnitude of the front has not gone unnoticed by nature. Its nearly continuous high elevation and numerous bedrock exposures provide habitat for many upland plant species that have their southernmost occurrences along the Front. One of these, the red spruce, is commonly found with branches extending only from one side, a consequence of the strong westerly winds that cross the high ridges and force the branches to grow in an easterly direction. Birds migrating in the fall follow the northeast-southwest orientation of the Allegheny Front as a guide to the warmer winters of the south. To the west, the Allegheny Mountains, highest at their eastern edge, gradually descend toward the lower portion of the Appalachian Plateaus Province.

West-looking view of the lower portion of the Appalachian Plateaus from the Coopers Rock Overlook in the Allegheny Mountains, with the Cheat River in the foreground. The view emphasizes the fairly level nature of the plateaus region when seen from above.

The Allegheny Front is also a major geological boundary. The rocks that cap it, and the majority of the Allegheny Mountains for that matter, were deposited during the Pennsylvanian Period, between 318 to 299 million years ago, and then moderately folded into a series of anticlines and synclines during the Alleghanian Orogeny. In contrast, most of the rocks in the Valley and Ridge Province to the east are much older, having been deposited during the Silurian and Devonian Periods between 444 to 359 million years ago. These rocks were also closer to the collision zone during the orogeny and thus are far more severely folded and faulted than the rocks of the Allegheny Mountains.

To the west, the difference between the landscapes of the lower and higher portions of the Appalachian Plateaus also can be attributed to the region's geology. Although there is considerable overlap in the ages of the rocks, those of the Allegheny Mountains were closer to the continental margin during the Late Paleozoic Alleghanian Orogeny and the final assembly of Pangea. As a consequence, they were compressed to a slightly higher degree, producing broad anticlines and synclines in a northeast-southwest orientation. Many of the anticlines are directly above deep thrust faults that fractured and pushed the rocks upward.

Erosion of the folds has produced bands of different rock types that stretch across the surface. Because different rocks tend to weather and erode at different rates, the high ridges correspond to bands of resistant sandstone, and the low valleys have been eroded into bands of soft shale. The most prominent ridge-forming rocks are sandstones of the Middle Pennsylvanian Pottsville Sandstone, which form ridges along the axes of anticlines, such as Chestnut Ridge along the Chestnut Ridge Anticline, or on the limbs of synclines, as is the case with Briery Mountain on the Kingwood Syncline.

Wetlands are a common feature of elevated valleys in the Allegheny Mountains Section of the Appalachian Plateaus.

PERIOD		FORMATIONS AND GROUPS
PENNSYLVANIAN	Pm	Monongahela Formation
	Pc	Conemaugh Group
	Pa	Allegheny Formation
	Ppv	*Pottsville Group: Kanawha Formation New River Formation
MISSISSIPPIAN	Mmc	*Mauch Chunk Group: Bluestone Formation Princeton Sandstone Hinton Formation Bluefield Formation
	Mg	Greenbrier Limestone
	Mp	Price Formation
DEVONIAN	Dhs	Hampshire Formation
	Dgg	Greenland Gap Group Foreknobs Formation Scherr Formation

Scaled thicknesses of sedimentary rocks in the Allegheny Mountains of the Appalachian Plateaus in West Virginia.
–Data from Matchen and others, 2008

1,000 feet

* The Pottsville and Mauch Chunk Groups are thinner in the northern part of the Allegheny Mountains and are considered formations.

Interstate 68
Morgantown—Maryland State Line
32 miles

Those interested in a comparatively quick introduction to the topography and geology of both the Appalachian Plateaus and the Valley and Ridge Provinces can do no better than to travel the 114 miles of I-68, from its junction with I-79 just south of Morgantown, West Virginia, to its eastern end at I-70 at Hancock, Maryland. As one of the Appalachian Corridor highways, I-68 is the ideal route to Baltimore and Washington, DC, for those traveling from the Midwest. The 32-mile stretch in the Mountain State traverses the eastern edge of the lower Appalachian Plateaus for 10 miles, and then ascends to the Allegheny Mountain Section and continues for another twenty or so.

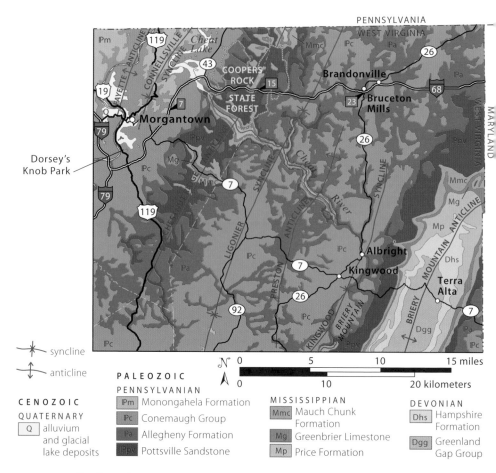

Geology along I-68 between Morgantown and the Maryland state line.

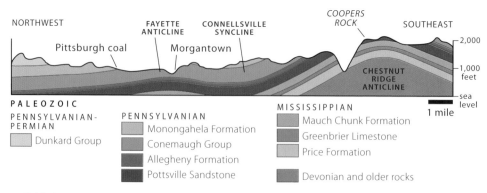

Folds in the lower, western portion of the Appalachian Plateaus are gentler compared to the fold of the Chestnut Ridge Anticline in the Allegheny Mountains. –Modified from Hare, 1957

Dorsey's Knob Park

A *knob* is a steep-sided hill set off from surrounding elevations. Once you are familiar with this landform, you'll see numerous instances throughout the Appalachian Plateaus. One mile north of exit 1 on US 119 is Dorsey's Knob, which is not only representative of this landform in general but also provides an extraordinary view of the transition between the lower part of the Appalachian Plateaus and the Allegheny Mountain Section. The knob is capped by an outcrop of Pittsburgh Sandstone, a part of the Monongahela Formation of Late Pennsylvanian age, which overlies the Conemaugh Group that crops out along I-68. The sandstone's comparative resistance to erosion accounts for the existence of the knob. Despite the resistant sandstone at its summit, the surrounding steep slopes are susceptible to erosion. You can see landslides directly adjacent to the site's parking lot and just across a small valley to the east. Eventually, as with the rest of the elevated terrain, the knob will be eroded away.

Views from the summit of Dorsey's Knob offer a clear picture of the different landscapes. To the west lies the crazy-quilt pattern of hills and valleys of the lower part of the Appalachian Plateaus, and to the east the view is dominated by Chestnut Ridge, a long ridge typical of the Allegheny Mountain Section.

Chestnut Ridge (on horizon), as seen from Dorsey's Knob, with numerous valleys cut by northwest-flowing streams. The ridge is the topographic expression of the Chestnut Ridge Anticline, the westernmost fold in the Allegheny Mountain Section.

The junction of I-79 and I-68 is situated in the Conemaugh Group, deposited in the Late Pennsylvanian Period. Typical of the rocks from this time in West Virginia, the Conemaugh Group is mostly shale and tends to form steep hillsides and deep valleys because of rapid erosion. Although there are anticlines and synclines here, the rocks dip at such a low angle that the folds do not influence the pattern of hills and valleys. This accounts in part for the seemingly random topography. The characteristic red beds of the Conemaugh Group are exposed on the north side of the highway near the junction with US 119 (exit 1).

East of Morgantown I-68 passes through typical lower plateau terrain produced by streams draining into the Monongahela River to the northwest, each named for an early European-American settler of the area: Cobun Creek, Aaron Creek, and Deckers Creek. The last of these, crossed near exit 4, runs along the hinge of the Connellsville Syncline. On the north side of the highway at exit 7, a shopping plaza is located on flat ground created during the mining of the Pittsburgh coal, the thickest coal in northern West Virginia. Shale and sandstone units just above the Pittsburgh coal are exposed in the outcrop under the plaza.

East of exit 7, I-68 begins to descend into the valley of the Cheat River, which runs along the west limb of the Chestnut Ridge Anticline. Just west of the bridge, the highway passes roadcuts of the Conemaugh Group, which includes the Ames cyclothem. The highway then crosses Cheat Lake, created by damming the Cheat River to generate electricity, and then ascends the west limb of the anticline.

Cross-bedded sandstone deposited in a river channel that cut into older, dark floodplain shales is exposed at the exit 7 off-ramp. The sandstone lies above the Pittsburgh coal, which was extensively mined in this area of the state.

Approaching the hinge of an eroded anticline is to proceed from younger rock to older rock. Exposures on the west side of Cheat Lake were in the middle of the Conemaugh Group, but at exit 10 the Buffalo Sandstone, one of the older units in the Conemaugh Group, is exposed and continues until the highway begins to follow a valley carved by Quarry Run.

As the highway continues east, it encounters rocks of the Middle Pennsylvanian Allegheny Formation. The Upper Kittanning coal appears, having a noticeable westward dip, and lies below the Upper Freeport coal, both thick Allegheny coals that were strip-mined along the north side of the highway.

By mile marker 12.5 the Homewood Sandstone member of the Middle Pennsylvanian Pottsville Sandstone is exposed. At this point, the grade of the highway and the dip of the Homewood Sandstone are more or less the same. Geologists refer to this correlation as a *dip slope*, thus as you continue to ascend the anticline eastward, the same rocks are exposed along the highway. Exposures of the Homewood Sandstone run continuously for about 1.5 miles to mile marker 14, where the road begins to flatten out a bit.

The roadcuts east of mile marker 14 expose the underlying Upper Connoquenessing Sandstone, the same unit that underlies the popular overlooks in Coopers Rock State Forest, where there are spectacular views of the Cheat River canyon. At the summit of Chestnut Ridge at exit 15 to Coopers Rock lies the Lower Connoquenessing Sandstone, the oldest of three major sandstones in the Pottsville. At the very bottom of the exposure is the Mississippian-Pennsylvanian

Exposure of the Upper Kittanning coal with a noticeable westward dip. The top of this hill was a surface mine in the Upper Freeport coal.

Coopers Rock State Forest

Coopers Rock State Forest, in large part the product of work done by members of the Civilian Conservation Corps during the 1930s, will reward those curious about the geology and topography of north-central West Virginia. Its principal attraction is the main overlook, which is situated on a large block of Upper Connoquenessing Sandstone that is slowly sliding away from the ridge. Looking west offers a broad view of the lower portion of the Appalachian Plateaus, where the topography is noticeably bumpy. Note that the horizons appear to be fairly level with only minor undulations. That gives a suggestion of the plateaus as a comparatively level region despite the weathering and erosional processes that resulted in its current contours. Turn to the left and you can see to the south the canyon carved by the Cheat River through the Chestnut Ridge Anticline, and beyond that the Allegheny Mountain Section of the plateaus.

The Cheat River flows northwesterly past the overlook through the anticline, following one of a series of *joints*, or stress fractures, that formed as a result of the compressional forces that also produced the folds in the Appalachian

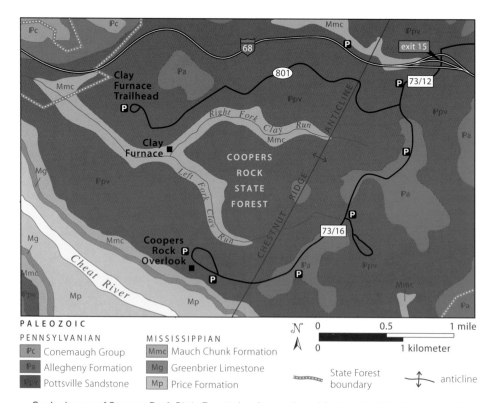

Geologic map of Coopers Rock State Forest showing roads and features highlighted in the text.
—Modified from McColloch and McColloch, 2003

Looking east (upstream) at the Cheat River valley as it cuts through the Chestnut Ridge Anticline on the western edge of the Allegheny Mountains.

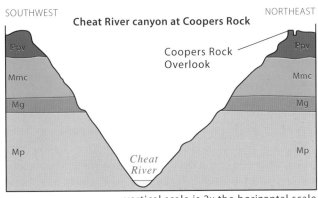

SOUTHWEST

Cheat River canyon at Coopers Rock

NORTHEAST

Coopers Rock
Overlook

Ppv

Mmc

Mg

Mp

Ppv

Mmc

Mg

Mp

Cheat River

PALEOZOIC
PENNSYLVANIAN
Ppv Pottsville Sandstone

MISSISSIPPIAN
Mmc Mauch Chunk Formation
Mg Greenbrier Limestone
Mp Price Formation

vertical scale is 2x the horizontal scale

Rock layers in the Cheat River canyon at Coopers Rock Overlook. River level is approximately 1,200 vertical feet below the overlook. –Modified from Hare, 1957

Mountains. Two predominant sets of joints are almost perpendicular in a north-west-southeast and a northeast-southwest direction in the rocks. In addition to influencing the direction of the Cheat River, these fractures also determine the pattern of weathering and erosion in the sandstones. The fractures divide the layers into blocks at nearly right angles. This is why many of the blocks of sandstone have flat sides that correspond to the joints and well-defined corners where two sets of fractures intersect. This pattern is also evident at the Rock City feature, a short trip to the northwest from the overlook.

Blocks of the Upper Connoquenessing Sandstone just north of the overlook at Coopers Rock State Forest. The sharp corners of the blocks correspond to the two sets of nearly perpendicular stress fractures, or joints, that cut through the rock.

A close inspection of the sandstone, especially along the Underlook Trail that winds around the base of the overlook, reveals many features that hint at the environmental conditions under which the sediments came to rest. Pebble-sized quartz grains indicate a fairly swift current was present during deposition. The Underlook Trail is often covered with quartz pebbles that eroded from the sandstone. Weathering has produced a distinctive honeycomb pattern in some of the sandstones. In addition, cross bedding found on nearly every outcrop of sandstone was formed by ancient river currents as they moved large amounts of sediment across the channels or downstream. Geologists can determine the direction of these ancient currents by measuring cross beds. Plant fossils are also common in the Upper Connoquenessing Sandstone. Many are the remains of ancient lycopods, or club mosses, which, when conditions were right, accumulated in great abundance and became some of the raw materials for coal. Overall, these features suggest that the Upper Connoquenessing Sandstone was deposited in a braided stream system.

Another destination in the park is the Henry Clay Iron Furnace, constructed in the early nineteenth century when small deposits of iron ore were mined throughout this part of the state. Furnaces such as this one dotted the region, transforming ore into iron to make implements for agriculture and industry, including rails for the developing network of railroads built to transport coal and timber. Directly behind the furnace, the trail cuts into one of many slag piles, impure waste that resulted from the separation of the usable iron from

Honeycomb weathering produced by the dissolution of cement in the sandstones at Coopers Rock State Forest.

Cross bedding in the Upper Connoquenessing Sandstone, produced during the movement of underwater dunes by river currents. The beds dip downward in the direction of the current, which in this case is to the left.

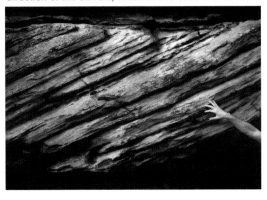

Fossil of the seed fern Neuropteris *from the Pottsville Sandstone.*

unusable rock. The iron deposits typically found in Pennsylvanian-age rocks were thin, isolated beds or small, fist-sized nodules of iron minerals. These deposits were worked out fairly quickly, and the entire industry in West Virginia came to an end when, in the 1880s, the industry began to draw on other sources of iron ore, the Mesabi Range of northern Minnesota being perhaps the most well-known in the United States. Pittsburgh, one of the major centers of steel manufacturing, made extensive use of iron ore, and though West Virginia ceased to provide iron, the state continued to be a major source of two other essential ingredients of steel manufacturing: coal and limestone.

The Henry Clay Iron Furnace stands as a reminder of the iron-producing operations that once dotted the region.

Slag, or waste rock, formed during the processing of iron in the Henry Clay Iron Furnace.

Diagonal bedding in the Pottsville Sandstone, produced by the migration of meandering streams, just east of the truck pull-off near the Coopers Rock exit of I-68.

boundary, marked by red beds of the Mauch Chunk Formation of Late Mississippian age. These are the oldest rocks along this stretch of I-68.

On the east limb of the Chestnut Ridge Anticline, the Homewood Sandstone forms a dip slope along the highway, just as it did on the west side. On the eastern horizon is Briery Mountain, a ridge running parallel to the northeast-southwest-oriented Chestnut Ridge. In the right light, I-68 can be seen climbing up the west slope of Briery Mountain in a series of lazy S-curves. If traveling this route from east to west, the western horizon is formed by Chestnut Ridge. There, the highway passes through a cut in the ridge that attentive westbound travelers can spot as they begin to descend Briery Mountain.

I-68 crosses Laurel Run at mile marker 18, a stream flowing along the hinge of the Ligonier Syncline, thus beginning the regular alternation of anticlines and synclines that characterizes much of the Allegheny Mountains. These structures are hard to see because the tilt of their limbs is subtle, dipping somewhere between 5 and 15 degrees. Thus, only knowledge of the specific rock types exposed in a particular location makes it possible to distinguish one of these larger folds from its neighbors. In the next 2 miles, exposures of Freeport Sandstone, which lie in the upper part of the Allegheny Formation, occur on both sides of the highway.

Just west of exit 23, the highway crosses Big Sandy Creek, which runs along the hinge of the Kingwood Syncline. East of that exit, the route climbs through Mahoning Sandstone, one of the oldest rocks of the Conemaugh Group. The sandstone outcrops on both sides of the highway. At and east of mile marker 27, the route is again passing by the Freeport Sandstone as it ascends the Briery Mountain Anticline. Two economically important coals, the Lower and Upper Freeport beds, follow the contour of the landscape here and were strip-mined on both sides of the highway at mile marker 28; note the low scrubby vegetation that is characteristic of reclaimed strip mines. At mile marker 30, I-68 reaches the summit of Briery Mountain. As the highway descends, exposures of Freeport Sandstone may be seen on either side as it enters Maryland.

US 33
I-79—BUCKHANNON—ELKINS—SENECA ROCKS
70 miles

US 33 is a four-lane divided highway known as Corridor H that runs between I-79 and Elkins. Although we begin this guide in the flatter part of the Appalachian Plateaus, the highway provides a good example of how the geology changes as you head east into the Allegheny Mountain Section. The rocks along the route get progressively older to the east, the farther we get from the center of the Appalachian Basin, which is near the Ohio River. The degree of folding and faulting also increases to the east, which at times can create duplication of the rocks. US 33 also crosses the boundary, or hinge line, between the Northern and Southern Basins. Rocks of Late Pennsylvanian age, typical of the Northern Basin, become less common to the east, and the thickness of rocks of Middle and Early Pennsylvanian age and Late Mississippian age begins to increase, a pattern that continues farther into the Southern Basin.

Between exit 99 of I-79 and Buckhannon, US 33 ascends the valley of Stonecoal Creek, climbing about 300 feet from its initial elevation of 1,040 feet at I-79. Exposures of the Conemaugh Group of Late Pennsylvanian age occur periodically along the road, easily identified by their distinctive red beds that formed on floodplains between ancient meandering streams. The river channels are represented by thick, tan or gray cross-bedded sandstones. Rocks of the overlying Monongahela Formation, its base marked by the Pittsburgh coal, cap many of the surrounding hills, though the Pittsburgh is much thinner and discontinuous here than to the north. Only a few surface mining operations have bothered to remove the coal.

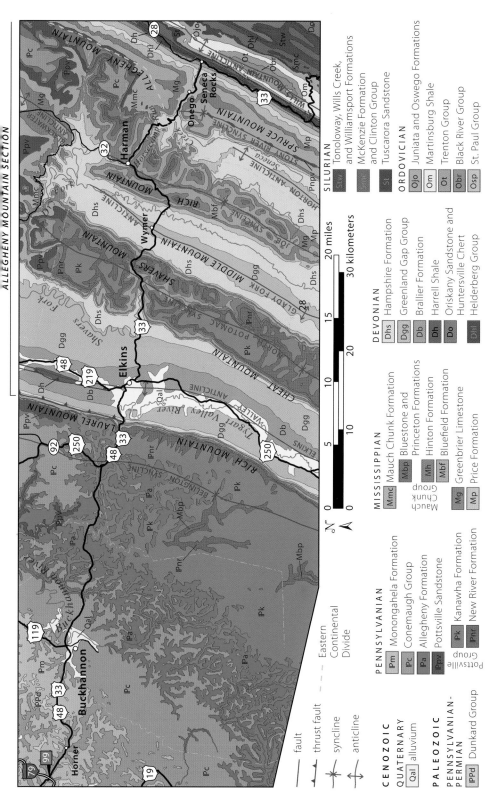

Geology along US 33 between I-79 and Seneca Rocks.

CENOZOIC

QUATERNARY
Qal alluvium

PALEOZOIC

PENNSYLVANIAN-
PERMIAN
IPPd Dunkard Group

PENNSYLVANIAN
IPm Monongahela Formation
IPc Conemaugh Group
IPa Allegheny Formation
Ppv Pottsville Sandstone

Pottsville Group
IPk Kanawha Formation
IPnr New River Formation

MISSISSIPPIAN
Mmc Mauch Chunk Formation

Mauch Chunk Group
Mbp Bluestone and Princeton Formations
Mh Hinton Formation
Mbf Bluefield Formation

Mg Greenbrier Limestone
Mp Price Formation

DEVONIAN
Dhs Hampshire Formation
Dgg Greenland Gap Group
Db Brallier Formation
Dh Harrell Shale
Do Oriskany Sandstone and Huntersville Chert
Dhl Helderberg Group

SILURIAN
Stw Tonoloway, Wills Creek, and Williamsport Formations
Smc McKenzie Formation and Clinton Group
St Tuscarora Sandstone

ORDOVICIAN
Ojo Juniata and Oswego Formations
Om Martinsburg Shale
Ot Trenton Group
Obr Black River Group
Osp St. Paul Group

— fault
╪ thrust fault
⟶⟵ syncline
⟵⟶ anticline
- - - Eastern Continental Divide

0   5   10   15   20 miles
0   10   20   30 kilometers

The lens-shaped sandstone layer was deposited by a river that cut a channel into the underlying layers. This exposure of the Conemaugh Group of Late Pennsylvanian age is just west of the Lewis-Upshur county line, on the north side of the highway.

The Redstone coal, however, which lies just above the Pittsburgh, was surface mined from the hillsides that line the route, but trees now cover the scars left by the mining operations. West of Horner, the road climbs out of the valley of Stonecoal Creek, and the Redstone coal drops below road level right around the Lewis-Upshur county line. North of the highway, the coal was extensively surface and underground mined from here north into Barbour County, which lies about 9 miles to the north.

As US 33 passes through Buckhannon, the seat of Upshur County, exposures of more red Conemaugh rocks are visible on the hillsides. East of Buckhannon, the highway gradually continues to climb. As it crosses the Laurel Fork of Sand Run, a tall exposure of Middle Pennsylvanian Allegheny Formation sandstones mixed with small layers of shale may be seen north of the highway. Although the Allegheny has river channel sandstones similar to those of the Conemaugh above it, its lack of red bed paleosols makes it easy to distinguish from the younger units. The upper boundary of the Allegheny Formation is the Upper Freeport coal, which was extensively underground mined south of Buckhannon.

Where US 33 crosses a small sliver of southernmost Barbour County, it crosses the hinge line, passing east into the Southern Basin. As the highway travels into Randolph County, it climbs rapidly toward the Allegheny Mountain Section of the plateaus, reaching an elevation of slightly more than 2,000 feet. The hills are now capped by the Allegheny Formation, with the northernmost

River sandstones of the Middle Pennsylvanian Allegheny Formation just west of Sand Run. Note the absence of red beds.

exposures of the Middle Pennsylvanian Kanawha Formation, part of the Pottsville Group, at road level (The Pottsville is undivided north of the hinge line but not here). The Tygart Valley River has cut down to reveal more of the Kanawha Formation. The highway remains in the Kanawha between the river crossing and the traffic light at the junction with US 250/WV 92. The Lower and Middle Kittanning coals near the base of the Allegheny were extensively mined in the area, both underground and on the surface. East of the river, the horizon is dominated by the westernmost major ridge of the Allegheny Mountains along US 33. Divided by a gap created by the Tygart Valley River, it is called Laurel Mountain to the north, and Rich Mountain to the south. Elevations along its crest locally exceed 3,000 feet.

Folding, which is more intense in the Allegheny Mountains than in the Appalachian Plateaus farther west, brings to the surface rocks of varying degrees of resistance to weathering and erosion. Where the rocks are more resistant, they create the long, high ridges typical of the Allegheny Mountains. In the case of Laurel and Rich Mountains, resistant quartz sandstones of the New River Formation of Early Pennsylvanian age (Pottsville Group) dip about 20 to 30 degrees to the west along the west limb of the Elkins Valley Anticline. This fold, the southern extension of the Deer Park Anticline, is thought to be underlain by a series of thrust faults that caused older layers in the subsurface to be fractured and forced upward in separate blocks. Another consequence of the faulting was an increase in the severity of the folding and uplift of the structure. The dip along the road is noticeable, with New River sandstones extending upward to the east, acting as a resistant cap for the ridge.

As the road curves to a more easterly direction, it crosses into the Mauch Chunk Group of Late Mississippian age. The unit is much softer than the overlying New River Formation, and it cannot be seen along the road until WV 92 diverges from the highway at a stoplight, and the road begins to climb. Small patches of red shale, typical of the Mauch Chunk, peek through the grassy slope

A resistant sandstone in the New River Formation of Early Pennsylvanian age. Although it is flat-lying here at mile marker 30, to the east the unit dips to the west, forming the hogback of Rich Mountain.

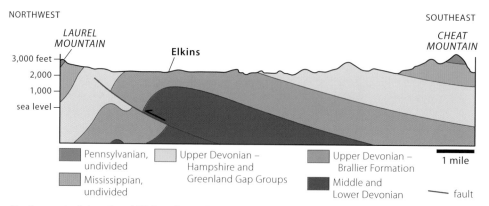

NORTHWEST · SOUTHEAST

LAUREL MOUNTAIN · Elkins · CHEAT MOUNTAIN

3,000 feet — 2,000 — 1,000 — sea level —

Pennsylvanian, undivided
Mississippian, undivided
Upper Devonian – Hampshire and Greenland Gap Groups
Upper Devonian – Brallier Formation
Middle and Lower Devonian
1 mile
fault

Rocks west of the city of Elkins dip to the west on the western limb of the Elkins Valley Anticline. Rocks east of the city are east-dipping on the east limb of the fold. The presence of a fault at depth is confirmed by the duplication of some of the Devonian layers. –Reger and Price, 1926

on the north side of the road near the traffic light. The Middle Mississippian Greenbrier Limestone is also present here but covered along the road. However, look to the south where both the Greenbrier and the Mauch Chunk are well exposed in the active JF Allen Quarry. The tall gray cliff rising from the floor of the quarry is the uppermost Greenbrier, while the red slopes above are the Mauch Chunk.

Red beds of the Mauch Chunk Group, exposed in a quarry south of the highway near the WV 92 stoplight, are protected from erosion by the New River sandstones that cap the west side of Rich Mountain. The Greenbrier Limestone, just below the Mauch Chunk, is quarried here.

The next outcrop, on the north side of the road east of the WV 92 junction, exposes the contact between the Price Formation of Early Mississippian time and the Hampshire Formation of Late Devonian time. The Hampshire, like the Mauch Chunk, has many distinctive red beds reflecting the arid climate at the time of deposition. The next series of roadcuts to the east, near the top of the hill, expose the Foreknobs Formation of Late Devonian age, which, along with the Hampshire and older Middle Devonian rocks to the east, are part of the Devonian Catskill clastic wedge. The sediments of the wedge were shed from the Acadian Mountains that rose to the east during the Acadian Orogeny, as a small microcontinent collided with the eastern margin of ancient North America. The crust west of these mountains subsided, producing the Catskill foreland basin, which filled with sediments from active deltas.

The continuous sequence of rock layers exposed in these roadcuts is typical of those that fill foreland basins. Subsidence tends to be rapid, and the initial sediments, generally mud sized, were deposited in quiet, offshore areas of the active delta lobes. As deposition continued, the sediments became coarser, reflecting a shift to nearshore and presumably shallow water environments at the front of the deltas. Eventually the top of the deltas emerged above water as they built new land out into the sea. Because of the folding, the sequence here is encountered in reverse order, with the Hampshire reappearing east of Elkins. For the most part, the red sediments of the Hampshire Formation were deposited in river channels and floodplains on the low-lying coastal plain that separated the Acadian Mountains from the shallow inland sea that occupied the Catskill foreland basin. The older Foreknobs Formation, along with the underlying Scherr and Brallier Formations, were deposited in offshore marine environments.

Just east of mile marker 32.5 on the north side of the road is the Devonian-Mississippian boundary along the western limb of the Elkins Valley Anticline. Overlying the red beds from the Hampshire Formation of Late Devonian age are gray sandstones of the Price Formation of Early Mississippian age.

Thin sandstone and shale beds of the Foreknobs Formation, deposited in Late Devonian time, feature ripple marks and marine fossils. The sandstone beds were deposited during storms when larger waves carried the sand offshore.

US 33 passes several more outcrops of alternating shale and sandstone in the Foreknobs Formation. Ripple marks in many of the sandstone layers were formed by currents that periodically reached the seafloor, most likely during storms. Invertebrate marine fossils are also common in this unit, confirming its marine origin. Several smaller scale anticlines and synclines related to the thrust faults below the Elkins Valley Anticline are common. US 33 leaves the divided highway, Corridor H, just east of mile marker 35 at the exit for Elkins. Between the exit and Elkins, only a few small exposures of Middle Devonian rocks are to be seen.

East of Elkins, US 33 climbs overland, crossing the spine of Cheat Mountain, a north-south ridge on the east limb of the Elkins Valley Anticline. The rock units that the route passed west of town are now dipping to the east and are encountered in normal stratigraphic order as the highway crosses the summit of Kelley Mountain (the local name for Cheat Mountain) and heads downhill toward Shavers Fork. Outcrops of the Hampshire along this stretch of US 33 have yielded a variety of early, primitive land plants, including the seed-bearing *Elkinsia polymorpha*. Although seed-bearing plants had diversified greatly by

Wave ripples in the Foreknobs Formation on the east side of the hill summit east of mile marker 33. The ripples formed during the waning phase of a storm, or just after the storm event.

Mississippian and Pennsylvanian times, *Elkinsia* is still recognized as the oldest seed-bearing plant in North America. The outcrop the route passes west of where it narrows to two lanes is an exposure of the Greenbrier Limestone, with large tunnels carved into it from now-abandoned quarrying operations.

Large tunnels, part of a now-abandoned quarry operation, were carved into the Middle Mississippian Greenbrier Limestone.

East of the Shavers Fork valley, US 33 climbs Shavers Mountain, located on the east limb of the North Potomac Syncline and capped by resistant sandstones of the New River and Kanawha Formations. East of the summit, the highway descends into the valley of Glady Fork and then climbs Middle Mountain, which lies near the axis of the Glady Fork Anticline. The Foreknobs Formation, exposed in small roadcuts near the town of Wymer, constitutes the oldest rock unit in this structure. The route descends again, this time into the valley of Laurel Run before climbing Rich Mountain, which tops out at an elevation of 3,370 feet. Like Shavers Mountain, Rich Mountain is on the limb of a syncline where the resistant New River Formation caps the highest elevations of the limb. Below the New River sandstones brightly colored red beds of the Mauch Chunk Group of Late Mississippian age appear at road level.

East of Rich Mountain, US 33 heads downhill into the valley of Dry Fork. For most of the descent the highway passes by red beds of the Mauch Chunk Group but eventually reaches gray layers of the Greenbrier Limestone. East of Harman, the route passes cross-bedded sandstones of the Price Formation of Early Mississippian age. It continues to climb to the east through roadcuts of the Price Formation along Horsecamp Run, which flows to the northwest, as do most of the streams up to this point. At an elevation of 3,295 feet, the highway crosses Allegheny Mountain, marking the top of the Allegheny Front, the boundary between the Appalachian Plateaus and the Valley and Ridge Provinces.

Red beds of the Mauch Chunk Group of Late Mississippian age. Similar to other red beds encountered around the state, these are likely paleosols that formed on river floodplains during a time with a predominantly arid climate.

Beds of the Greenbrier Limestone, exposed west of Harman, were deposited when the North American continent was covered by a shallow tropical sea.

Cross beds produced by water currents in sandstones of the Price Formation east of Harman. Flow direction was to the right.

Horsecamp Run, the valley of which the highway follows to ascend the west side of Allegheny Mountain, flows north-northwest to the Dry Fork and then on to the town of Parsons, where it joins Shavers Fork to form the Cheat River, a tributary of the Monongahela River, which joins the Allegheny at Pittsburgh to form the Ohio. US 33 descends Allegheny Mountain by way of the valleys of Walmsley and McIntosh Runs, both of which flow into Seneca Creek, which flows into the North Fork of the South Branch of the Potomac. The Potomac flows into Chesapeake Bay; the Ohio into the Mississippi River and ultimately the Gulf of Mexico. Thus, the summit of Allegheny Mountain constitutes the Eastern Continental Divide.

East of the divide, which is also the Randolph-Pendleton county line, the road plunges down the Allegheny Front, first passing exposures of the Price Formation and then those of the older Hampshire Formation, including distinctive gray cross-bedded sandstones and dark-red interbedded shales. At the bottom of the descent, the road follows Seneca Creek, which flows to the east, and encounters the Price Formation again on the east limb of the Horton Anticline. East of the town of Onego (pronounced "one-go" by its residents) the Hampshire Formation appears again, this time dipping steeply to the west on the east limb of the Stony River Syncline, the easternmost structure in the Allegheny Mountain Section. After a short climb, look up and you will see one of West Virginia's most celebrated natural sites: Seneca Rocks.

The intersection of US 33 and WV 28 lies at the base of the Allegheny Front and in the Valley and Ridge Province. The elevation here is lower, at 1,600

River sandstones and floodplain shales of the Hampshire Formation of Late Devonian time along the Allegheny Front.

feet, than the floor of the easternmost valley of the Allegheny Mountains at Harman, which was at 2,370 feet. In addition to the elevation, the geology has also changed significantly. Unlike the gentler folds in the Appalachian Plateaus, Seneca Rocks lies on the steeply dipping west limb of the Wills Mountain Anticline. The layers of hard Tuscarora Sandstone that make up Seneca Rocks are vertical, having been forced into this orientation by westward movement along a series of thrust faults just below the surface.

Although the stress that caused the intense deformation here is the same that folded the layers in the Appalachian Plateaus, this region was closer to the collision zone when Pangea was in its final stages of assembly at the end of the Paleozoic Era. As a consequence, the rocks in the Valley and Ridge Province were deformed to a much greater degree. Tight folds and thrust faults are commonplace here and form the distinctive Valley and Ridge topography characterized by ridges composed of repeated exposures of resistant rock. The amount of corresponding uplift is also much greater. The Tuscarora Sandstone is Early Silurian in age, nearly 100 million years older than the New River sandstones that cap the ridges in the Allegheny Mountains. West of Seneca Rock, the Tuscarora lies 8,000 to 10,000 feet below the surface. At Seneca Rocks, it is over your head. The highest point of Seneca Rocks has an elevation of a little more than 2,000 feet above sea level, approximately 500 feet above the floodplain of the North Fork of the South Branch of the Potomac River, just to its west.

For more information about Seneca Rocks, see the sidebar in the road guide for US 33: Seneca Rocks—Franklin—Virginia State Line.

US 50
Skyline—Grafton
60 miles

We begin this road guide at the intersection of US 50 and WV 42 on the Allegheny Front: the eastern edge of the Appalachian Plateaus along its boundary with the Valley and Ridge Province. Here, the village of Skyline is situated at an elevation of approximately 2,700 feet above sea level in a wind gap on Allegheny Mountain. To the south, the mountain reaches a height of 3,020 feet. Along this ridge you can see wind turbines. When their height is added to that of the ridge, it's safe to say that they are at times driven by wind currents originating on the east side of the Rocky Mountains that encounter no obstacles until reaching the Allegheny Mountains.

Skyline and the Allegheny Front are situated on the eastern extent of the Middle Pennsylvanian Pottsville and Allegheny Formations. Between the Front and Backbone Mountain to the west, rocks of the Conemaugh Group, primarily shales, siltstones, and sandstones, dip very gently in a broad, unnamed syncline. The Bakerstown coal in the Conemaugh has been extensively mined, both at the surface and underground. US 50 passes over an underground mine just east of Mt. Storm. Although there are few exposures along the level portions of the

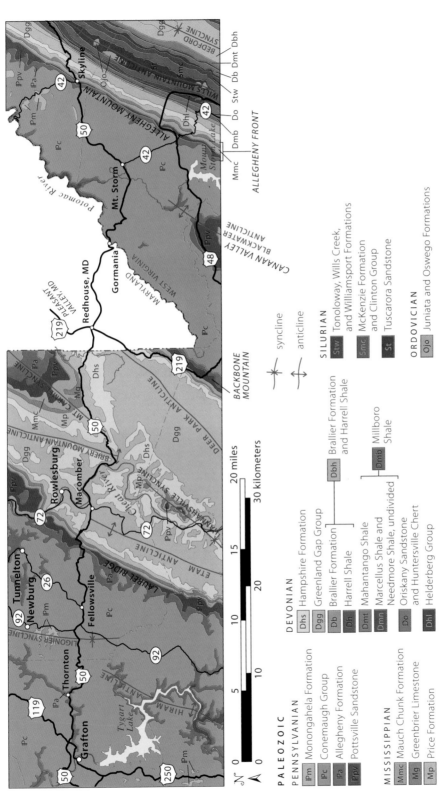

Geology along US 50 between Skyline and Grafton.

PALEOZOIC

PENNSYLVANIAN
- ℔Pm Monongahela Formation
- ℔Pc Conemaugh Group
- ℔Pa Allegheny Formation
- ℔Ppv Pottsville Sandstone

MISSISSIPPIAN
- Mmc Mauch Chunk Formation
- Mg Greenbrier Limestone
- Mp Price Formation

DEVONIAN
- Dhs Hampshire Formation
- Dgg Greenland Gap Group
- Db Brallier Formation
- Dh Harrell Shale
- Dbh Brallier Formation and Harrell Shale
- Dmt Mahantango Shale
- Dmn Marcellus Shale and Needmore Shale, undivided
- Dmb Millboro Shale
- Do Oriskany Sandstone and Huntersville Chert
- Dhl Helderberg Group

SILURIAN
- Stw Tonoloway, Wills Creek, and Williamsport Formations
- Smc McKenzie Formation and Clinton Group
- St Tuscarora Sandstone

ORDOVICIAN
- Ojo Juniata and Oswego Formations

syncline
anticline

One of the many rows of wind turbines located along the Allegheny Front.

route, outcrops of the Conemaugh Group are exposed as US 50 descends into the Potomac River valley east of Gormania.

Gormania, West Virginia, and Gorman, Maryland, are twin settlements separated by the North Branch of the Potomac River, which serves as the state line. West of Gorman, the highway continues crossing Backbone Mountain at an elevation of 3,100 feet and then passing onto the east limb of the Deer Park Anticline. The rocks become progressively older as the road drops through Pennsylvanian-to-Mississippian-age strata before reaching the floor of Pleasant Valley, where no rocks are exposed along the road. US 50 crosses the approximate position of the axis of the Deer Park Anticline at the junction with US 219 in Redhouse, Maryland, and then reenters West Virginia.

Looking east from the Allegheny Front at the repetition of ridges in the Valley and Ridge Province. The low spot in the first ridge is a large wind gap called Doll Gap.

West of Cathedral State Park, the highway passes along a gray sandstone bench in the Price Formation of Early Mississippian age near the axis of the Mount Carmel Syncline. West of Dayton, US 50 plunges nearly 1,200 feet into the Cheat River valley. Drivers are cautioned to be careful negotiating the numerous switchbacks and should anticipate the presence of heavily loaded and slow-moving coal, stone, and timber trucks around every turn.

Outcrops of red and gray cross-bedded sandstones and red shale of the Hampshire Formation of Late Devonian age are exposed along the road. They give way to interbedded sandstone and gray to brown shale of the Foreknobs Formation of the Greenland Gap Group, also of Late Devonian age, at the bottom of the valley. There US 50 parallels the meandering course of the river, which has a long history of wreaking havoc within the narrow confines of this valley. Significant flooding events are a consequence of steep topography and heavy rains.

Just west of Macomber, the highway parallels Flag Run, a tributary of the Cheat, for several miles before beginning its steep climb out of the valley, a route that involves two tight switchbacks. The succession of formations encountered in the descent on the east side of the Cheat River is now reversed. US 50 first passes sandstone and shale outcrops of the Foreknobs Formation of Late Devonian age, dipping slightly to the northwest along the northwest limb of the Etam Anticline. As the road climbs it passes by younger Devonian and Mississippian rocks until it crests Laurel Ridge, capped by the Middle Pennsylvanian Pottsville and Allegheny Formations.

Once the road leaves the Cheat River valley, it begins a gradual descent toward Fellowsville. Although the rocks of the Conemaugh Group lie at the surface here, just east of town US 50 crosses over an extensive underground mine that targeted the Middle Kittanning coal in the Allegheny Formation.

The stout construction of the US 50 bridge over the Cheat River is necessary to withstand the force of floodwaters that periodically rush through the valley.

Sandstones of the Foreknobs Formation dip to the northwest away from the axis of the Etam Anticline.

West of Fellowsville, US 50 approaches the western limit of the Allegheny Mountains, and the landscape begins to transition from northeast-southwest-oriented ridges to the more unorganized topography characteristic of the lower portion of the Appalachian Plateaus Province.

Only a few fold axes intersect the highway along the 12 miles between Fellowsville and Grafton, but they are so gentle that only exposures of the Conemaugh Group can be seen between Fellowsville and Thornton. At the valley of Three Fork Creek west of Thornton, sandstone and shale of the Allegheny Formation are visible, the creek having cut down through the Conemaugh Group to reach these rocks. West of the creek, the road climbs back into rocks of the Conemaugh Group. Just south of the highway, you can see the extraction of the Middle Kittanning coal of the Allegheny Formation at an active underground mine a few miles east of Grafton.

US 219
Marlinton—Elkins—Maryland State Line
109 miles

The northern portion of US 219, a highway that follows the Seneca Trail, passes through the heart of the Allegheny Mountains. As US 219 heads north out of Marlinton it leaves the Greenbrier River valley. The route climbs not only the valley wall but upward through geologic time until it reaches the rather bumpy high ground eroded into the Bluefield Formation of Late Mississippian time. Distant ridges to the west are capped by younger rocks of the Hinton and Bluefield Formations, as well as the New River and Kanawha Formations of Early to Middle Pennsylvanian age.

East at Slaty Fork, the highway heads east along Big Spring Fork to Linwood. At the junction with WV 66, US 219 climbs north out of the Greenbrier River watershed and enters the Allegheny Mountains. Crossing the drainage divide situated near the village of Mace, at the boundary of Randolph and Pocahontas Counties, the road descends north into the elevated valley of the Tygart Valley River. It will follow the river's course to Elkins. The Tygart Valley is carved into one of the most extensive folds along this route, the Elkins Valley Anticline. There are few, if any, rocks exposed in the valley bottom because the Tygart Valley River has eroded fairly soft, shaley rocks of Middle and Late Devonian age.

North of Valley Head, where the highway crosses the Tygart Valley River near Spangler, outcrops of the Greenland Gap Group of Late Devonian age dip to the northwest, indicating that the road is running along the west limb of the Elkins Valley Anticline. Similar exposures appear farther north near Dailey, where the highway crosses the axis of the anticline and runs along its eastern limb. As expected, the rocks, this time those of Devonian Brallier Formation, are dipping to the southeast.

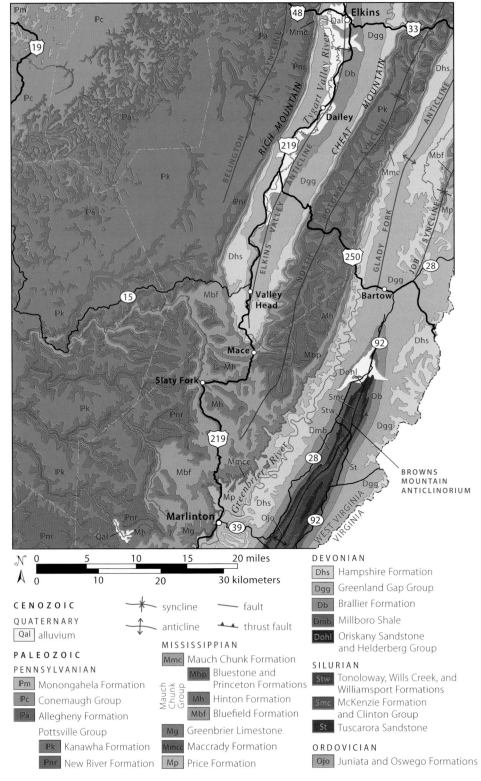

Geology along US 219 between Marlinton and Elkins. For the route north of Elkins, see the map on page 158.

CENOZOIC

QUATERNARY
Qal alluvium

PALEOZOIC

PENNSYLVANIAN
IPm Monongahela Formation
IPc Conemaugh Group
IPa Allegheny Formation
Pottsville Group
IPk Kanawha Formation
IPnr New River Formation

syncline
anticline
fault
thrust fault

MISSISSIPPIAN
Mmc Mauch Chunk Formation
Mbp Bluestone and Princeton Formations
Mauch Chunk Group
Mh Hinton Formation
Mbf Bluefield Formation
Mg Greenbrier Limestone
Mmcc Maccrady Formation
Mp Price Formation

DEVONIAN
Dhs Hampshire Formation
Dgg Greenland Gap Group
Db Brallier Formation
Dmb Millboro Shale
Dohl Oriskany Sandstone and Helderberg Group

SILURIAN
Stw Tonoloway, Wills Creek, and Williamsport Formations
Smc McKenzie Formation and Clinton Group
St Tuscarora Sandstone

ORDOVICIAN
Ojo Juniata and Oswego Formations

Thin-bedded sandstones and shales of the Brallier Formation on the east limb of the Elkins Valley Anticline near Dailey. These beds accumulated offshore in the Catskill foreland basin during the Acadian Orogeny.

Another interesting feature of this valley is the relationship between topography and folds. Many tend to associate upward-arching anticlines with high elevations, and downward-dipping synclines with low elevations. But in this area, like many others in the Appalachian Mountains, synclines cap the tops of mountains while eroded anticlines make up the valleys. While resistance to erosion and other contributing factors may promote this unusual relationship, it seems that the way rock layers respond to folding has much to do with it. Think of an ordinary cleaning sponge for a moment. If you were to bend the sponge upward, like an anticline, you would see the small holes in the middle of the sponge get larger. Conversely, if you bent the sponge downward the holes would get smaller, with many of them closing entirely. The same seems to hold

In anticlines, the upper surface is stretched, which opens pores and fractures, increasing weathering and erosion rates. In synclines, the upper surface is compressed, which closes pores and slows weathering and erosion.

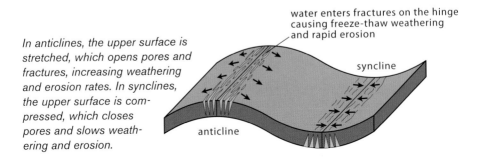

true for rock layers as well. As the rocks are stretched across the top of an anticline, the side facing the surface stretches, widening the pores in the rock and opening fractures. Water can then enter the rock more easily, speeding up the weathering process. On a syncline, the side facing the surface is compressed, causing the pores to get smaller and fractures to become narrower, thus armoring the surface against water and slowing the rates of weathering and erosion.

Elkins, seat of Randolph County, is situated on a large meander loop of the Tygart Valley River. Tightly folded rocks of the Brallier Formation can be seen where hillsides have been carved to make room for buildings and roads. Some of the dips are quite steep and can appear almost vertical in

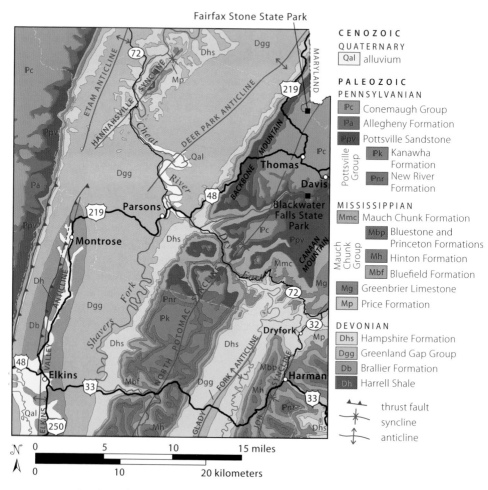

Geology along US 219 between Elkins and the Maryland state line.

places. As the highway turns north and heads out of town, it joins a portion of Corridor H, one of six such four-lane highways cutting through some of the most mountainous terrain in the state. This was also the route of the Western Maryland Railway, which transported timber and coal out of this area. At the on-ramp to Corridor H, note tightly folded layers of the Greenland Gap Group, dipping in many different orientations.

As the route continues north, it runs along Leading Creek and the axis of the Elkins Valley Anticline. Exposures of the same Late Devonian units continue along the route. About 1 mile north of Montrose, the highway turns east and crosses into Tucker County. It proceeds east along Haddix Run toward Parsons. In the vicinity of Moore, small folds are also visible along the road as the highway approaches Porterwood. There, Haddix Run flows into Shavers Fork, which US 219 follows to Parsons, where the highway merges with WV 72.

At the north end of Parsons, Shavers Fork and Black Fork flow together to form the Cheat River, which flows north and west to join the Monongahela River just north of the Mason-Dixon Line, the state's boundary with Pennsylvania. At the point where US 219 leaves WV 72, the route begins the ascent of Backbone Mountain. Rocks of Late Devonian through Late Pennsylvanian age pass by as the road heads toward the axis of the North Potomac Syncline.

Parsons is roughly 1,800 feet above sea level, so by the time US 219 reaches its highest point on Backbone Mountain at 3,500 feet, it has climbed more than 1,700 feet. The landscape east of the summit resembles an elevated plateau supported by resistant rocks of the Pottsville Sandstone of Early Pennsylvanian time. A modest amount of relief does exist at the surface due to the erosion of younger, and much softer, rocks of the Middle Pennsylvanian Allegheny Formation and Late Pennsylvanian Conemaugh Group. Both the Upper Freeport coal in the Allegheny and the Bakerstown coal in the Conemaugh were extensively mined in this area. In fact, US 219 passes over abandoned underground mines on both sides of the North Fork of the Blackwater River as it enters the town of Thomas, which was almost completely undermined.

North of Thomas, the highway heads north and then northwest, passing south of Fairfax Stone State Park, where the Potomac River originates. Just north of the Fairfax Stone turnoff, US 219 passes the Fairfax Stone quarry, which targets Middle Pennsylvanian sandstone. North of the quarry is a wonderful view of the Allegheny Mountains as US 219 descends Backbone Mountain, passing through the reverse sequence of rocks you encountered north of Parsons. Only a few rocks can be seen, but at the bottom of the grade there is a small exposure of the Price Formation sandstone dipping to the southeast. Here we are briefly in the valley of the Youghiogheny River (pronounced "Yock-a-gany"), another tributary of the Monongahela River, which it joins near Pittsburgh, Pennsylvania. North of the junction with WV 24, the highway leaves the valley, where no rock is exposed along the road, before entering Maryland.

WV 7
MORGANTOWN—MARYLAND STATE LINE
38 miles

The route begins in the immediate vicinity of exit 155 from I-79 on Chaplin Hill Road. There are at least seven distinct coal beds from the Pennsylvanian Period mined in this area, none more economically important than the Pittsburgh coal. Not only was it the thickest of the coals, but it also lay comparatively close to the surface here and was easily mined. The surrounding hills were extensively mined, but operations ceased to be economical. South of the highway a number of restaurants and the University Town Centre are located on the site of former underground and strip mines. A quick trip up University Town Centre Drive to the first of the restaurants on the south (left) side of the road reveals

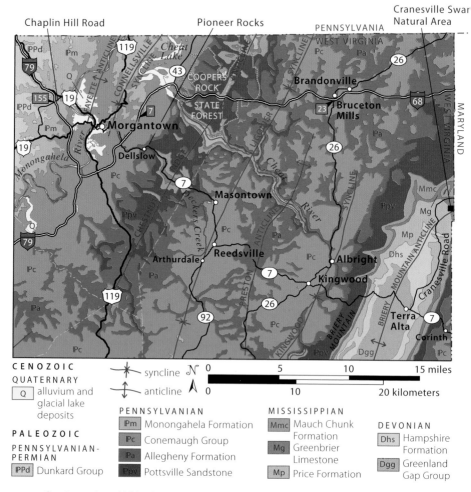

CENOZOIC

QUATERNARY

Q alluvium and glacial lake deposits

PALEOZOIC

PENNSYLVANIAN-PERMIAN

ℙPd Dunkard Group

syncline N°
anticline A

PENNSYLVANIAN

ℙm Monongahela Formation
ℙc Conemaugh Group
ℙa Allegheny Formation
ℙpv Pottsville Sandstone

MISSISSIPPIAN

Mmc Mauch Chunk Formation
Mg Greenbrier Limestone
Mp Price Formation

0   5   10   15 miles
0   10   20 kilometers

DEVONIAN

Dhs Hampshire Formation
Dgg Greenland Gap Group

Geology along WV 7 between Morgantown and the Maryland state line.

Jumbled beds of shale above the Sewickley coal in a cut along University Town Centre Drive near exit 155. The shales collapsed into a void created by mining in the Sewickley.

a large cut into the hillside exposing the Sewickley coal. Shales above the coal subsided into the void created by mining from below, a common consequence of underground mining.

To the west of the intersection of Chaplin Hill Road with WV 7 and US 19 lies the town of Osage, the center of many mining operations situated along Scotts Run, which the highway parallels. During the early 1930s, when the Great Depression was at its most critical, the poverty of those living in company towns near Osage captured the attention of First Lady Eleanor Roosevelt. She not only drew national attention to the plight of the unemployed miners and their families but subsequently oversaw the creation of a planned community known as Arthurdale, located about 20 miles to the east in rural Preston County, to which a number of these families relocated. WV 7 passes within 3 miles of Arthurdale when it reaches Reedsville.

WV 7, which shares the highway with US 19 for several miles, approaches the axis of the Fayette Anticline and passes by exposures of Connellsville Sandstone in the Conemaugh Group of Late Pennsylvanian age as it nears the Monongahela River bridge. East of the river, the highway, here known as Monongahela Boulevard, proceeds through Star City and climbs out of the valley. Before descending into Morgantown, Monongahela Boulevard intersects with WV 705, or Patteson Drive, directly across from the West Virginia University Coliseum. Patteson Drive overlies an ancient oxbow lake. Such lakes occupy abandoned meandering river channels, and the presence of this feature indicates that a meander loop of the ancient Monongahela River once flowed along the course of Patteson Drive.

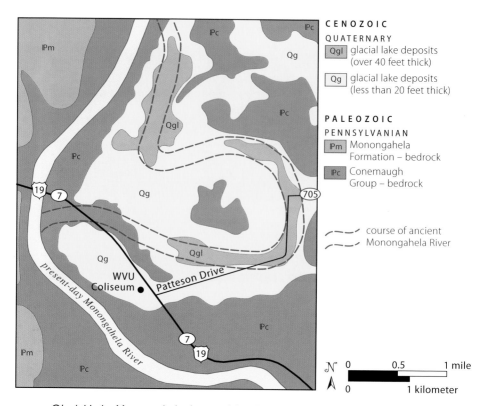

CENOZOIC
QUATERNARY
Qgl glacial lake deposits
(over 40 feet thick)

Qg glacial lake deposits
(less than 20 feet thick)

PALEOZOIC
PENNSYLVANIAN
Pm Monongahela
Formation – bedrock

Pc Conemaugh
Group – bedrock

- - - - course of ancient
Monongahela River

Glacial Lake Monongahela drowned the channel and floodplain of the ancient Monongahela River, covering the area with lake sediments. The thickest deposits of lake clays (tan) accumulated in the ancient Monongahela River channel and can be used to trace the former course of the river.

Even more significant than the presence of the buried oxbow lake are the laminated silty clays that filled it. The presence of these fine sediments indicates they were deposited under very quiet-water conditions, while the laminations record seasonal changes in runoff from nearby streams. These characteristics are common in lakes formed as a result of the damming of streams by glaciers or glacial sediment. In this instance the ice sheets were those that advanced during the Pleistocene Epoch. Essentially, the small oxbow lake records the presence of a much larger lake, Glacial Lake Monongahela, which formed during the Pleistocene. The extent of the lake has been mapped by using the presence of these lake clays. Geologists have also determined that Glacial Lakes Monongahela and Teays, to the southwest, existed at the same time during some of the earliest advances of the ice sheets, and they may have reappeared during later ones.

As Monongahela Boulevard descends into the Monongahela River valley, a tall, river-deposited outcrop of rock on the north side of the road exposes rocks of the Conemaugh Group, the most common rocks visible in the Morgantown

Laminated clay and silt layers deposited on the bed of Glacial Lake Monongahela record seasonal changes in runoff caused by glacial ice advances during the Pleistocene Epoch.

Pleistocene fossil leaf preserved by a brightly colored iron mineral in the Glacial Lake Monongahela clay deposits.

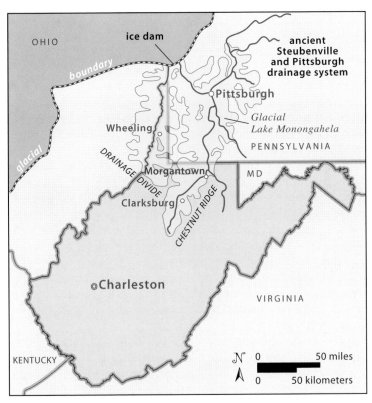

Extent of Glacial Lake Monongahela. –Modified from Kavage Adams and others, 2017; drainage from Teller and Goldthwait, 1991

area. An approximately 40-foot section in the lower portion of this outcrop contains another exposure of the very well-developed Ames cyclothem. The cyclothem contains, in ascending order, the Pittsburgh Red Shale, the Harlem coal, and the Ames marine zone. It is overlain by the Grafton Sandstone. The entire exposure ranges from the Pittsburgh Red Shale at the base to the lower Connellsville Sandstone near the top. At this point, the road veers to the southeast and becomes Beechurst Avenue.

Where the road passes through downtown Morgantown, there are no exposures to be observed, but as Beechurst Avenue parallels the Monongahela it is following the river's meandering course, which was in part influenced by the same joints in the underlying rocks that dictated the course of other rivers in the vicinity, including the Cheat. Here the flow of the Monongahela River is turning from northwest to northeast (it turns to the northeast again downstream of the bridge you previously crossed).

Beechurst Avenue bears to the right and merges with University Avenue. WV 7 proceeds for two blocks before turning left onto Pleasant Street and ascending onto a river terrace created by the southward meandering of Deckers Creek, the modern valley of which WV 7 will subsequently follow. Prior to that ascent, the route runs along a lower terrace created by the Monongahela River as it cut down through its valley. After two blocks, WV 7 turns left onto Spruce Street, and a block later it turns right onto Walnut Street, crosses Deckers Creek at a comparatively high elevation, turns left once more, and descends into Deckers Creek valley. The contrast in elevations is significant. The heights to the north and south, which constitute parts of Morgantown's Woodburn and South Park neighborhoods, respectively, are roughly 400 feet above the creek. Once the road reaches the bottom of the valley, small exposures of Conemaugh shale and sandstone can be seen as the road bears right, and then, in a left-hand switchback known locally as the "hogback turn," it crosses over the creek again before settling down to run close to the creek's north bank.

The valley opens up somewhat thanks to the work of the creek and its tributaries: Hartman Run from the north, Aaron Creek from the south, and Knocking Run from the east. Similar to many other parts of Morgantown, this valley was occupied by Glacial Lake Monongahela in Pleistocene time. It is now home to Sabraton, another Morgantown neighborhood. Until the 1960s, there were several heavy industries here getting their energy from coal mined in the immediate vicinity. Even a cursory glance at Deckers Creek will reveal the legacy of coal mining operations: orange iron oxide caused by acid mine drainage from abandoned operations upstream coats the streambed. Along the valley walls, more exposures of the Ames marine zone are visible north of the intersection with I-68.

East of I-68, the road twists and turns on its way through Rock Forge, the first of several unincorporated settlements that were formerly coal company towns. Rock Forge has been described as a "twice-born" town. In 1796 it was the site of an iron furnace and forge, one of many that were once located in the northern part of the state. By the late 1840s, local deposits of iron ore were exhausted. In 1905 Rock Forge was reborn as a coal company town, with underground and

The blocky Harlem coal is overlain by shales of the Ames marine zone in an outcrop along on WV 7 at the intersection with Hartman Run Road. The coal, which was deposited in low-lying coastal swamps, was inundated by a shallow sea that covered this region in one of the many warmer interglacial periods during the Late Paleozoic ice age.

A cephalopod fossil from the Ames marine zone. This swimming mollusk was a predator in the Pennsylvanian seas.

surface mines targeting the Upper Freeport coal in the Middle Pennsylvanian Allegheny Formation. Subsequently, Rock Forge became the home for people working in the industries in Sabraton or in nearby mining operations.

The now-defunct mining operations in Rock Forge and Richard were able to extract Upper Freeport coal profitably because it lies much closer to the surface here along the west limb of the Chestnut Ridge Anticline. The coal from these mines was transformed into a form of purified carbon, called coke, in nearby ovens that used to line the valley walls.

On the east side of Dellslow, the road crosses to the north side of Deckers Creek and, east of Tyrone Road, passes an outcrop of the Homewood Sandstone member at the top of the Middle Pennsylvanian Pottsville Sandstone. (We are in the Northern Basin here, so the Pottsville has only formation status, not the group status it has in the Southern Basin.) Locally known as the Pioneer Rocks, this sandstone marks the western margin of the Allegheny Mountain Section along this route. The Homewood continues along the north side of the road as WV 7 climbs above Deckers Creek along the dip slope of the rock. The slope under the sandstone is covered with large boulders that have fallen from the outcrop, evidence of the ongoing process of erosion that is slowly wearing the mountains away. Farther east, the road passes an exposure of the Upper Connoquenessing Sandstone that contains plant fossils, as well as large quartz pebbles that were rounded and deposited by fast river currents.

The erosion of the Chestnut Ridge Anticline by Deckers Creek exposes older Mississippian-age rocks in the core of the fold. WV 7 passes by slopes of the easily weathered red shales of the Mauch Chunk Formation of Late Mississippian age and exposures of light-gray Middle Mississippian Greenbrier Limestone. The Greenbrier contains marine brachiopod and crinoid fossils, as well as prominent cross bedding formed by underwater currents flowing in the shallow tropical sea that once covered most of the contiguous United States. Horizontal layers of Greenbrier Limestone are the oldest rocks exposed in the Chestnut Ridge Anticline along this route.

The road passes through a large limestone quarry that has been in operation for a number of generations. It was a source of the limestone necessary for steel production as well as aggregate. In the vicinity of the boundary of Preston and Monongalia Counties, WV 7 travels over the east limb of the Chestnut Ridge Anticline, and thus the rock units appear in reverse. Near Masontown the Upper Freeport coal is once again at the surface and was extensively mined.

East of Masontown, the road leaves Deckers Creek valley, and exposures of Conemaugh Group sandstones appear frequently. Coal was extensively mined here. The road travels over two former underground mines in the Upper Freeport coal, and to the north you can see a series of rounded, grassy hills, the result of the restoration of the land's contour following surface mining of Bakerstown coal of the Conemaugh Group. At the junction with WV 92 in Reedsville, those interested in exploring Arthurdale, Eleanor Roosevelt's planned community for displaced miners and their families, should proceed 3 miles south on WV 92.

East of Reedsville, WV 7 offers a view of Chestnut Ridge to the north. Note the geologic marker at Cows Run describing early gas drilling operations in the region. The highway crosses the axis of the Preston Anticline, which, though not influencing the topography at this point, was the site for natural gas wells. This resource typically accumulates in anticlinal traps. Sandstones from both the Allegheny Formation and Conemaugh Group are exposed along the route. From the higher ground east of Kingwood you can see Briery Mountain dominating the eastern horizon. It roughly parallels Chestnut Ridge.

Reclaimed grassy hills between Masontown and the WV 92 junction hide the evidence of coal mining.

East of Kingwood, the highway descends into the Cheat River valley, crossing the axis of the Kingwood Syncline. Rocks of the Conemaugh Group and Allegheny Formation can be observed. West of the Cheat River bridge, the highway begins to climb Briery Mountain, on the west limb of the Briery Mountain Anticline.

Unlike the valley of Deckers Creek on the Chestnut Ridge Anticline, no deep valley was carved through the core of the Briery Mountain Anticline. WV 7 climbs the dip slope of the Pottsville Sandstone, reaching the summit at approximately 2,700 feet and remaining at essentially the same elevation for several miles. Platy sandstones of the Foreknobs Formation of Late Devonian age, the oldest rocks in the anticline, are exposed on the high ground adjacent to a Lions Club school bus shelter to the south. East of the shelter, the road follows Saltlick Creek into Terra Alta. At approximately 2,560 feet above sea level, the name Terra Alta is appropriately derived from the Latin phrase meaning "high land."

The Briery Mountain Anticline, like many in the region, trapped natural gas and petroleum resources underground and thus became the site of what was known as the Terra Alta Gas Field. At one time as many as fifty wells were drilled down more than 1 mile below the surface to the porous Oriskany Sandstone of Early Devonian age, which contained the gas. Today, the field is exhausted, though it has continued to serve as an underground storage reservoir for natural gas.

Just west of Terra Alta, where the CSX Railroad parallels WV 7, both cross the axis of the Briery Mountain Anticline. No exposures of rock are visible on its east limb until east-dipping sandstones of the Price Formation of Early Mississippian age form the ridge on which the Hopemont Hospital is situated.

Cranesville Swamp

Unlike many of the side trips presented in this volume, Cranesville Swamp contains no spectacular outcroppings of rock, yet this unique ecosystem owes its existence to many of the geological events that shaped the modern landscape in West Virginia. The swamp is located about 9 miles north of WV 7 and can be accessed from Terra Alta. Turn north onto CR 42, known as Toy Street, and then turn onto Oak Grove Road. Continue for approximately 2 miles to a Y in the road. Veer right at the Y onto CR 47, or Cranesville Road. Continue northeast for 5.5 miles and turn right onto CR 49, Burnside Camp Road. After about 1 mile, turn left onto CR 47/1, or Feather Road. Follow Feather Road for just over 0.1 mile until you reach a utility line right-of-way. The access road for a parking area is on your right, from which you can stroll into the swamp on a boardwalk.

Standing water provides the right conditions to accumulate and preserve thick layers of peat moss in the Cranesville Swamp.

High ground around Cranesville Swamp traps cold air and provides a refuge for the northern flora that inhabits the swamp.

Straddling the Maryland–West Virginia border, the majority of this unique microenvironment is found in the Mountain State. Cranesville Swamp contains a rare ecosystem situated in a *frost pocket,* an elevated, low-lying area with cooler temperatures and poor drainage that permits localized pooling of water. The swamp lies along the axis of the Briery Mountain Anticline. As in other interactions with this fold, the resistant Pottsville Sandstone forms the walls of an upland valley with softer Mississippian shale and limestone units providing the floor. The swamp is perched at an elevation of 2,560 feet and is surrounded by hills that are upward of 2,900 feet. These hills trap moisture and cool air in the valley, which provide the optimal climate for an ecosystem more characteristic of those found in Canadian latitudes.

The unique plants that inhabit the swamp are a legacy of the last glacial advance of the Pleistocene ice age, which reached its maximum extent approximately 20,000 years ago. Although ice never covered this region, the cooler climate of the time led to the establishment of more northern, or boreal, plant species in this area. Even after the climate began to warm, and the ice started to retreat about 15,000 years ago, the cool, moist climate of Cranesville Swamp continued to provide favorable conditions and, thus, a southerly refuge for the boreal species that remain today. These species were replaced at lower elevations by flora adapted to a warmer climate.

The flat ground just to the east of the ridge is developed upon the easily weathered Greenbrier Limestone and Mauch Chunk Formation. The land becomes hilly again, a consequence of Pottsville and Allegheny sandstones at the surface near Corinth, west of the Maryland border.

WV 32
THOMAS—HARMAN
23 miles

WV 32 crosses through the heart of the Allegheny Mountains, passing three of the Mountain State's most iconic sites: Blackwater Falls State Park, Canaan ("Kuh-naan") Valley, and Dolly Sods Wilderness Area. Whichever route you traveled to arrive at WV 32, it likely involved a long ascent up Allegheny, Backbone, or Cabin Mountain to what resembles an elevated plateau with gently sloping ridges and a few deeply incised stream valleys. High elevations and abundant precipitation produce unique upland forests and wetlands, many of which are frost pockets inhabited by plant species that originally colonized the region during glacial advances in the Pleistocene Epoch.

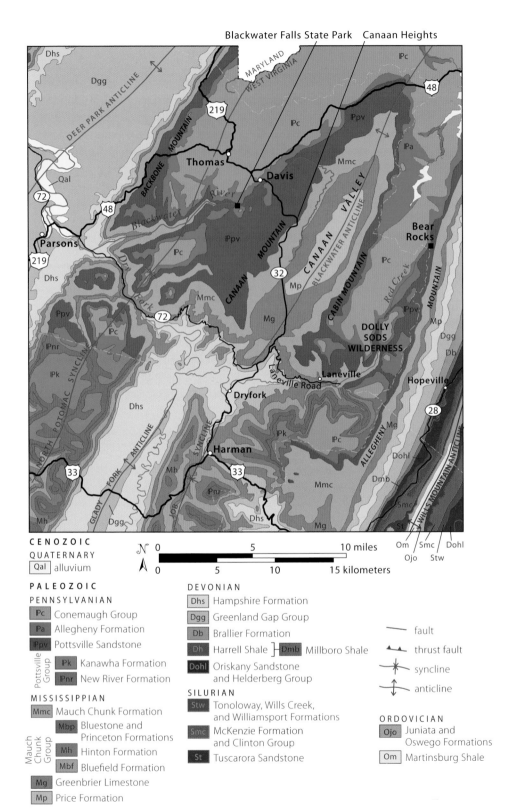

Geology along WV 32 between Thomas and Harman.

Labels on map:

Blackwater Falls State Park Canaan Heights

Dhs
Dgg
DEER PARK ANTICLINE
MARYLAND
WEST VIRGINIA
219
IPc
IPpv
48
IPa
Mmc
Thomas
Davis
CANAAN VALLEY
Qal
72
River
Blackwater
BACKBONE MOUNTAIN
IPpv
IPc
CANAAN MOUNTAIN
BLACKWATER ANTICLINE
CABIN MOUNTAIN
48
Parsons
Dry Fork
32
Mp
IPc
Red Creek
Bear Rocks
219
Dhs
Mmc
Mg
DOLLY SODS WILDERNESS
IPpv
Mp
IPpv
72
IPc
Dgg
Db
IPnr
IPk
Laneville
Hopeville
NORTH POTOMAC SYNCLINE
Dhs
Laneville Road
Dryfork
ALLEGHENY MOUNTAIN
Mg
28
IPk
IPc
Dohl
SYNCLINE
HORTON ANTICLINE
Harman
Dmb
33
Mh
33
Mmc
GLADY FORK ANTICLINE
JOB
IPnr
Smc
WHITES MOUNTAIN ANTICLINE
Mh
Dgg
Dhs
Mg
St
Om Smc Dohl
Ojo Stw

CENOZOIC
QUATERNARY
Qal alluvium

N
0   5   10 miles
0   5   10   15 kilometers

PALEOZOIC
PENNSYLVANIAN
IPc Conemaugh Group
IPa Allegheny Formation
IPpv Pottsville Sandstone
Pottsville Group
IPk Kanawha Formation
IPnr New River Formation

MISSISSIPPIAN
Mmc Mauch Chunk Formation
Mauch Chunk Group
Mbp Bluestone and Princeton Formations
Mh Hinton Formation
Mbf Bluefield Formation
Mg Greenbrier Limestone
Mp Price Formation

DEVONIAN
Dhs Hampshire Formation
Dgg Greenland Gap Group
Db Brallier Formation
Dh Harrell Shale ⎤ Dmb Millboro Shale
Dohl Oriskany Sandstone and Helderberg Group

SILURIAN
Stw Tonoloway, Wills Creek, and Williamsport Formations
Smc McKenzie Formation and Clinton Group
St Tuscarora Sandstone

─── fault
▲▲▲ thrust fault
⚹ syncline
⬍ anticline

ORDOVICIAN
Ojo Juniata and Oswego Formations
Om Martinsburg Shale

Although the topography is quite dramatic in places, the geology of the area is quite simple. The resistant Pottsville Sandstone of Early to Middle Pennsylvanian age is rather gently folded and covered by erosional remnants of younger rocks—the Allegheny Formation of Middle Pennsylvanian age and Conemaugh Group of Late Pennsylvanian age. For the first few miles east of Thomas, WV 32 passes over these younger rocks. Coals within both units, the Upper Freeport in the Allegheny and the Bakerstown in the Conemaugh, were extensively mined in this area. In fact, nearly all of the road between Thomas and Davis was undermined, although little evidence to attest to this lies on the surface. At Davis, you can head southwest to Blackwater Falls State Park.

Blackwater Falls

For those wanting to visit Blackwater Falls, turn west on Blackwater Falls Road just west of Davis. The park has two easily accessible viewing platforms. The first is a level, paved walkway from a parking area that offers an elevated view from near the top of the Blackwater River valley. To access the platform, turn left onto Blackwater Lodge Road at the triangle intersection with Blackwater Falls Road. The second platform, accessed using stairs that descend to the lower part of the valley, gives visitors a close-up view of the falls.

River channel sandstones of the Pottsville Sandstone at Blackwater Falls State Park form the valley walls and the resistant caprock at the falls.

The falls are situated in a steep, V-shaped valley that is nearly 500 feet deep. The Blackwater River, named for the water's dark tint from tannic acids released by decaying vegetation, flows over a ledge of Pottsville Sandstone. The falls drop 57 feet to the valley bottom, and the sandstones in both the riverbed and the valley walls contain numerous cut-and-fill channel structures and cross bedding formed by rivers that transported the sand. Deposited during the Pennsylvanian Period, the sand was ultimately lithified into sandstone. Many of the stone steps that lead to the lower platform contain plant fossils, ripple marks, and cross beds.

How was the river able to cut down through the hard Pottsville Sandstone? The answer is found in the soft shales that underlie the sandstone. The river carved a valley in the upstream direction in a process called *headward erosion.* Shales below the dipping Pottsville Sandstone were eroded to a lower elevation ahead of where the river encountered the Pottsville Sandstone at the surface. As the soft shales were eroded from below they no longer supported the weight of the overlying sandstone, which then collapsed, causing the falls to migrate upstream, or in the headward direction. The collapse of many of the blocks is aided by joints in the sandstone, which provide a plane of weakness and cause the blocks, and the falls itself, to have even, flat faces. Evidence of this ongoing process lies at the base of the falls, where large, angular blocks of sandstone that collapsed sometime in the past still remain.

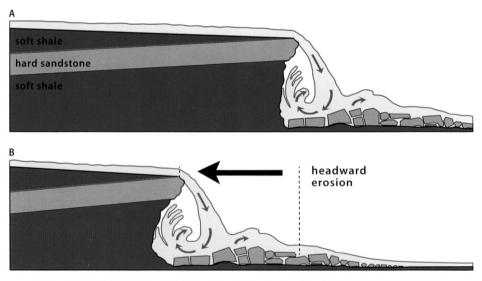

The effect of headward erosion on soft shales (green) and hard sandstones (brown). The sandstone layer is undercut by the river, causing it to break into blocks and collapse.
—Modified from Renton, undated

South of Davis, which incidentally has the highest elevation of any incorporated community in West Virginia at 3,200 feet, the highway crosses the Blackwater River upstream from the falls. We are west of the Eastern Continental Divide, so the stream flows west and is a tributary of the Cheat River. Between the river and Canaan Heights, WV 32 climbs Canaan Mountain, the slope of which follows the gently dipping west limb of the Blackwater Anticline. The road is lined with blocks of pebbly Pottsville Sandstone, which forms the slope and underlies Canaan Heights at the western edge of Canaan Valley. The elevation of Canaan Heights is approximately 3,700 feet, and when the trees lose their leaves it offers a nice view of the valley.

South of Canaan Heights, WV 32 begins its descent into Canaan Valley, dropping roughly 400 feet to the valley floor. To the south lies Cabin Mountain, which is the eastern wall of the valley and constitutes the eastern horizon. Like Canaan Mountain, Cabin Mountain is capped by Pottsville Sandstone, but it's on the eastern limb of the Blackwater Anticline. Timberline and Canaan Valley Resort ski areas are also visible. Occasionally visible along the road are small gas wells and storage tanks painted green, the wells tapping into the anticlinal trap formed by the Blackwater fold. Those wells, dating from the 1980s, were among the earliest to make use of directional drilling, an innovative technology that, as the name implies, allows the drill stem to be steered in the subsurface. The technology revolutionized the drilling industry.

Anticlines tend to be susceptible to erosion because their rock layers are stretched over the fold axis, creating fractures and expanding pores, thus increasing the rate of weathering by water. Erosion follows thereafter, hollowing these features out. Canaan Valley is essentially the result of the hollowing out of the Blackwater Anticline. Imagine the resistant Pottsville Sandstone arching up and over the valley, connecting the outcrops on Canaan and Cabin Mountains just as they did prior to erosion. Then imagine that once the Pottsville was eroded away, older rocks of Late Mississippian age—the Mauch Chunk Formation and Greenbrier Limestone—were subsequently removed, exposing

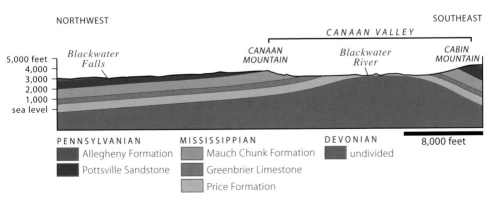

Geologic cross section of the Blackwater Anticline at Canaan Valley. Hard Pottsville Sandstone forms Canaan and Cabin Mountains. –Modified from Matchen and others, 2008

the top of the Price Formation of Early Mississippian age. The result is the valley through which the highway now runs.

As WV 32 continues south, it crosses the North Branch of the Blackwater River and then the Blackwater River itself north of where the highway veers west and passes Cabin Mountain, with its ski trails. South of Canaan Valley Ski Resort, the road descends below the elevation of the Canaan Valley floor, and you can see a small quarry in the Greenbrier Limestone to the west. Down-hill from the quarry, roadcuts reveal more of the Greenbrier Limestone, which continue about a half mile until the junction with Laneville Road: the route to Dolly Sods. Be cautious if you choose to turn onto Laneville Road. It takes a left-hand hairpin off WV 32.

South of Laneville Road, WV 32 descends into Red Creek valley. You can see sandstones of the Price Formation along the road. The highway crosses Red Creek at the Tucker-Randolph county line. South of the creek, the route crosses a low drainage divide and enters the valley of the Dry Fork, passing the community of the same name in the process. Between Dry Fork and Harman, WV 32 follows the Dry Fork valley, passing flat-lying red beds and dark-red cross-bedded sandstones of the Hampshire Formation of Late Devonian age in the lower part of the valley. WV 32 climbs back into Mississippian rocks, where the Greenbrier Limestone is exposed in a roadside quarry just to the north of Harman. A historical marker at the quarry refers to the Greenbrier as the "Big Lime."

Dolly Sods Wilderness Area

Dolly Sods Wilderness, part of the Monongahela National Forest, is situated in the easternmost part of the Allegheny Mountains between Cabin Mountain, the eastern wall of Canaan Valley, and the imposing Allegheny Front. To reach Dolly Sods, turn east on Laneville Road, which heads generally southeast, winding through hilly farmland until it turns east and hugs the northern valley wall of Red Creek. The road follows the outcrop belt of both the Greenbrier Limestone and the Mauch Chunk Formation, which lie at the surface in Canaan Valley but here are encountered at a lower elevation because the layers continue to dip to the southeast on the east limb of the Blackwater Anticline. Outcrops are sparse until the road descends to the level of Red Creek near the town of Laneville. Here, red beds and sandstones of the Mauch Chunk line the north side of the road until it crosses Red Creek and becomes Forest Road 19. The road then turns upward and climbs to the Allegheny Front. The road makes a long, gradual turn to the northeast and intersects FR 75. Although there are many places to stop along the way, continue on FR 75 for about 7.5 miles until you can see the road veering sharply to the right and large blocks of white

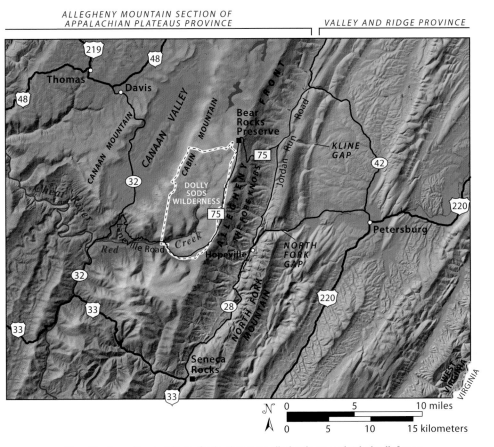

The Allegheny Front at Dolly Sods shows up distinctly on a shaded relief map.

Pottsville Sandstone ahead. Here at the Bear Rocks Preserve there are parking areas on both sides of the road.

Dolly Sods was named after the Dahle family that settled here in the 1800s. "Sods" is a local term for a grassy mountaintop meadow. The boundary of Dolly Sods essentially outlines the watershed of Red Creek, which is shaped like an elongated bowl. Similar to the area around Thomas and Davis to the west, the high ground is supported by the Pottsville Sandstone that was gently folded into the Stony River Syncline. These resistant sandstones line the edges of the bowl and make up the rims, while erosional remnants of the Allegheny Formation and Conemaugh Group cover the middle. Bear Rocks Preserve lies on the eastern rim.

Many of the surface features and ecosystems are remnants of the cooler climate that existed during the last glacial advances in the Pleistocene Epoch. Plant species more common in the northern latitudes of Canada have found a refuge in the cold and windy conditions here, which has stunted the growth

At Dolly Sods the Pottsville Sandstone forms the eastern edge of the Allegheny Mountains. Many of the spruce trees are flagged, with their branches pointing downwind of the prevailing winds.

of many of the red spruce trees on the rims and even caused their branches to grow mostly in the lee side of the trunk—that is, pointing to the east. This condition is known as "flagged."

The many weathered and tilted boulders of sandstone in Bear Rocks Preserve also have their origins in the Pleistocene Epoch, when cooler climates led to intense frost wedging. Repeated freezing and expanding of water in joints helped wedge the Pottsville apart, forming the numerous flat-sided blocks. The sandstone here is very coarse, with large, rounded quartz pebbles visible on the rock surfaces and weathered out as loose grains on the trails. Cross bedding is also common here and, combined with the abundance of large pebbles, indicates that very swift currents transported this material in what was likely a braided stream system that drained the ancestral Appalachian Mountains to the east.

Aside from what lies on the ground, the main attractions of Dolly Sods are, of course, the views. It is easy to be overwhelmed looking in almost any direction from the lofty heights of the Allegheny Front, which here is just under 4,000 feet above sea level here. Look west across the Sods to see Cabin Mountain, the western rim. To the north, the land gradually descends. The Bakerstown and Upper Freeport coals were mined there and used in the Mt. Storm Power Plant. Now lines of wind turbines extend along the front to the Maryland state line. The most spectacular and geologically significant view is to the east, where the eastern edge of the Allegheny Mountains, the Allegheny Front, plummets

Eastward view of the Valley and Ridge Province from Dolly Sods.

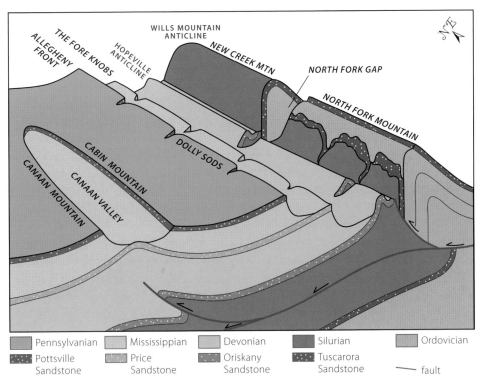

ALLEGHENY FRONT

THE FORE KNOBS

HOPEVILLE ANTICLINE

WILLS MOUNTAIN ANTICLINE

NEW CREEK MTN

NORTH FORK GAP

NORTH FORK MOUNTAIN

DOLLY SODS

CABIN MOUNTAIN

CANAAN VALLEY

CANAAN MOUNTAIN

Pennsylvanian	Mississippian	Devonian	Silurian	Ordovician
Pottsville Sandstone	Price Sandstone	Oriskany Sandstone	Tuscarora Sandstone	fault

Like much of the Appalachian Mountains, gently folded, resistant sandstones form the prominent landforms of Canaan Valley, Dolly Sods, and the Allegheny Front. East of the Front in the Valley and Ridge Province, folds are much tighter and thrust faults are common at the surface. The ridge-forming sandstones have a dotted pattern on the map. —Modified from Renton, undated

nearly 2,000 feet to the town of Hopeville, along WV 28, and the western edge of the Valley and Ridge Province. Looking out over the series of ridges it should be plainly obvious how that province got its name.

The first, or westernmost, ridge is known as New Creek Mountain to the north and North Fork Mountain to the south. It is the topographic expression of the Wills Mountain Anticline, the westernmost of the major fault-propagation folds that characterize the geology of the Valley and Ridge Province. This is one of the best places in the state to see the difference in tectonic uplift between the Allegheny Mountains and the Valley and Ridge Province.

As you look across New Creek Mountain, note Kline Gap, recognizable by the roughly circular outcrop of white sandstone that arches over the mountain on both sides. The white rock is the Tuscarora Sandstone of Early Silurian age, and its resistance to erosion makes it a prominent ridge former in the Valley and Ridge. Here, in the Allegheny Mountain Section of the Appalachian Plateaus, the same sandstone is around 10,000 feet below the surface of both Dolly Sods and Canaan Valley. The difference in elevation is the work of large thrust faults that underlie the Valley and Ridge Province. Essentially these faults permitted large slabs of sedimentary rock to be shoved westward during the Alleghanian Orogeny. Many slabs became stacked like toppled dominos, and the rock above them was uplifted, broken, and bent into numerous anticlines and synclines. The rock above the Tuscarora, including the Pottsville you are standing on, was eroded away, exposing a landscape of highly deformed older rock.

Another feature worth noting is the outcrop of Tuscarora Sandstone in North Fork Gap, just to the south of Kline Gap. There, the white cliffs have been eroded away and do not extend over the summit of North Fork Mountain. Instead the Tuscarora, on the east limb of the Wills Mountain Anticline, forms a hogback, where resistant rock forms one slope of a mountain, often protecting softer rocks underneath from erosion.

One reason for the difference in the degree of erosion between the two gaps is related to the *plunge*, or downward tilt of the axis, of the Wills Mountain Anticline. While many fold axes appear to run parallel to the surface, over long distances they tend to intersect the surface and continue belowground. In this case, the Wills Mountain Anticline plunges to the north. The Tuscarora on North Fork Mountain was at higher elevation and exhumed by erosion earlier than it was to the north, where it is now just beginning to erode.

VALLEY AND RIDGE PROVINCE

Approximately three-quarters of the Mountain State lies within the westward-sloping Appalachian Plateaus Province. Its topography seems capricious with valleys seemingly running in every direction. Streams carving into a landscape covered more or less by soft shale, which weathers uniformly, establishes nature's default dendritic drainage pattern. The Valley and Ridge Province is altogether different. Here, roughly parallel ridges extend for miles in a northeast-southwest orientation, separated from one another by deep valleys. The ridges consistently funnel streams in the same orientation, though some occasionally cross the ridges at nearly right angles through water gaps, producing the distinctive trellis drainage pattern—think of a garden trellis in which slats of wood cross each other at right angles. Because most of the Valley and Ridge Province lies to the east of the Eastern Continental Divide, the streams drain into the Potomac River and eventually the Atlantic Ocean. The main exception is the New River, which carved its northwestward path millions of years before the land was uplifted and began to be eroded.

The drainage, and the topography as a whole, are the surface expressions of rock layers that were subjected to increased compression during the Late Paleozoic Alleghanian Orogeny, which completed the final assembly of Pangea. Unlike the gently dipping rocks of the plateaus, the layers here were lying closer to the collision zone between the African and North American Plates and

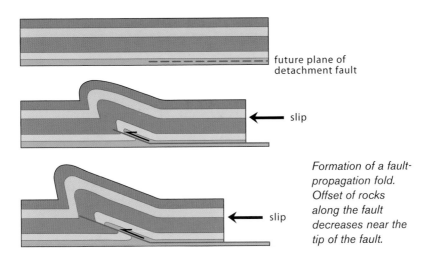

future plane of
detachment fault

slip

slip

Formation of a fault-propagation fold. Offset of rocks along the fault decreases near the tip of the fault.

179

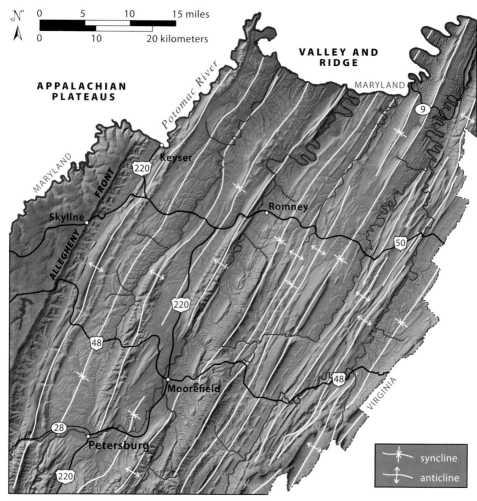

Shaded relief map of major rivers (blue) and fold axes (white) in the northern part of West Virginia's Valley and Ridge Province. Resistant, ridge-forming sandstones direct drainage into and along the valleys, forming a trellis drainage pattern.

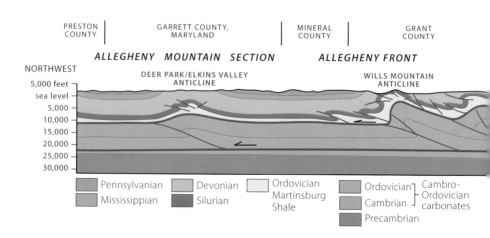

therefore were severely deformed. Outcrops of nearly vertical and even over-turned layers, the latter of which are now upside down, are common in folds in the region. Many of these folds are fault-propagation folds, produced by rocks dragging along the surfaces of thrust faults, which, unlike those found in the Appalachian Plateaus Province, can reach the surface in the Valley and Ridge. These folds are asymmetrical, with one limb of the fold, usually the northwest limb, dipping more steeply than the southeastern one.

In a way, the small-scale folding and thrust faulting visible at the surface mimics the larger-scale deformation at great depth, which ultimately led to the overall pattern of rocks as well as the surface topography. The Cambro-Ordo-vician carbonates, a package of rock nearly 10,000 feet thick and lying about 3 miles below the surface, was cut into a series of slabs by thrust faults that connected major detachment faults above and below the carbonates. A *detach-ment* is a horizontal thrust fault in which one rock layer slides, or is thrust, over another. The smaller thrust faults permitted the large slabs to be shoved westward and stacked like toppled dominos between the detachments that propagated through weaker layers.

Rocks above the Cambro-Ordovician carbonates were uplifted, broken, and bent to a much greater degree than those on the plateaus. It is, however, surprising to learn that while the topographic relief in the Valley and Ridge equals or surpasses that of the Allegheny Mountain Section of the Appalachian Plateaus, elevations along the ridges in the Valley and Ridge are generally lower. During the Alleghanian Orogeny the Valley and Ridge was at a higher eleva-tion, as part of the highlands adjacent to the ancestral Appalachian Mountains. Erosion at such an elevation tends to be more rapid because high precipitation, wider temperature variations, and steeper slopes lead to faster weathering and lowering of the land. In fact, sandstones of the Pottsville Group in the Appa-lachian Plateaus contain clasts of Early Paleozoic rocks from the Valley and

Geologic cross section from the Allegheny Mountain Section of the Appa-lachian Plateaus to the Valley and Ridge. Major detachment faults, which bracket the Cambro-Ordovician carbonate slabs, are highlighted in thick red.
–Modified from Kulander and Dean, 1986

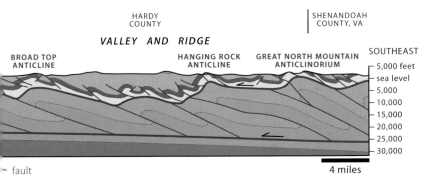

Ridge. This suggests that even as uplift was occurring during the orogeny, the Valley and Ridge was an erosional landscape while the low-relief landscape of the plateaus was a site of deposition.

Given the faster rates of erosion described above, it should be no surprise that the rocks encountered in the Valley and Ridge Province also tend to be older than those of the Appalachian Plateaus Province. Early and Middle Paleozoic rocks deposited during the Ordovician, Silurian, and Devonian Periods compose most of the surface rocks in the region, while Late Paleozoic rocks from the Pennsylvanian and Permian Periods cover most of the area in the plateaus.

The topography in the Valley and Ridge Province reflects the difference in weathering and erosion between the resistant sandstones that make up the ridges and the more easily weathered shales and limestones that line the valley floors. It may be difficult at first to visualize how streams running through the low valleys could carve water gaps through the ridges at their present elevation. But as was true of the Appalachian Plateaus Province to the west, several thousand feet of rock have been removed by streams carving down into the landscape for hundreds of millions of years. As they did, their courses followed joints in the rock that generally run perpendicular to the axes of folds. This permitted streams to cut through the folds, often by means of stream capture, connecting drainages in adjacent valleys, thus producing the right angles of trellis drainage.

The road guides for the Valley and Ridge Province, like the drainage pattern, can also be thought of as trellised, although many of the water gaps are too narrow for a highway. Where this is the case the east-west routes have to climb up and over the ridges, providing numerous scenic views of the landscape. The north-south routes generally remain in the valleys. The variety and age of the rocks encountered depend on the direction of travel. East-west routes cross numerous fold axes and the surface traces of thrust faults. Different, often repeated rock layers are often encountered in rapid succession. In contrast, the valley-hugging north-south routes parallel these geologic structures and tend to follow the same rock unit for many miles.

US 33
SENECA ROCKS—FRANKLIN—VIRGINIA STATE LINE
45 miles

At Seneca Rocks, US 33 joins WV 28 and heads south up the North Fork of the Potomac's South Branch. To the west lies Allegheny Mountain, the eastern edge of the Appalachian Plateaus capped by the Pottsville Sandstone of Early Pennsylvanian age. The ridge on the east side of the valley that includes Seneca Rocks is known as the River Knobs. Seneca Rocks is a large exposure of vertical Tuscarora Sandstone, and to the south along the midline of River Knobs, occasionally you can see smaller exposures of the vertical beds. In between the

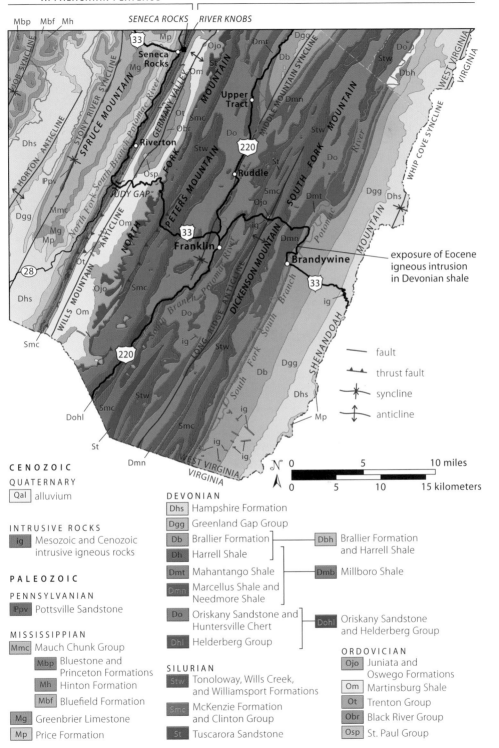

APPALACHIAN PLATEAUS | VALLEY AND RIDGE

SENECA ROCKS RIVER KNOBS

exposure of Eocene
igneous intrusion
in Devonian shale

—————— fault

⏶⏶⏶ thrust fault

✳ syncline

⇕ anticline

N

0   5   10 miles

0   5   10   15 kilometers

CENOZOIC

QUATERNARY

Qal alluvium

INTRUSIVE ROCKS

ig Mesozoic and Cenozoic
intrusive igneous rocks

PALEOZOIC

PENNSYLVANIAN

Ppv Pottsville Sandstone

MISSISSIPPIAN

Mmc Mauch Chunk Group

Mbp Bluestone and
Princeton Formations

Mh Hinton Formation

Mbf Bluefield Formation

Mg Greenbrier Limestone

Mp Price Formation

DEVONIAN

Dhs Hampshire Formation

Dgg Greenland Gap Group

Db Brallier Formation

Dh Harrell Shale

Dbh Brallier Formation
and Harrell Shale

Dmt Mahantango Shale

Dmn Marcellus Shale and
Needmore Shale

Dmb Millboro Shale

Do Oriskany Sandstone and
Huntersville Chert

Dhl Helderberg Group

Dohl Oriskany Sandstone
and Helderberg Group

SILURIAN

Stw Tonoloway, Wills Creek,
and Williamsport Formations

Smc McKenzie Formation
and Clinton Group

St Tuscarora Sandstone

ORDOVICIAN

Ojo Juniata and
Oswego Formations

Om Martinsburg Shale

Ot Trenton Group

Obr Black River Group

Osp St. Paul Group

Geology along US 33 between Seneca Rock and the Virginia state line.

Seneca Rocks

Seneca Rocks is located on the east side of the North Fork of the South Branch of the Potomac, across the valley from the base of the Allegheny Front, the boundary between the Appalachian Plateaus and Valley and Ridge Provinces. Extending more than 500 feet above the valley floor, Seneca Rocks consists of the Tuscarora Sandstone, a very dense, quartz-rich rock, which accounts for its resistance to erosion and its comparatively light color. It was deposited as beach sands along a coast in Early Silurian time.

Vertical beds of the resistant Tuscarora Sandstone form Seneca Rocks on the west limb of the Wills Mountain Anticline, the westernmost fold in the Valley and Ridge.

To visit Seneca Rocks, either head north on WV 28 from the junction of US 33 and WV 28 and make a quick right into the Seneca Rocks Picnic Area, or head south and then left into the Seneca Rocks Discovery Center. While the Discovery Center provides much information about Seneca Rocks and the surrounding area in a modern facility, the picnic area lies at the head of a 1.5-mile trail that utilizes several switchbacks in a gentle climb to an observation platform near the top of Seneca Rocks. Once at the platform, the entire vertical extent of the Allegheny Front is visible to the west, quite possibly one of the best views of this important topographical and geological boundary in the Mountain State.

Standing close to the base of Seneca Rocks, say near the visitor center or the picnic area in the park, both of which lie between the river and the cliff, you might easily conclude that the rocks are horizontal and the outcrop is simply the result of erosion that removed the weaker rocks and let the stronger sandstone remain. Not so. Instead, the Tuscarora Sandstone at Seneca Rocks is

View from the top of Seneca Rocks looking to the south along the North Fork of the South Branch of the Potomac River. The ridge visible in the distance (at right) is part of the Allegheny Front.

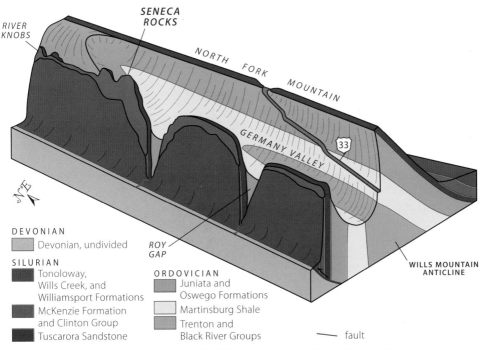

SENECA ROCKS

RIVER KNOBS

NORTH FORK MOUNTAIN

GERMANY VALLEY

33

WILLS MOUNTAIN ANTICLINE

ROY GAP

DEVONIAN
Devonian, undivided

SILURIAN
Tonoloway, Wills Creek, and Williamsport Formations
McKenzie Formation and Clinton Group
Tuscarora Sandstone

ORDOVICIAN
Juniata and Oswego Formations
Martinsburg Shale
Trenton and Black River Groups

—— fault

Schematic cross section of the Wills Mountain Anticline at Seneca Rocks.
—Modified from Renton, undated

nearly vertical and part of the western limb of the asymmetrical Wills Mountain Anticline. This fold is the westernmost structure in the Valley and Ridge Province and thus farthest away from the collision zone between the North American and African Plates during the Alleghanian Orogeny.

The fold's presence here suggests that the irresistible force to the east, namely the push of the African Plate, could not overcome what in this location had become an immovable object: the North American Plate. The latter would not yield any more territory. Instead, the intense compressional stress that was being transmitted by a subsurface thrust fault was directed upward, and the layers of rock, including the Tuscarora Sandstone, folded as they were dragged along the fault. The upward movement, or displacement, of rock becomes evident because the Tuscarora Sandstone at the surface here lies nearly 2 miles below the Appalachian Plateaus to the west.

knobs, gaps in the ridge appear, resulting from streams cutting down through stress fractures, or joints, in the sandstone.

The vertical orientation of the Tuscarora continues under the valley floor on the west limb of the Wills Mountain Anticline. Younger rocks above the sandstone, which include the remainder of the Silurian and much of the Devonian section, are easily weathered carbonates and shales that have been worn down as the river has meandered from one side of the valley to the other. Occasionally, US 33 passes exposures of Middle and Late Devonian rocks, including an exposure of the Oriskany Sandstone that lines the west side of the highway at Riverton. In between the Oriskany exposure and the Tuscarora to the east lie the entire Silurian and Early Devonian sections. This would be difficult to accomplish across the width of the valley unless the rocks were vertical.

The rocks in the valley were laid down in the Appalachian Basin in the Silurian and Early Devonian Periods, a time of relative calm between the Taconic and Acadian Orogenies. For most of this time, the basin was relatively shallow, with clastic sediments accumulating only for brief periods. Both the Tuscarora and Oriskany are essentially beach or barrier island sands deposited along the edge of a sea that occupied the basin. Most of the remaining rocks are carbonates formed from the remains of organisms that flourished in the warm sea.

US 33 turns east toward Judy Gap, while WV 28 continues south. Within this major gap in the River Knobs, US 33 passes the Tuscarora Sandstone and enters the core of the Wills Mountain Anticline. The highway climbs a 3.5-percent grade for almost 7 miles en route to the summit of North Fork Mountain. As it does, it passes the older Martinsburg Shale, deposited in a foreland basin in Ordovician time during the early stages of the Taconic Orogeny. The basin formed as the region was flexed downward by the collision of the North American Plate and a small island arc that had formed during subduction in the

Iapetus Ocean. The sediments of the Martinsburg Shale accumulated in deeper water than did the Silurian units and contain the fossils of a small, blind trilobite called *Cryptolithus*, which had no use for eyes in the dark, deep water.

As US 33 climbs toward the summit of North Fork Mountain, it passes bright-red outcrops of shales and sandstones of the Juniata Formation of Late Ordovician age. This unit, lying above the Martinsburg Shale, is the late-stage

The head shield of the Ordovician trilobite Cryptolithus *from the Martinsburg Shale.*

In Judy Gap vertical beds of the Tuscarora Sandstone form outcrops similar to Seneca Rocks.

Germany Valley Overlook

As US 33 ascends the west side of North Fork Mountain, look for a blue sign with white lettering announcing a scenic overlook. It is well worth a stop, but use caution both entering and exiting because the road curves sharply in both directions. The overlook is approximately 3,350 feet in elevation; at Judy Gap, the elevation was 1,940 feet, and the summit of North Fork Mountain is 3,580 feet. As the sign at the overlook indicates, to the north lies Germany Valley–the hollowed-out core of the Wills Mountain Anticline, which is plunging to the north. The floor of the valley slopes down to the west.

Spruce Mountain (Allegheny Front)

View to the north from Germany Valley scenic overlook. Ordovician rocks in the valley constitute the core of the Wills Mountain Anticline, while the younger Tuscarora Sandstone on North Fork Mountain to the east (far right) and the River Knobs to the west (left center) are the limbs. The Allegheny Front rises in the distance.

The Wills Mountain Anticline is asymmetrical, and the less steep east limb, visible to the upper right (northeast), dips about 40 degrees to the east. The tall cliffs on top of North Fork Mountain create a common topographic feature of the Valley and Ridge Province called a *hogback*, a vernacular term adopted by geologists to identify steeply sloped ridges, 20 degrees or more, with narrow summits. The hogbacks form when resistant rock caps one side of a ridge, protecting the softer units underneath from erosion.

To visualize the entire anticline, imagine a time when German Valley did not exist. The cliffs of Tuscarora that cap the North Fork Mountain hogback were connected to the vertical Tuscarora of the River Knobs in a continuous layer, arching above the older units that made up the core of the anticline before erosion hollowed it out. Weathering and erosion of anticlines in the Valley and Ridge are often aided by extensional fractures that form on the upper surface of the rock as it is stretched during folding. Think of an anticline as comparable to a sponge that has been folded. The holes in the middle of the upper surface of

River Knobs   **North Fork Mountain**

the sponge get wider as it is bent. In rock layers, water then enters the pores and fractures and breaks the layers into pieces as it alternately freezes and thaws.

To the west beyond River Knobs is the elevated edge of the high plateaus and the Allegheny Front. This is a particularly good location to see the Front in its entirety. Of note are the Fore Knobs, which are the eroded remnants of the Late Devonian rock unit that bears their name. The Fore Knobs give the face of the Front a "stepped" appearance as it slopes down to the Valley and Ridge Province. Such striking contrasts in elevation are characteristic of the Valley and Ridge Province.

portion of the foreland basin fill. It was deposited by rivers carrying sediments eroded from the uplifted Taconic Mountains. The Juniata got its red color from exposure to the atmosphere under arid conditions, which oxidized iron minerals in the sediments after they were deposited, a common outcome for ancient floodplain deposits seen elsewhere in the state. As the road descends the eastern slope of the mountain, it passes the contact between the Juniata and Tuscarora, coinciding with the boundary between the Ordovician and Silurian Periods. The descent also offers a great view of how the east-dipping Tuscarora Sandstone forms the slope of the North Fork Mountain hogback.

After crossing to the east side of a small valley created by Reeds Creek, US 33 again passes exposures of Juniata and Tuscarora rocks on the west side of Peters Mountain. Their reappearance is the result of displacement along a thrust fault that drove a section of these two layers up and over another layer like toppled dominos. The units were folded as the ends of the beds were dragged along a fault in a fashion similar to the fault drag of the Wills Mountain Anticline. Like North Fork Mountain to the west, Peters Mountain is a hogback capped by Tuscarora Sandstone. On the east side of its summit, the highway descends through folded and faulted Juniata rocks and the Oriskany Sandstone, roughly 44 million years younger than the Juniata units higher up the mountain.

West of Franklin, US 33 passes several exposures of the Oriskany Sandstone and two limestone quarries that expose the Devonian Helderberg Group. Unlike the faulted Tuscarora to the east, the repeated exposures of these rocks

The contact between the Ordovician Juniata Formation (red rock at left) and the Silurian Tuscarora Sandstone (white rock at right) on the east slope of North Fork Mountain. The Tuscarora is the resistant caprock that forms this hogback.

An anticline in the Juniata Formation is exposed on the east slope of Peters Mountain as the road turns southeast. Its asymmetrical shape (steep on west side, gradual on east side) is the result of drag along a thrust fault, which formed this fault-propagation fold.

are due to small folds. Approximately one-half mile west of its northern junction with US 220, US 33 enters a narrow valley of eroded Middle Devonian Marcellus Shale in the axis of the Middle Mountain Syncline.

Both in Franklin and east of town, folding has produced repeated exposures of the Devonian Helderberg Group, Oriskany Sandstone, and Millboro Shale. The highway follows the valley of Trout Run as it heads east, then climbs South Fork Mountain. As it does, it crosses the axes of several small folds responsible for the changing dip of Silurian and Devonian rocks and several ridges. Where it passes through a tight gap in Long Ridge, white cliffs of the Tuscarora Sandstone are perched high above the road. Its presence here, well above younger Silurian and Devonian rocks, is the result of another thrust fault, which also produced the Long Ridge Anticline, the west limb of which is marked by the Tuscarora Sandstone at road level.

At the summit of South Fork Mountain, elevation 2,365 feet, US 33 begins to descend the east limb of the Long Ridge Anticline. While you might expect to follow Silurian rocks down the east limb, the route passes exposures of dipping Devonian Helderberg and Oriskany rocks at Kisner Gap Road. The rocks are on the footwall of a fault that displaced older Silurian rocks in the headwall to the east, a feature called a *back thrust*. These faults are the result of "push back" from the resistance of the North American Plate to the major faults displacing rock to the west.

Just east of the bridge over Paddy Run the Tuscarora Sandstone reappears in the west limb of the Long Ridge Anticline.

Along the grade west of Oak Flat are limestones and thin-bedded cherts of the Helderberg Group of Early Devonian age, part of a back thrust associated with the Long Ridge Anticline.

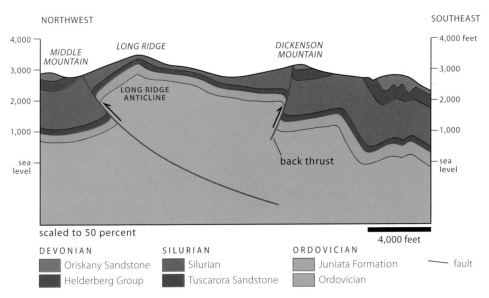

Geologic cross section of the Long Ridge Anticline south of US 33. The core of the anticline along the route has been eroded, exposing the Tuscarora Sandstone and rocks of Late Ordovician age. East-dipping Devonian Helderberg rocks east of the anticline are in the footwall of the back thrust near Dickenson Mountain. –Modified from McDowell and others, 2005

In the valley of the South Fork of the South Branch of the Potomac, the eastern horizon is dominated by Shenandoah Mountain, with the boundary between West Virginia and Virginia running along its spine. Like many of the large valleys encountered thus far, this one is also eroded into black Devonian shales, which are visible in several outcrops along the road. One of these exposures, about 1.5 miles north of the town of Brandywine, also contains one of several small igneous intrusions found in Pendleton County. Radiometrically dated at around 50 million years old, these intrusions solidified during the Eocene Epoch of the Cenozoic Era, a time when present-day West Virginia, and the rest of the eastern shore of North America for that matter, was a passive margin formed along the Atlantic Ocean. With no clear tectonic mechanism available to generate magmas in the area at that time, these intrusions remain an issue of much debate among geologists and one of the unsolved mysteries of West Virginia's geological history.

A nearly vertical Eocene-age igneous dike cuts across the Middle Devonian Millboro Shale. The sample shows large black crystals of iron-rich minerals in the igneous rock.

The erosion of soft, Middle Devonian black shales forms many of the valleys in the Valley and Ridge. This exposure is on the north side of the road (west of the outcrop with the igneous intrusion), about 3.5 miles east of Brandywine. In places you can see whitish weathering residue on the shales that develops when sulfur is exposes to atmospheric oxygen. Sulfur tends to become concentrated in low-oxygen environments that also preserve organic-rich rocks like the black shales.

US 33 follows the shales south to Brandywine, the last community west of the road's dramatic ascent of Shenandoah Mountain, the west limb of the Whip Cove Syncline. Along the climb, the route passes most of the units deposited in the Catskill clastic wedge during Devonian time. The dark shales at the base grade into the lighter-colored interbedded sandstones and shales of the Brallier and Foreknobs Formations, the latter having thicker—greater than 1 foot—sandstone beds. The contact between the two is located near the intersection of the highway and the National Forest Shooting Range access road. As the route winds through several switchbacks, it reaches the red rocks of the Hampshire Formation, the youngest Devonian rocks in West Virginia.

All the units along the western ascent of Shenandoah Mountain are dipping southeast into the hillside toward the axis of the Whip Cove Syncline. It may seem strange that a mountain of this size is the eroded remnant of a syncline, but this is in fact quite common. Remember how the axis of the Wills Mountain Anticline had eroded to form Germany Valley? The folding of the Tuscarora into an anticline increased the rate of weathering and erosion by stretching pore spaces and opening fractures. Here, the effect is the opposite. Folding the units into a syncline actually compressed the upper surface, which limits the ability of water to enter the rock and break it into pieces.

River channel sandstones and floodplain mudstones in the Hampshire Formation near the first big turn about 0.5 mile west of the Shenandoah Mountain summit. The intense red color likely indicates that the sediments were deposited in an arid climate.

Near the summit, a scenic overlook provides a spectacular view of the many mountains crossed by US 33, and a safe place to turn around if you are not headed into Virginia. If you continue east, the route passes by exposures of the Hampshire Formation at an elevation of 3,450 feet. This, however, is not the highest elevation on Shenandoah Mountain. A few eroded sandstone remnants of the Price Formation of Early Mississippian age cap the mountain to the south at elevations over 4,000 feet.

US 48
DAVIS—MOOREFIELD—VIRGINIA STATE LINE
72 miles

Corridor H is a work in progress. Intended to link I-79 in the west-central part of the Mountain State with I-81 in western Virginia, it currently consists of two stretches of limited-access four-lane divided highway with comparatively easy grades and gentle curves. This road guide covers the completed stretch between Davis and the Virginia border. Like several other east-west running highways in the Mountain State, Corridor H provides an extraordinary survey of nearly 200 million years of geological history, from rocks of the Pennsylvanian Period at the western end to those of the Ordovician at its eastern end. The many dramatic exposures provided by roadcuts reveal continuous layers of Paleozoic formations as well as spectacular evidence of the folding and faulting that resulted from the

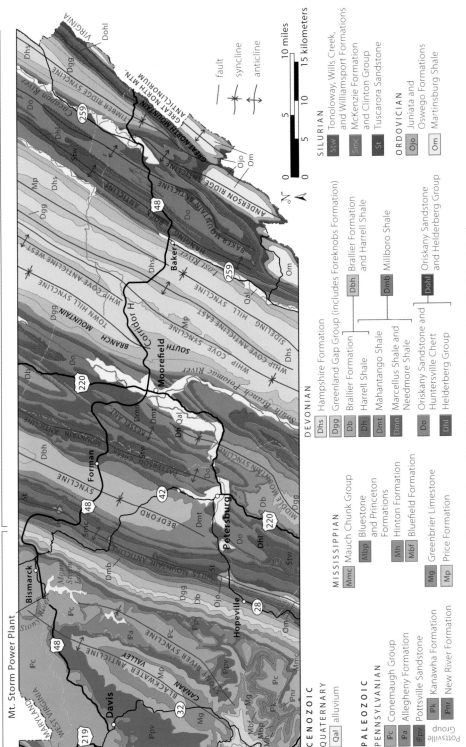

Geology along US 48 between Davis and the Virginia state line.

Alleghanian Orogeny. The relatively wide shoulders provide opportunities to pull over and examine individual samples of the rock types characteristic of the formations in this part of the Mountain State.

The western end of this section, currently marked as WV 93, begins in the Allegheny Mountains, where it intersects WV 32 in Davis. Initially, it follows the west limb of the Blackwater Anticline, its fold axis located to the south in Canaan Valley. Most of the surrounding rock is either part of the uppermost Middle Pennsylvanian Allegheny Formation or the Conemaugh Group of Late Pennsylvanian age, separated by the Upper Freeport coal. This coal has been extensively mined in the area, both on the surface and underground, with many currently active operations supplying some of the coal required by the nearby Mt. Storm Power Plant. Evidence of active mining can be seen on both sides of the highway. In general, the Upper Freeport coal dips gently to the northwest away from the fold axis of the Blackwater Anticline. South of the route, this coal lies close to the surface and is strip-mined, whereas north of the highway it is at depth and is mined underground.

The Allegheny Formation is exposed in several locations and is easily distinguished from the overlying Conemaugh Group by the lack of red beds that characterize the Conemaugh. Just west of the Tucker-Grant county line, a large pile of waste rock from former mining operations may be seen to the south.

Where not disturbed by mining operations, the area is dotted with wetlands, the result of high precipitation, poor drainage, and comparatively cool temperatures. The wetlands are typical of this area of the Allegheny Mountain Section of the Appalachian Plateaus, where gentle folds produce wide and shallow troughs

Mining operations have exposed beds of the Middle Pennsylvanian Allegheny Formation.

in which drainage moves slowly and thus moisture accumulates. Many of the wetlands contain plant species generally found at cooler more northern latitudes. They are the remnants of the floras established during the Pleistocene Epoch.

Near the Stony River, the Mt. Storm Power Plant dominates the view. West of it, the highway passes only a few small and isolated exposures. East of the power plant a series of wind turbines can be seen, one of many such installations along US 48 as it continues east. In terms of technological developments, the power plant could be seen to represent the past, the wind turbines one part of the future of electrical generation.

As the highway winds around the power plant, outcrops containing red beds indicate the presence of the Conemaugh Group, exposed in the Stony River Syncline, the easternmost structure in the Allegheny Mountains. Just west of the intersection of US 48 and WV 93, an exposure of the Conemaugh Group on the north side of the highway reveals beds that have been cut and displaced by a series of normal faults that define large slump blocks. A *slump* is a type of landslide that forms as a mass of earth slides along a curved normal fault, slowly rotating in the process. The displacement in slumps is typically short, and using the Bakerstown coal located in the outcrop as a reference, you can visualize the preslumping configuration of the layers.

Although slumping is basically caused by the pull of gravity, it generally needs a trigger to put the blocks in motion. There are several possible explanations, but the simplest is that the blocks were originally the walls of an ancient stream valley. In this scenario, erosion by the stream undercut the walls and caused the slope to become so steep that the blocks slumped downslope. The result is seen in the disruption of the boundaries between various rock layers. To reconstruct the original order of strata from bottom to top requires close attention to the rock types involved. It must be noted that the event that caused this slump occurred while the sediments were still unlithified, before the Alleghanian Orogeny folded and lifted the rocks to their present elevation of approximately 3,000 feet.

East of Bismarck, US 48 reaches the eastern limit of the Allegheny Mountain Section of the Appalachian Plateaus and offers an excellent view of the Valley and Ridge Province. Outcrops of the resistant Pottsville Sandstone of Early to Middle Pennsylvanian age form the edge of the plateaus. The highway turns to the north and descends the Allegheny Front. In doing so, it crosses the Mississippian-Pennsylvanian boundary and encounters the bright-red rocks of the Mauch Chunk Formation of Late Mississippian age. Like the Conemaugh Group to the west, the Mauch Chunk was deposited when the climate was arid to semiarid, creating the right conditions for the formation of red beds.

Like most of the overlying Pennsylvanian units, the Mauch Chunk is largely composed of river and floodplain deposits with a few marine zones caused by the periodic transgressions of a shallow sea to the east. One such marine zone is marked by a light-gray limestone that clearly dips to the west on the east limb of the Stony River Syncline. Marine fossils are common at this locality.

As the route continues to descend, it passes the Greenbrier Limestone and Price Formation, the lowermost Mississippian unit. Just below the Price

Formation lies the Spechty Kopf Formation, a sedimentary deposit of pebble-to-cobble-sized clasts surrounded by finer mud-sized material. It has been interpreted as a lithified glacial deposit, called a *diamictite*, due to the presence of cobbles with scratches and gouges typical of glacial erosion and transport. The diamictite is capped by an unusual, thin, light-gray unit with highly contorted beds that clearly formed while the sediments were unlithified. Their deformation could have been caused by the weight of the ice, or they may have slumped in response to some disturbance in a lake or sea.

A brachiopod from one of the marine limestones in the Mauch Chunk Group of Late Mississippian age.

At mile marker 83.25, a layer of jumbled, highly contorted beds lies on top of glacially deposited diamictites in the Spechty Kopf Formation, just below the Devonian-Mississippian Boundary.

At mile marker 87, the highway passes outcrops of the Hampshire Formation, deposited in Late Devonian time during the final stages of the Acadian Orogeny. The road abruptly turns south passing a roadcut of the thin-bedded Tonoloway Limestone of Late Silurian age. The dip of the rocks is noticeably steeper as the route encounters the west limb of the Wills Mountain Anticline, the westernmost structure in the Valley and Ridge Province. The highway is now running just west of the fold axis, and as a consequence the tops of many thin Tonoloway beds are visible. Not surprisingly, a large limestone quarry on the west side of the road parallels the outcrop belt.

The carbonate sediments of the Tonoloway and overlying Helderberg Group were deposited during a tectonically calm period between the Taconic and Acadian Orogenies, at a time when the area was covered by a warm, shallow sea just south of the equator. The sea was ringed by broad tidal flats where carbonate sediments accumulated in thin layers. Those who stop near mile marker 86 to look more closely can see mud cracks in the characteristic thin beds of the Tonoloway. Mud cracks form when wet sediment is exposed to the atmosphere and shrinks in response to drying. They are very common on tidal flats, where sediments are alternately wet and dry as a consequence of the coming and going of the tides. Cubic casts of halite, or rock salt crystals, are also common and indicate elevated levels of salt in these tidal flat waters

East of this north-south section of US 48 lies Greenland Gap, where the core of the Wills Mountain Anticline is exposed by the downcutting of the North Fork of Patterson Creek. Here, the Tuscarora Sandstone of Early Silurian age can be seen dipping in both directions away from the axis. The anticline is asymmetrical, with a steeply dipping, often vertical, west limb and a more gently dipping east limb. Incidentally, the Tuscarora on the west limb is the

Mud cracks preserved on thin-bedded carbonates of the Silurian Tonoloway Limestone. These structures formed when wet sediments dried out upon exposure to the atmosphere.

same part of the structure responsible for the vertical Tuscarora Sandstone at Seneca Rocks, about 25 miles to the south as the crow flies.

The highway turns east once again and approaches the fold axis. The Tuscarora is very well exposed at mile marker 89, dipping about 30 degrees to the west just before it changes dip direction on the east limb. A dark shale, not often seen in natural exposures of the Tuscarora because of weathering, lies between an upper and lower sandy zone. The dark shale was likely deposited in a protected lagoon behind the quartz-rich barrier island sands that make up most of this unit. At mile marker 90.5, east-dipping Oriskany and Helderberg units of Early Devonian age form a small ridge on the flank of the Wills Mountain Anticline.

The highway now enters a large valley, which in a broad sense marks the Bedford Syncline. Most of the units at the surface in this fold are shales of

Cubic casts of halite, or rock salt, preserved in the Tonoloway Limestone.

The Tuscarora Sandstone on the west limb of the Wills Mountain Anticline at mile marker 89.

Middle to Late Devonian age that have weathered rapidly to form the valley. There is a slight difference in the topography within the valley, with the center slightly elevated and bumpy, and the edges lower and smoother. The difference corresponds to the weathering of bedrock, with the more easily eroded Middle Devonian shales along the edges of the valley and the Brallier Formation, which has thin sandstone beds, in the middle. As is often the case with weak shales, numerous smaller-scale folds within them cause frequent changes in the dip direction and make their outcrop belt wider than if they were all dipping in the same direction.

At the exit for Patterson Creek Road and the town of Forman, roadcuts have exposed the contact between two Middle Devonian shales: the black Marcellus Shale and the younger, dark-gray to brown Mahantango Shale. The two units can be distinguished by prominent weathering and oxidation of the Marcellus and thin siltstone beds and limestone nodules containing marine fossils within the Mahantango.

These rounded hills result from soft shales of Middle Devonian age eroding rapidly, forming many of the valleys in the Valley and Ridge Province.

The shales, along with the Brallier Formation, were deposited in the early stages of the Acadian Orogeny as a collision between ancient North America and a small microcontinent, commonly referred to as Avalonia, produced the Catskill foreland basin and the Acadian Mountains to the east. During deposition of the Marcellus Shale, the basin was relatively deep, with mud slowly accumulating in quiet water. Plankton once living in the surface waters mixed with the muds, creating an organic-rich deposit. The organic matter is responsible for both the black color of the Marcellus Shale and its importance as a source rock for oil and gas in the Mountain State.

East of Forman, US 48 climbs to a series of ridges produced by weathering of the Patterson Creek Mountain Anticline. The core of the structure consists of carbonates of the Helderberg Group and Tonoloway Limestone that contain smaller-scale folds within the larger anticline. The first of these is located at mile marker 96.5 with folding in the Helderberg Group. At mile marker 97, the highway crosses from Grant County into Hardy County near the axis of the anticlinorium, where beds of the Tonoloway Limestone are folded into several anticlines and synclines. At mile marker 98, US 48 returns to Helderberg units, this time dipping east in a tall exposure above an eastbound service pull off. East of mile marker 98 the highway returns to a valley formed by Middle Devonian shales and makes a broad sweeping turn to the south. During the course of the next several miles, it passes exposures of Mahantango and Marcellus Shales.

East of the valley, the highway climbs Timber Ridge, formed by the Kessel Anticline. As the highway crosses the ridge, a long roadcut transects the fold. At the western end of the roadcut at mile marker 102, Middle Devonian shales, the Oriskany Sandstone, and the Helderberg Group are exposed on both sides of the road, all dipping to the west. It is worth noting that the contact between the Oriskany and Devonian shales is a regional unconformity. It separates the last rock (Oriskany Sandstone) deposited during the tectonic calm that followed the Taconic Orogeny in Late Ordovician time and the first rocks (Devonian shales) deposited in the subsiding Catskill foreland basin that formed during the Acadian Orogeny in Middle Devonian time.

Folded Helderberg Group limestones on the west limb of the Patterson Creek Mountain Anticline at mile marker 96.5.

A series of folds in the Tonoloway Limestone in the core of the Patterson Creek Mountain Anticlinorium at mile marker 97.

The Oriskany Sandstone (left, gray to orange) and dark Middle Devonian shales (right) dipping to the west on the Kessel Anticline at mile marker 102. Sands of the Oriskany were the last to be deposited during the passive margin stage between the Taconic and Acadian Orogenies. The dark shales represent the first pulse of sediments shed from the newly formed Acadian Mountains in the Middle Devonian Period.

All but the western end of the enormous roadcut exposes the Helderberg Group at the core of the Kessel Anticline. The flat-lying rocks near the fold axis (at middle of roadcut) are heavily weathered compared to the dipping rocks on the limbs, another example of the intense fracturing that occurred near the axes of anticlines, where the upper surface of the beds stretched and fractured as they were folded. In this case, the fractures have allowed groundwater to flow into the Helderberg rocks and form a series of caves by dissolving the carbonates. A cross section of this is now exposed by the roadcut and offers travelers an inside view of an otherwise underground cave system. The caves are also filled with bright-orange terra rossa, a common soil type produced by iron oxidation in the limestones.

In the vicinity of Moorefield, US 48 crosses the wide valley of the South Branch of the Potomac. Flat and comparatively wide valleys, far different from those in the Appalachian Plateaus, are characteristic of the Valley and Ridge Province. This valley is about 3.5 miles wide, and like the other valleys encountered to the west, it formed in Middle Devonian shales with numerous smaller-scale folds contributing to its width. The elevation is also considerably lower than it is at the highest part of the Appalachian Plateaus. Recall that at Bismarck, just east of the Mt. Storm Power Plant, the elevation is around 3,000 feet. The floor of the South Branch valley is roughly 900 feet above sea level, and Timber Ridge is only 400 feet higher where the highway crosses it.

East of Moorefield, the broad valley gives way to South Branch Mountain, composed of rocks of the Catskill clastic wedge, deposited during the Acadian

A large limestone block of the Helderberg Group collapsed into an underlying void created by the dissolution of limestone.

Orogeny. The Middle Devonian shales that make up the valleys were deposited offshore in quiet waters. The younger units were deposited in a series of progressively more nearshore and subsequently onshore environments. Thus, the frequency of these sandstone beds and their thickness increases upward through the section. The layers were subsequently folded into a series of anticlines and synclines.

A series of roadcuts between mile markers 108 and 110 expose the Brallier and Foreknobs Formations of Late Devonian age dipping to the east in the west limb of the Town Hill Syncline. The two formations can be difficult to distinguish, but in general sandstones in the Brallier are less than 1 foot thick while the Foreknobs contains sandstone beds over 1 foot thick. The Foreknobs Formation, part of the Greenland Gap Group, is exposed along several roadcuts, and its dip angle changes in the Whip Cove Anticline West and again at mile marker 113, where US 48 intersects North River Road. In this exposure of the core of the Whip Cove Syncline, the dip angle of the bright-red Hampshire Formation changes, rising steeply before leveling off. Two miles east of the North River Road intersection, rocks of the Hampshire Formation dip to the west on the west side of the Whip Cove Anticline East. At mile marker 116.5, folded Foreknobs sandstones in the center of this fold contain ripple marks, which suggests that the sand was deposited on a nearshore shelf within the reach of increased wave action during storms.

West of the North River Road intersection, an asymmetrical fold in the Hampshire Formation of Late Devonian age suggests the presence of a thrust fault below.

At mile marker 116.5 are wave-rippled sandstone beds in the Fore-knobs Formation of Late Devonian age, likely formed by large waves during storms.

Between mile marker 117 and the exit for Baker, the Devonian units are folded into the Sideling Hill Syncline, the same structure exposed in rather dramatic fashion in a deep roadcut on I-68 in Maryland. Like many of the other major folds encountered along the route, the Sideling Hill Syncline contains smaller-scale folds and faults that are well developed in the Foreknobs Formation, which extends east to mile marker 118.5. Flat-lying Hampshire rocks are exposed in a tall outcrop at Diamond in the Rough Road at the center of the syncline. This outcrop provides an excellent cross section of a river system that drained the eroded Acadian highlands to the east. Here, purple to tan cross-bedded channel sandstones with sharply delineated lower erosional surfaces cut into floodplain shales. The Hampshire, like many other red units in the area, was deposited under arid to semiarid conditions. Iron in the floodplain muds was extensively oxidized, giving them a bright-red color. Approaching the exit for Baker from the west, Corridor H crosses the east limb of the Sideling Hill Syncline, and the Devonian units you have encountered since Moorefield are exposed almost continuously with a very steep west dip.

Folding, likely along small-scale thrust faults, in the Foreknobs Formation near mile marker 118.5.

River channel sandstones and red floodplain mudstones, deposited during the Acadian Orogeny, in the Hampshire Formation at Diamond-in-the-Rough Road.

Folded Tuscarora Sandstone in the Hanging Rock Anticline at mile marker 121. The sandstone has a much different appearance in fresh roadcuts compared to the weathered Tuscarora along old WV 55, just north of the highway.

Baker rests in the narrow valley of Lost River, which turns east north of the highway where it has cut a water gap through the next major fold, the Hanging Rock Anticline. The river parallels the highway here for a short distance. At mile marker 121, west-dipping Helderberg rocks appear along the west limb. A long roadcut exposes the Tuscarora Sandstone of Early Silurian age and the overlying Rose Hill Formation of the Clinton Group in the core of the anticline.

As the highway crosses Lost River by way of the John and Freda Rudy Memorial Bridge, you can look north into the heart of this structure thanks to the water gap created by the river. This is a great opportunity to view a natural exposure of the Tuscarora in the gap and a human-made one in a recent roadcut along US 48. East of the anticline, the route turns to the northeast, roughly paralleling the axis of smaller-scale folds east of the Hanging Rock Anticline. There are fewer fresh roadcuts here, and many of them are carved into Middle Devonian shales. Only a few exposures of the Helderberg and Oriskany units are visible until you reach the end of the four-lane road at mile marker 126, where Corridor H ends and the route becomes WV 55/US 259.

In Wardensville, WV 55 crosses the Cacapon River and continues for 7.5 miles before entering Virginia. A mile east of where US 259 departs WV 55 and heads north, east-dipping Devonian shales in the west limb of the Timber Ridge Syncline may be seen where WV 55 begins to climb Great North Mountain, which has dominated the eastern horizon for a number of miles. The highway soon passes the steeply west-dipping Oriskany Sandstone that lies on the west limb of the Great North Mountain Anticlinorium.

Most of the units east of the Oriskany have an east dip that suggests that the route has crossed the axis of this fold and is now on the east limb. Not so. The Silurian rocks in the core of the fold are upside down, having been overturned by the tremendous forces associated with the Alleghanian Orogeny. The last clearly visible rocks exposed in the Mountain State are those of Tuscarora Sandstone, overturned and dipping steeply to the east as the summit of Great Northern Mountain is approached, along with the state line.

US 50
Virginia State Line—Romney—Skyline
51 miles

US 50 bears the distinction of being the oldest east-west highway in the Mountain State. It began life as the Northwestern Virginia Turnpike, chartered in 1827 by the Virginia legislature to run from Winchester, Virginia, to Parkersburg on the Ohio River. Construction of the turnpike was overseen initially by Claudius Crozet (1790–1864), who was born in France, served in Napoleon's headquarters, and migrated to the United States after the Battle of Waterloo. He joined the faculty at the US Military Academy at West Point and was later appointed state engineer for Virginia. In this capacity, he laid out the route of the turnpike, one of several highway projects with which he was involved.

A close study of the US Geological Survey's topographic maps of the region through which the highway runs reveals Crozet's priorities, which determined the highway's route through the Valley and Ridge Province in West Virginia. Keep the route as level as possible. If there must be grades, keep them as low as possible. If these goals mean a more circuitous route to make use of a water gap through a ridge, so be it. If no such gaps present themselves, then make the angles of ascent and descent over a ridge as low as possible, even if doing so adds more miles to the route. Above all else, make use of the knowledge of those who had traveled through this region for centuries, both animals and indigenous people who knew the territory well, to sketch out the route. As a consequence, the modern two-lane highway winds its way through the Valley and Ridge Province.

US 50 enters the Mountain State on the east limb of the Bear Garden Anticline. The mostly open topography here reflects the soft nature of the shale-dominated units deposited in the Catskill foreland basin during the Acadian Orogeny, in Middle to Late Devonian time. The highway crosses over Timber Ridge, formed by the Foreknobs Formation with an elevation of approximately 1,200 feet, and descends into the valley of Mill Brook. On the west side of that stream the route ascends west to the first of numerous gaps, this one a wind gap in Bear Garden Mountain. Within the gap are east-dipping exposures of the Oriskany Sandstone in the core of the Bear Garden Anticline

Unlike the younger Devonian units encountered earlier, the Oriskany was deposited during the short-lived passive margin phase in Early Devonian time that separated the Taconic Orogeny from the Acadian Orogeny. The abundance

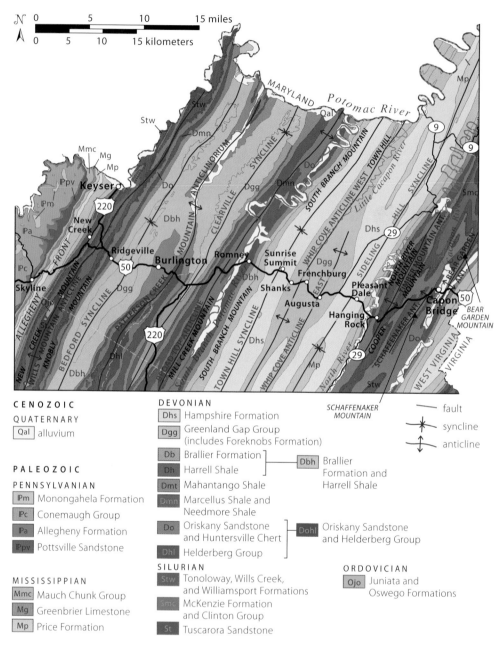

Geology along US 50 between Virginia state line and Skyline.

CENOZOIC

QUATERNARY

Qal alluvium

PALEOZOIC

PENNSYLVANIAN

Pm Monongahela Formation

Pc Conemaugh Group

Pa Allegheny Formation

Ppv Pottsville Sandstone

MISSISSIPPIAN

Mmc Mauch Chunk Group

Mg Greenbrier Limestone

Mp Price Formation

DEVONIAN

Dhs Hampshire Formation

Dgg Greenland Gap Group
(includes Foreknobs Formation)

Db Brallier Formation ⎫
Dh Harrell Shale ⎭ Dbh Brallier Formation and Harrell Shale

Dmt Mahantango Shale

Dmn Marcellus Shale and Needmore Shale

Do Oriskany Sandstone and Huntersville Chert ⎫
Dhl Helderberg Group ⎭ Dohl Oriskany Sandstone and Helderberg Group

SILURIAN

Stw Tonoloway, Wills Creek, and Williamsport Formations

Smc McKenzie Formation and Clinton Group

St Tuscarora Sandstone

ORDOVICIAN

Ojo Juniata and Oswego Formations

—— fault

⚹ syncline

⤧ anticline

East-dipping beds of the Oriskany Sandstone in the Bear Garden Anticline on the north side of US 50, just east of the summit over Bear Garden Mountain.

of quartz sand grains and common marine fossils, including brachiopods and crinoids, suggests that the Oriskany was originally a beach sand that extended into the shallow marine realm. Shortly west of the gap, you can see the Oriskany dipping to the west away from the fold's axis as the highway enters the valley of the Cacapon River, which has carved into soft shales of Middle Devonian age.

After crossing the Cacapon (pronounced "kuh-KAY-pon") River, a tributary of the Potomac, in the village of Capon Bridge, the highway angles west up and over Schaffenaker Mountain. The Oriskany returns again, this time on the east limb of the Schaffenaker Anticline, illustrating its prominence as a resistant ridge former along this route.

US 50 continues in a southwesterly direction and crosses over another Oriskany ridge, Cooper Mountain, which has exposures of that sandstone along its western slope. At the village of Loom, note the numerous rounded boulders of weathered Oriskany rock. The Timber Mountain Anticline, on which the Oriskany lies, is a larger fold than those to the east. It has rocks of Early Devonian through Early Silurian age near its axis. The route curves sharply around Timber Mountain, and the core of the anticline of the same name can be seen along the road. Several Silurian units, including the Keefer Sandstone and Rose Hill Formation, all more than 25 million years older than the Oriskany and other Devonian rocks outcropping farther east, are dipping in both directions, away from the axis.

The next ridge is North River Mountain, through which the stream that US 50 has paralleled west of Loom has cut a gap large enough to accommodate the

Silurian rocks in the Timber Mountain Anticline on the north side of US 50 at the sharp turn past Timber Mountain.

Just east of the eastern junction with WV 29 is a tree growing between near-vertical beds of the Oriskany Sandstone.

highway. To the west of that gap is the village of Hanging Rock at which point the route passes the Oriskany Sandstone in a series of small-scale folds.

The highway continues northwest in the broad, open valley of North River. The valley parallels the axis of the Sideling Hill Syncline, a regional structure encountered on many of the east-west routes in this chapter. The axis of the syncline lies near the town of Pleasant Dale, where the youngest unit in the core, the red rocks of the Hampshire Formation, is exposed. Several miles to the west, near the western junction of US 50 and WV 29, outcrops of the Hampshire and the older Foreknobs Formation are dipping east toward the axis of the Sideling Hill Syncline.

Several folds are encountered near and west of the village of Augusta, although they are fairly gentle and do not bring the ridge-forming Oriskany to the surface. Beds of the Foreknobs and Hampshire Formations can be seen dipping steeply to the east and west along the route.

At Bell Hollow, the route turns north, following the South Fork of the Little Cacapon River for a few miles and then turns west where that stream joins the North Fork of the same river at Frenchburg. Throughout this section, small folds in the Brallier and Foreknobs Formations produce steeply dipping exposures. Almost vertical exposures of the Foreknobs stand across from the roadside park in a water gap through Town Hill, just west of Shanks. The smaller folds then give way to the Town Hill Syncline, with small exposures of

The Foreknobs Formation of Late Devonian age in the Sideling Hill Syncline on the north side of US 50 at the western WV 29 junction. The red beds likely formed during low sea level when iron in the sediments was exposed to oxygen in the atmosphere.

A small, tightly folded syncline in the Foreknobs Formation east of Shanks.

red shales in the Hampshire Formation visible in the town of Sunrise Summit. Sandstones within the Hampshire form a small plateau at this town, on the west side of which the road turns sharply southwest and follows the valley of Big Run. Here the east-dipping Foreknobs forms a series of ridges that make up South Branch Mountain.

Romney, the seat of Hampshire County, lies just east of the South Branch of the Potomac River, which has formed a comparatively wide valley in soft Middle Devonian shales. Dominating the western horizon is Mill Creek Mountain, the topographic expression of the Broad Top Anticline. The highway passes through a water gap created by Mill Creek, providing a great opportunity to look at the smaller structures in the anticline.

West of Romney, US 50 crosses the South Branch and veers to the south, passing between a ridge of Oriskany Sandstone and Mill Creek Mountain. The route continues along Mill Creek, which has carved a small valley into Middle Devonian shale. At Core Road, both Mill Creek and the highway turn sharply to the northwest and into the heart of the Mill Creek Mountain Anticline, the centerpiece of the Broad Top Anticline. Just west of the turn, a tall exposure of limestones of the Helderberg Group of Early Devonian age below the Oriskany Sandstone is visible on the east limb. A half mile west of Core Road, the axis of the anticline is clearly evident in an abandoned quarry of Tonoloway Limestone of Late Silurian age, which shows the beds dipping in both directions. Although access to the quarry is restricted, a quick peek through the gates on the access road is worth a stop. Here thin beds of the Tonoloway, deposited on a series of tidal flats that ringed a shallow Silurian sea, help to define the anticline. Just east of Mechanicsburg, west of where the highway exits the water gap, beds of the

A large exposure of east-dipping Helderberg limestones of Early Devonian age in the Mill Creek Mountain Anticline near the junction with Core Road.

Oriskany Sandstone on the west limb of the anticline are visible on the north side of the road.

US 50 follows Mill Creek for several miles. Just east of the eastern junction with US 220, US 50 crosses the axis of the Clearville Syncline, west of which you can see exposures of Devonian-age Brallier Formation and Mahantango Shale that dip to the east. The same units continue to be visible between US 220 and Burlington, where US 50 crosses Patterson Creek in a broad valley of Middle Devonian shale. West of Burlington, Mill Creek cuts through small ridges of Late Devonian units.

Between Ridgeville and New Creek, the highway passes through the Wills Mountain Anticline. Immediately west of Ridgeville is a water gap in Knobly Mountain, a ridge of Oriskany Sandstone on the east limb of the anticline. At other places in the Valley and Ridge this anticline is defined by the Tuscarora Sandstone, but US 50 took advantage of an area where the axis of the anticline plunges, so here the Tuscarora is underground. As a consequence, most of the core of this fold is composed of shale-dominated Silurian units that are younger than the Tuscarora, so there are almost no exposures except for a few Helderberg Group quarries in a water gap of New Creek Mountain, on the west side of the anticline.

Between the towns of New Creek and Claysville, US 50 runs along the eastern edge of the New Creek valley. The view to the west shows that the topography is dramatically different from that to the east. West of the junction with WV 93, where the elevation is a little less than 1,200 feet, US 50 begins to climb, first gently, and then more steeply up the Allegheny Front. By the time it reaches the top of Allegheny Mountain, the elevation is close to 2,800 feet. To do so, it climbs a comparatively steep grade and does so with a number of sharp turns and switchbacks. Caution is recommended on this stretch of road.

From the base to the top of the Front, US 50 crosses over rocks from the Middle Devonian Period to the Early Pennsylvanian Period, a span of nearly 50 million years. The same soft rocks of Middle and Late Devonian age you encountered many times along the route are crossed in the gentle portion of the climb at the base of the Front. The remaining units in the steep part of the grade, from bottom to top, are red rocks of the Hampshire Formation, the Price Formation of Early Mississippian age, the Middle Mississippian Greenbrier Limestone, and red rocks of the Mauch Chunk Formation of Late Mississippian age. At the summit, high on the eastern edge of the Appalachian Plateaus, you can see a boulder field of Pottsville Sandstone of Early to Middle Pennsylvanian age.

US 460 AND US 219
BLUEFIELD—LEWISBURG—MARLINTON
115 miles

Not only is US 219 the longest highway in the state, it has one of the oldest histories as well. Native peoples created a route that became known as the Seneca Trail, and it was regularly traveled by members of this Haudenosaunee (Iroquois) nation when European settlers first moved into this region in the late eighteenth century. The trail traversed a variety of terrains, but its course was dictated for the most part by the orientation of the surrounding ridges. It would eventually become the right-of-way for major portions of both US 460 and US 219.

Unlike the western part of the state, eastern West Virginia is characterized by landforms and streams that run in a northeast-southwest orientation, the result of the Late Paleozoic collision from the southeast with Africa during the Alleghanian Orogeny. To put it simply, think of a head-on collision between two cars. The energy released by the collision causes the hoods of the cars to crumple, creating ripples with crests running perpendicular to the direction of the collision. The continental collision produced similar ripples, or folds, and their erosion created northeast-southwest-trending stream valleys and high ridges that the highway faithfully follows.

At its southern end, this route is situated just east of the Allegheny Front, the western boundary of the Valley and Ridge Province. As the route heads north, it crosses that boundary and enters the Appalachian Plateaus, hugging its eastern edge for a number of miles between Salt Sulphur Springs and Hillsboro. Then for about a dozen miles it returns to the Valley and Ridge around Marlinton.

The dominant landform of the southern part of this route is East River Mountain to the southeast, which US 460 roughly parallels for 31 miles before it turns southeast into Virginia. Like most mountains in the region it is a northeast-southwest-trending ridge. It has an almost formidable presence, rising in

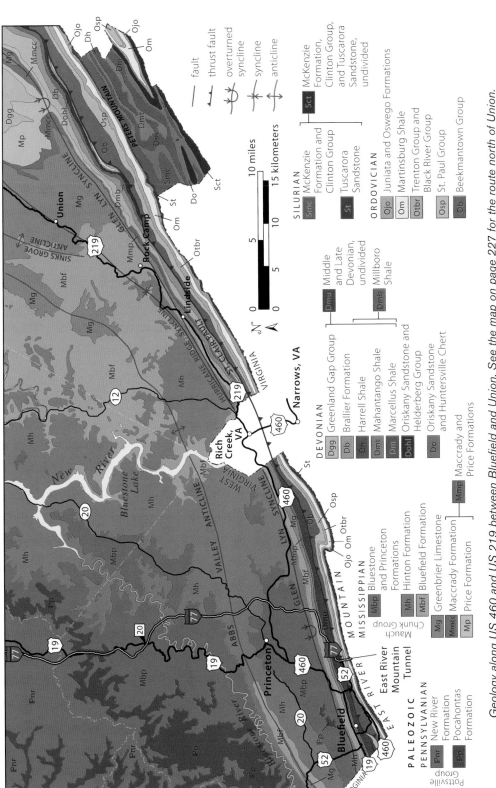

Geology along US 460 and US 219 between Bluefield and Union. See the map on page 227 for the route north of Union.

places to 3,600 feet above sea level, more than 1,000 feet higher than the valley in which the highway runs. It serves as the boundary between the two Virginias. It is not just any ridge either: in this region it is the topographic expression of rocks uplifted by the St. Clair Fault, a major thrust fault that marks the boundary between the Appalachian Plateaus and Valley and Ridge Provinces.

US 460 runs around the southern edge of Bluefield, where you are east of the St. Clair Fault in the Valley and Ridge Province. Small exposures of dolostone and limestone of the Beekmantown Group of Early Ordovician age are found along the route as it heads east. The Beekmantown Group is part of a large block of the Earth's crust that was shoved north and west along the St. Clair Fault. Its rocks, like others in the region east of the St Clair fault, are dipping about 40 degrees to the southeast. If you were to travel to the top of East River Mountain you would pass over southeast-dipping Middle and Late Ordovician rocks and reach the Tuscarora Sandstone of Early Silurian age, which caps the mountain.

On the east side of Bluefield and just north of the split with US 52, US 460 passes a fantastic exposure of the St. Clair Fault on the northbound on-ramp from US 52. It is unusual to see an exposure of this fault. Most faults are a series of fractures that shatter the rocks and cause them to erode away rapidly, especially in the humid climate of the eastern United States. At the interchange, roadcuts have exposed Beekmantown carbonates on top of the younger black Millboro Shale of Middle Devonian age, which includes the Marcellus Shale in the northern part of the state. This strange juxtaposition was produced as the Beekmantown carbonates were shoved westward as much as 20 miles and uplifted nearly 6,000 feet along the St. Clair Fault. It is no surprise that the fault cut the Devonian rocks at the level of the Millboro Shale. Thrust faults tend to propagate, or progress, through layers of soft, weak rock like the black shales.

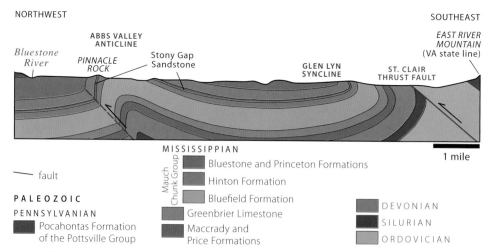

Movement along the St. Clair Fault shoved older rocks on top of younger rocks in and east of Bluefield. The force also folded and faulted the rocks west of the fault, including the Stony Gap Sandstone at Pinnacle Rock. –Modified from Whisonant and Schultz, 1986; Reger and Price, 1926

The St. Clair thrust fault is exposed at the US 52/US 460 interchange. Here the gray Beekmantown carbonates of Early Ordovician age are thrust over the Middle Devonian Millboro Shale (black rock on left). The Millboro Shale is upside down on the east limb of the overturned Glen Lyn Syncline.

The soft, black Millboro Shale provided a zone of weakness for the progression of the St. Clair Fault at shallow depths.

North of the interchange, steeply dipping, thin-bedded, gray to tan sandstones and shales of the Brallier Formation of Late Devonian age are exposed along the road. These rocks, like the Millboro Shale at the US 460 interchange, appear to be dipping to the southeast. If that were true, the younger Brallier rocks would have to lie under the older Millboro Shale, violating the basic rule of superposition: older layers underlie younger ones. Instead, the Late Devonian rocks are upside down, part of the east limb of the overturned Glen Lyn Syncline. They were overturned as the block of crust under and to the east of the St. Clair Fault was dragged over the block west of the fault.

US 460 encounters younger rocks to the northwest as it approaches the axis of the Glen Lyn Syncline. Just south of Green Valley, the road crosses the axis and passes over more gently dipping Late Mississippian rocks on the western limb of the fold. The reduced dip causes these rocks to remain at the surface as the road heads northeast toward Princeton.

In the vicinity of Princeton, you can see exposures of Late Mississippian age, specifically weathered shales and sandstones of the Bluestone, Princeton, and Hinton Formations of the Mauch Chunk Group. The low angle of dip in these rocks is clearly visible at mile marker 17, where sandstone and red and gray shales are flat-lying. Because the rocks are flat, you may be able to visualize the amount of uplift along the St. Clair Fault. Consider this: the Late Mississippian–age rocks under US 460 are nearly 1.25 miles above the Tuscarora Sandstone of Early Silurian age. However, to the east, the Tuscarora Sandstone caps East River Mountain—you have to look up to see it! This suggests that the minimum vertical displacement along the St. Clair Fault exceeded 1.25 miles.

The highway crosses back over to the south side of the axis of the Glen Lyn Syncline near the exit for Oakvale. At mile marker 20.5 overturned rocks on the east limb are exposed dipping to the southeast. US 460 then enters Virginia, crossing the New River and passing through the town of Glen Lyn, Virginia. The road hugs the north bank of the New River. At Rich Creek, Virginia, US 219 begins its journey north. Travelers wanting another look at the St. Clair Fault are encouraged to continue on US 460 to Narrows, Virginia, where the New River cuts through East River Mountain.

Narrows Gap through East River Mountain

As with all the ridges of this province, you have three ways to cross East River Mountain: climb it, tunnel through it, or follow a river gap. Climbing it on a road means long grades, both ascending and descending, as the route edges up one side and down the other. I-77 tunnels through the mountain just south of Princeton, West Virginia, just as it will do when it encounters another ridge, Walker Mountain, farther south in Virginia. US 460 takes the third option, following a river gap cut by the New River through the thick sequence of rock that forms East River Mountain. Indeed, the New River created water gaps across many of the Appalachian Mountains as it flowed north-northwest from North Carolina before turning west as it entered present-day West Virginia. The New River is a superimposed stream, one that flowed over the land long before erosion created the modern landscape. It has been cutting down through rock and sediment ever since.

The purpose of this side trip, a loop that starts and ends in Rich Creek, is to view the results of the Late Paleozoic Alleghanian Orogeny, a continental collision that occurred during the assembly of the supercontinent Pangea. The effect of this orogeny is not only visible in the topography of the Valley and Ridge Province but also in the rocks, including at Narrows Gap, located 8 miles east-southeast of Rich Creek, just off US 460 near the village of Narrows, Virginia. Here, the New River's water gap is just wide enough to accommodate the river, the highway on the east bank, and the tracks of the Norfolk Southern Railway and Lurich Road on the west bank.

On US 460, traffic moves at a high rate of speed in both directions. Through the gap there is no wide shoulder on which to pull off, nor are there any guardrails between the cliff and the right lane of the highway. Readers are cautioned against trying to study the rock structures while driving on this route. Rather, they should take US 460 east to the junction with VA 61, turn left at the traffic light, follow the road over the river, and after driving under the railroad take the first right onto Lurich Road. A paved two-lane county road having little traffic, it allows for slower speeds and the chance to stop to look at the core of the ridge.

As you travel north on Lurich Road, after a couple of miles the valley walls close in, and the vegetation gives way to naked cliffs of the aforementioned

The Tuscarora Sandstone of Early Silurian age on the headwall of the St. Clair Fault. The resistant unit projects above the New River's bed, forming the rapids in the foreground.

Tuscarora Sandstone running down the east side of the ridge. As the road heads north, there are pullouts available to study the rocks. Follow the dipping rock on the opposite side of the valley and you will find that as soon as the cliffs disappear into the ground, two small sets of rapids appear in the New River. These rapids are caused by highly resistant beds of the Tuscarora Sandstone sticking out of the bed of the New River, creating small obstacles for the water to flow across. The same cliffs appear above you on the south side of the valley as the Tuscarora Sandstone climbs to the top of the ridge. Immediately under the Tuscarora are red beds of the Juniata Formation of Late Ordovician age and older Ordovician shales and carbonate rocks.

The aforementioned rocks have been displaced along the St. Clair Fault. Heading north again on Lurich Road you will pass rocks of Middle and then Early Ordovician age and reach the Beekmantown carbonates of Early Ordovician age. These were thrust over the Middle Devonian Millboro Shale along US 460 near Bluefield. As Lurich Road turns to the southwest following a large meander bend in the New River, outcrops of steeply dipping, overturned rocks of Late Mississippian age are exposed along the road. The rocks, on the east limb of the Glen Lyn Syncline, get their steep dip from the drag force associated with movement of the St. Clair Fault, which caused the rocks here to curl as a result of the intense friction along the fault. Continue down the river and on to Glen Lyn. The road intersects with US 460 here, where you can turn right and head east again to Rich Creek.

Steeply dipping beds of the Mauch Chunk Group of Late Mississippian age were folded by drag along the St. Clair Fault.

Ripple marks in the Mauch Chunk Group were produced by waves shifting sand back and forth along the bottom of a shallow sea.

A few miles northeast of Rich Creek, US 219 enters West Virginia at Peterstown, traveling in a narrow valley created by Trigger Run, which flows between Chimney Ridge to the northwest and Little Mountain to the southeast, both capped by sandstone of the Price Formation of Early Mississippian age. South of Little Mountain and more than 1,000 feet higher rises Peters Mountain, the continuation of East River Mountain, forming the Allegheny Front. The valley's geology consists primarily of easily weathered limestone and shale of the Middle Mississippian Greenbrier Limestone and Late Mississippian–age Bluefield Formation on the east flank of the Glen Lyn Syncline. Gentle slopes and low rolling hills in this valley attest to the easily weathered nature of the rock.

The highway, like many in the Appalachian Plateaus, follows the valleys of a succession of small streams. It leaves the Trigger Run valley for one that may have been the former course of Rich Creek, and then it enters that stream's current valley, which leads to the community of Lindside. US 219 follows

Hans Creek north of Lindside while passing exposures of tan sandstones of the Hinton Formation of Late Mississippian age in the core of the Glen Lyn Syncline. Crossing a low drainage divide, it enters the valley of Bradley Brook and then the Rock Camp Creek valley as it turns once again to the north en route to the village of Rock Camp. There, you can see beds of red shale and limestone, members of the Bluefield Formation. Just to the north of Rock Camp, sandstone and brown shales of the Bluefield Formation dip gently to the northwest; we are now at the eastern edge of the Appalachian Plateaus.

The highway follows the meandering Rock Camp Creek for a few more miles and then follows Indian Creek where the highway turns east. As it once again turns north, US 219 moves from clastic rocks of the Bluefield Formation into a landscape developed on the Greenbrier Limestone. Regions with carbonate rocks at and near the surface tend to develop a unique set of features that characterize karst topography.

Karst topography is perhaps best described as bumpy with circular depressions of various depths scattered randomly. It forms because limestone consists of calcium carbonate, in this case the remnants of shells and skeletons of marine organisms. Exposed to the comparatively humid climate of the region, the limestone began to dissolve due to the presence of naturally acidic rain and groundwater. Eventually, the water worked its way deeper and deeper into the bedrock. Fractures widened, and streams that had flowed along the surface disappeared into the rock to flow underground. These disappearing streams produced extensive networks of caves, some running for several miles. Where those caves were close to the surface, sinkholes formed when the overlying rock became too thin and collapsed. For more information on the origins of this distinctive topography, see the road guide for I-64: Beckley—White Sulphur Springs—Virginia State Line.

The karst region here extends from around Union to just north of Frankford, with just a couple of exceptions. Along US 219 several caves have been commercially developed. Those wishing to see how water over millions of years has transformed the subsurface of this region are encouraged to visit one or another of them.

Three miles south of Ronceverte, a town with a French name that translates to "Greenbrier," the route travels north out of the Greenbrier Limestone temporarily as it crosses the axis of the Sinks Grove Anticline. It passes over the older Maccrady Formation of Early Mississippian age—characterized by red shales, thin limestones, and sandstones—and the still older sandstones of the Price Formation. Then, almost as quickly, the highway returns to the Maccrady and then once again to the Greenbrier Limestone and karst terrain as it approaches Lewisburg from the south.

Lewisburg, the seat of Greenbrier County, lies on the Greenbrier Limestone, and it is arguably the center of the West Virginia caving community. Miles of mapped caves underlie the region, and the town is host to national conferences on cave research. One of the area's most popular commercial caves, Lost World Caverns, lies just north of town. See the sidebar about the caverns in the road guide for I-64: Beckley—White Sulphur Springs—Virginia State Line.

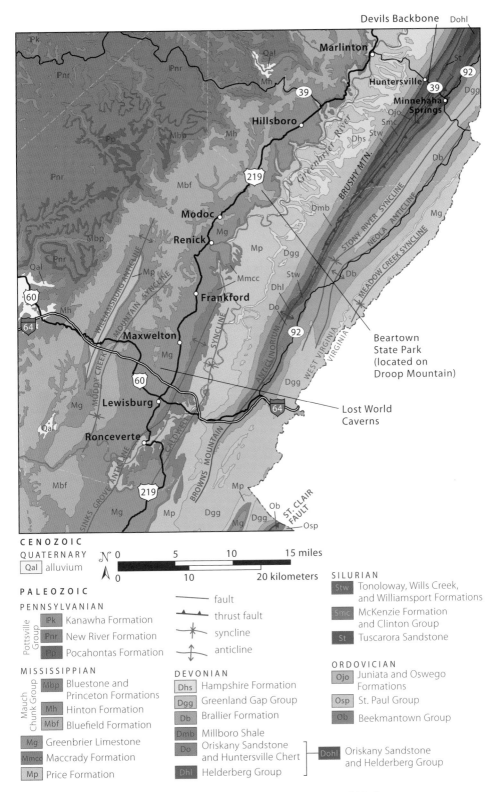

Geology along US 219 between Ronceverte and Marlinton.

North of I-64, US 219 passes through more karst terrain. Numerous examples of sinkholes can be seen across from the airport access road south of the town of Maxwelton. Karst terrain continues along the highway, with many small outcrops of limestone dotting the landscape, until the road briefly climbs onto an erosional remnant of Bluefield Formation shales and sandstones north of Renick. It then returns to the Greenbrier Limestone at the community of Modoc. Throughout this part of the route, the Appalachian Plateaus to the west is capped by resistant sandstones of the Pennsylvanian-age New River Formation. To the east in the Valley and Ridge Province lies the Greenbrier River valley and Brushy Mountain, which is the surface expression of the intensely folded and faulted Browns Mountain Anticlinorium. North of Modoc, the

These sinkholes, typical of karst terrains, developed in carbonate rock of the Middle Mississippian Greenbrier Limestone just north of Lewisburg.

Beartown State Park

Five miles north of Renick is the entrance to Beartown State Park, 1.5 miles east of US 219 on a single-lane paved road (not open in winter). Here, large house-sized blocks of the Droop Sandstone member of the Bluefield Formation have broken away from the hillside and are slowly sliding downslope. The shapes of the blocks are strongly controlled by stress fractures, or joints, running at right angles to one another. Walkways have been established among the blocks to make it easy to walk around and examine them.

The Droop Sandstone was deposited along the shore and in shallow waters of a Late Mississippian sea, resulting in a rock composed primarily of sand and pebble-sized quartz grains. Minor amounts of mica and clay are also present in the rock. The cement that binds the grains together is not uniform, and areas with minimal cement erode more rapidly. This gives the rock a pitted appearance in places where it is not well cemented. Cross bedding is also common, reflecting the movement of sand under the influence of various currents.

Blocks of the Droop Sandstone along the boardwalk at Beartown State Park.

Dissolution pits in the Droop Sandstone form in poorly cemented zones in the rock.

highway begins to climb Droop Mountain, another erosional remnant of the more resistant Bluefield Formation.

North of the community of Spice, the terrain becomes gentle and rolling again as the route passes onto the Greenbrier Limestone, which it traverses through Hillsboro and to the northeast. Look north for an active limestone quarry at Mill Point. To the northwest, ridges of Late Mississippian and Early to Middle Pennsylvanian rocks are visible.

Northeast of Hillsboro, the highway begins to encounter clastic rocks of Early Mississippian age, and the relief again increases. Note the flat bases of Price Formation beds, a characteristic of deposition along a relatively flat seafloor as opposed to the bottom of a concave stream channel. These same exposures appear periodically as the road descends into the Greenbrier River valley on its way to Marlinton. There, the Price contains numerous marine fossils as well as trace fossils that record the activities of animals on the seafloor.

Devils Backbone along WV 39

The short trip to Devils Backbone gives travelers a look at the inside of one of the more complicated folds in West Virginia, the Browns Mountain Anticlinorium. Studying it provides a better understanding of the distinctive landforms in the Valley and Ridge Province. The intense deformation seen along the road is what warrants the use of the term *anticlinorium.* Unlike an anticline, where

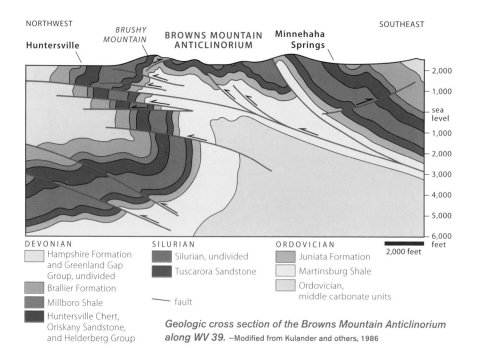

Geologic cross section of the Browns Mountain Anticlinorium along WV 39. —Modified from Kulander and others, 1986

the units simply change dip direction, the rocks in the core of an anticlinorium contain numerous smaller-scale folds and faults.

From Marlinton, take WV 39 east. The route runs through the valley of Knapp Creek, a westward-flowing tributary of the Greenbrier River. East of Marlinton, the road crosses progressively older rocks as you approach the center of the Browns Mountain Anticlinorium. While Marlinton is situated on sandstones of the Price Formation of Early Mississippian age, farther east Knapp Creek has cut into Late and Middle Devonian rocks. By the time it reaches Huntersville, the landscape opens up because soft Middle Devonian shales lie at the surface. East of Huntersville, the highway crosses over the central portion of the anticlinorium, where much older Silurian and Ordovician rocks are exposed. Farther east, the succession of rock is reversed.

East of Huntersville, Knapp Creek has cut a water gap through Brushy Mountain, which sits on the spine of one of the many anticlines in the core

The Devils Backbone, a small anticline within the Browns Mountain Anticlinorium, exposes the Tuscarora Sandstone of Early Silurian age.

*Intense compression has forced shales in the Tuscarora Sandstone upward,
bending the overlying sandstone beds into a box fold.*

of the anticlinorium. Approximately 7 miles east of Marlinton, the highway
crosses this creek on the Trooper Douglas Wayne Bland Memorial Bridge. Pull
over on the south side of the road on the west side of the bridge. After a very
short walk on the side road to the east, you will see a small anticline known as
the Devils Backbone.

Examine the outcrop from bottom to top. In the center of the fold a small
triangle of red mudstones of the Juniata Formation of Late Ordovician age is
exposed, deposited more than 435 million years ago. Arching over the Juniata is
the Tuscarora Sandstone of Early Silurian age, thus permitting one the opportunity to touch the Ordovician-Silurian boundary at the formation contact.
Looking up at the bottom of the Tuscarora beds, you can observe the crisscrossing tracks and trails of marine organisms that crawled across the seafloor
before it was buried by sand.

The material for these rocks was a product of the Late Ordovician Taconic
Orogeny, when Laurentia collided with island arcs that formed during subduction off its eastern margin. Mountains created during the collision weathered,
producing sediments of the Queenston clastic wedge, which included the material in the Juniata Formation and Tuscarora Sandstone. Folding of the anticline,
as well as the entire Browns Mountain Anticlinorium, happened during the
subsequent Late Paleozoic Alleghanian Orogeny. If time permits, you may want

The white Tuscarora Sandstone and red Juniata Formation on the east limb of the Browns Mountain Anticlinorium. They are located in the headwall of one of the many faults present in the anticlinorium.

to continue east for 2 miles on WV 39 to observe many additional folds and dipping strata of the resistant Tuscarora Sandstone along the way.

East of the bridge, outcrops of Tuscarora Sandstone occur to the north at road level; it and the Juniata were gently folded into small folds. About 1 mile east of the bridge, also on the north side of the road, the Tuscarora Sandstone was folded into a roughly square shape called a box fold. The northwest corner of this fold was cut from below by soft shales that were forced through the sandstone as it was tightly compressed. The sandstone is on the lower block of a major thrust fault, which extends nearly 20 miles along the surface and displaced these rocks nearly 1,500 vertical feet. About 1.5 miles east of the bridge (and just west of the WV 92 junction), the contact between the oldest rock of the Silurian Period, the white Tuscarora Sandstone, and the youngest unit of the Ordovician Period, the bright-red Juniata Formation, is exposed along on the north side of the road. Both of these units are within the upper block, or hanging wall, of a thrust fault.

US 220
KEYSER—MOOREFIELD—
PETERSBURG—VIRGINIA STATE LINE
90 miles

Broadly speaking, the highways through the Valley and Ridge Province follow a trellis-like pattern, with those running east-west crossing over ridges or through water gaps, and those running roughly northeast-southwest traveling along the floors of the intervening valleys. Because the valley routes run parallel to the axes of folds, they remain in the same rock unit for many miles. Although valley routes may not have the variety of rock types, they certainly present travelers with many scenic landscapes and great exposures, especially when the route jogs from one valley to the next.

US 220 enters the state 13 miles south of Cumberland, Maryland, when it crosses the North Branch of the Potomac, which serves as the state boundary between the Maryland and West Virginia panhandles. The Potomac originates at the Fairfax Stone in Tucker County, West Virginia. Situated on the south bank of the river is the town of Keyser. The ridge to the east is New Creek Mountain, formed by the near-vertical west limb of the Wills Mountain Anticline. The axis of the fold lies at a lower elevation here than it does farther south, and the Tuscarora Sandstone lies below road level. The Oriskany Sandstone of Early Devonian age is the ridge former, and it outcrops along New Creek Mountain.

To the west of Keyser is Dans Mountain, in this part of the state the eastern limit of the Allegheny Mountains Section of the Appalachian Plateaus. It is capped by the resistant Pottsville Sandstone of Middle Pennsylvanian age. Like most of the valleys in this part of the state, the floor of the valley east of the mountain consists of soft shale-dominated units of Middle to Late Devonian age.

South of Keyser, US 220 travels along the base of New Creek Mountain, then slips through a water gap and heads down the east side of the mountain before merging with US 50. The road passes more exposures of Oriskany and Helderberg rock, easily seen at a quarry at the base of New Creek Mountain.

The next major ridge to the east, Knobly Mountain, is formed by the east limb of the Wills Mountain Anticline. Near the fold axis, there are a few exposures of Silurian shales and sandstones. The road, now joined with US 50, crosses Knobly Mountain through a wind gap, a former water gap in which the stream changed course as erosion of the land lowered the gap to its present elevation. East of the gap lies the Oriskany Sandstone, the counterpart to the beds exposed in a quarry at the bottom of New Creek Mountain. Between Ridgeville and Burlington, about 4 miles, Mill Creek has carved a broad valley out of folded shales of Middle and Late Devonian age.

The route passes more exposures of folded shales as US 220 passes the Mill Creek Country Club and the village of Markwood before crossing the Bedford Syncline, where contorted beds appear in the Brallier Formation of Late Devonian age. The village of Burlington lies on the west side of the Patterson Creek

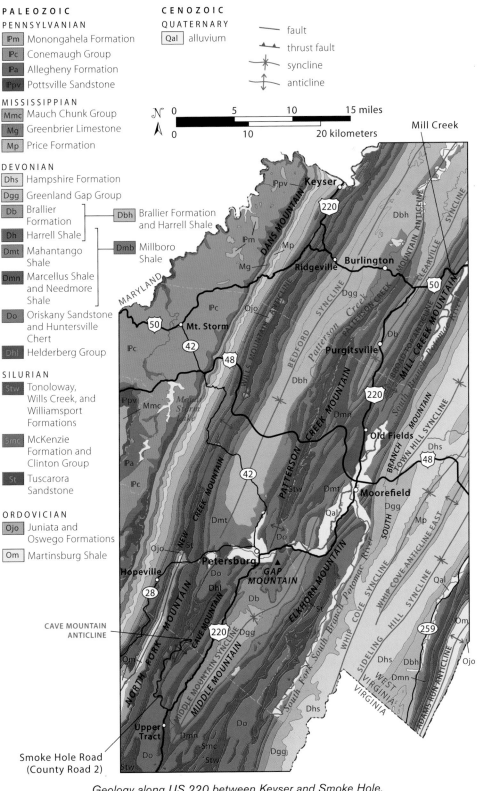

PALEOZOIC

PENNSYLVANIAN
- Ppm Monongahela Formation
- Ppc Conemaugh Group
- Ppa Allegheny Formation
- Ppv Pottsville Sandstone

MISSISSIPPIAN
- Mmc Mauch Chunk Group
- Mg Greenbrier Limestone
- Mp Price Formation

DEVONIAN
- Dhs Hampshire Formation
- Dgg Greenland Gap Group
- Db Brallier Formation
- Dh Harrell Shale
- Dbh Brallier Formation and Harrell Shale
- Dmt Mahantango Shale
- Dmn Marcellus Shale and Needmore Shale
- Dmb Millboro Shale
- Do Oriskany Sandstone and Huntersville Chert
- Dhl Helderberg Group

SILURIAN
- Stw Tonoloway, Wills Creek, and Williamsport Formations
- Smc McKenzie Formation and Clinton Group
- St Tuscarora Sandstone

ORDOVICIAN
- Ojo Juniata and Oswego Formations
- Om Martinsburg Shale

CENOZOIC

QUATERNARY
- Qal alluvium

- ⎯ fault
- ◣◣◣ thrust fault
- ⎯✳⎯ syncline
- ⎯↕⎯ anticline

N

0   5   10   15 miles

0   10   20 kilometers

Mill Creek

Keyser

220

Dbh

Ppv

Ppm

Mp

Mg

Ridgeville   Burlington

50

Dgg

Db

DANS MOUNTAIN ANTICLINE

MILL CREEK MOUNTAIN ANTICLINE

CLEARVILLE SYNCLINE

Ppc

Ojo

MILLS MOUNTAIN ANTICLINE

BEDFORD SYNCLINE

Patterson Creek

PATTERSON CREEK

BROAD FORD ANTICLINE

South Branch Potomac River

MARYLAND

50   Mt. Storm

42

48

Ppc

Dbh

Purgitsville

220

Dmn

Old Fields

Dhs

48

PATTERSON CREEK MOUNTAIN

BRANCH MOUNTAIN

TOWN HILL SYNCLINE

Ppv   Mmc

Moun Storm Lake

Ppa

Ppc

42

Dmt

Do

Stw

Dmt

Moorefield

Qal

Dgg

Mp

SOUTH BRANCH MOUNTAIN

WHIP COVE SYNCLINE

WHIP COVE ANTICLINE EAST

Qal

Petersburg

GAP MOUNTAIN

Do

Dhl

Db

St

ELKHORN MOUNTAIN

Om

259

Hopeville

28

NORTH FORK MOUNTAIN

Ojo

St

CAVE MOUNTAIN ANTICLINE

CAVE MOUNTAIN

220

Dgg

MIDDLE MOUNTAIN SYNCLINE

MIDDLE MOUNTAIN

SIDELING HILL SYNCLINE

Dhs   Dbh

WEST VIRGINIA

Dmn

Ojo

ADAMS RUN ANTICLINE

Dhs

Do

Upper Tract

Dmn   Smc

Do   Dgg

Stw

Smoke Hole Road (County Road 2)

Geology along US 220 between Keyser and Smoke Hole.
See map on page 183 for the southern section of the road.

A small quarry at the base of New Creek Mountain has exposed the contact between the Oriskany Sandstone on the left and the Helderberg Group on the right.

valley, which is eroded in Middle Devonian shales. East of the valley, the route takes advantage of water gaps to cross Patterson Creek Mountain and the anticline of the same name. You can see both the Mahantango and Marcellus Shales along the road. At the aptly named community of Junction, US 220 leaves US 50 and turns south, traveling along the trough of the Clearville Syncline between Patterson Creek Mountain to the west and Mill Creek Mountain to the east. Both mountains are capped by the Oriskany Sandstone that dips toward the route. As the road continues south, rock exposures decrease.

Between US 50 and Purgitsville, US 220 follows the valley of Mill Creek. Near the village of Rada, a few exposures of east-dipping Middle Devonian shales are visible along the west limb of the Clearville Syncline. On the north side of Purgitsville, the highway crosses the axis of the syncline, south of which are exposures of the Brallier Formation dipping to the west. South of the Hampshire-Hardy county line, the valley begins to open up with many exposures of shale along the road. At Old Fields, it enters the valley of the South Branch of the Potomac. East of Mill Creek Mountain, South Branch Mountain dominates the eastern horizon.

Between Old Fields and Moorefield, the shale bedrock is covered by recent sediments deposited by the South Branch. These materials, known as alluvium, constitute weathered rock transported and deposited by the river as it has meandered within its valley in Quaternary time. Unlike the underlying bedrock, these sediments are rich during nutrients and thus facilitate the agricultural industry in the valley.

Tight folding in the Brallier Formation of Late Devonian age in the Bedford Syncline between Markwood and Burlington.

In Moorefield, the highway crosses the South Fork River, a tributary of the South Branch. A levee system along its banks was constructed after the record-setting flood of 1985, which caused devastating flooding along the Cheat River to the north. During the flooding of the South Fork, over 80 percent of the agricultural bottomland experienced some erosion, the floodwaters transported boulders over 3 feet in diameter, and several lengthy sections of railroad track were found twisted into spirals downstream.

From Moorefield to the border with Virginia, approximately 42 miles, US 220 mainly follows the South Branch valley when it is not in the valley of one of its tributaries. Between Moorefield and Petersburg, here and there small hills consisting of shale are situated in the valley. Look to the east when passing the Valley View Country Club to see vertical beds of Oriskany Sandstone on Elkhorn Mountain, which constitutes the eastern horizon at this point.

At Durgon, as the valley turns west, the highway hugs the southern valley wall above the alluvium and its associated farmland to the north, eventually entering a narrow water gap near Welton. The South Branch carved the gap in Patterson Creek Mountain, known as Gap Mountain south of the gap, and erosion has exposed rocks within the Patterson Creek Mountain Anticline. Where US 220 passes Welton Park in the gap, you can see the fold axis of the anticline clearly defined by the exposures of the Helderberg and Oriskany units dipping away from it.

West-dipping beds of the Helderberg Group in the Patterson Creek Mountain Anticline south of Welton Park along US 220.

South of Petersburg, the highway leaves the South Branch valley, travels overland for a few miles, and then enters the valley of North Mill Creek, which flows just west of the fold axis of the Middle Mountain Syncline. The route once again follows an outcrop belt of Middle Devonian shales. Late Devonian units in the core of the syncline are coarser and more resistant than the shales along the road and thus form Middle Mountain to the east. The younger Helderberg and Oriskany form Cave Mountain to the west. Just south of Brushy Run the highway leaves this valley and makes its way once again to that of the South Branch, crossing that river north of Upper Tract. At Ruddle, the river and the highway slip through a water gap, with outcrops of east-dipping Oriskany Sandstone. US 220 now roughly follows the axis of the Middle Mountain Syncline, and exposures of Oriskany and Helderberg become commonplace between this point and the town of Franklin.

Smoke Hole

The Smoke Hole region is situated within a narrow canyon carved by the South Branch of the Potomac River. It is part of the Spruce Knob–Seneca Rocks National Recreation Area within the Monongahela National Forest. The side trip begins at the intersection of Smoke Hole Road and US 220 about 1 mile north of the town of Upper Tract. Turn onto Smoke Hole Road, County Road 2, at the west end of the bridge over the South Branch of the Potomac River. If approaching from the north, prepare to make a sharp right after crossing the river.

Smoke Hole Road follows the course of the South Branch, which has carved a water gap into Cave Mountain and then turns north, running between Cave Mountain to the east and North Fork Mountain to the west. The route follows the river until Smoke Hole Road turns west and leaves the valley, gradually ascending the east slope of North Fork Mountain before plunging into the valley of the North Fork of the South Branch and intersecting WV 28.

The geology of the southern portion the Smoke Hole Canyon is dominated by the Cave Mountain Anticline, an asymmetrical fold with a steep-to-overturned northwest limb. Two rock units of Early Devonian age, the Helderberg Group and Oriskany Sandstone, make up most of the outcrops seen in this part of the canyon. Several small-scale folds and other deformational features visible along the road have led to differing interpretations of the geology of the area. Essentially, there are two contrasting ideas. One is that the rocks are cut by numerous thrust faults that led to small-scale folding and the repetition of rock units in the canyon. The other idea, illustrated in the cross section below, suggests that folding was the predominant style of deformation that produced the repetition of the rocks. The debate continues.

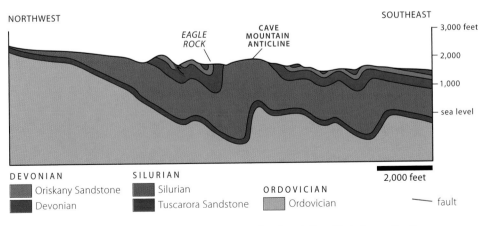

Cross section of the Smoke Hole area showing the relationship between the Cave Mountain Anticline and Eagle Rock. —Modified from Gerritsen, 1988

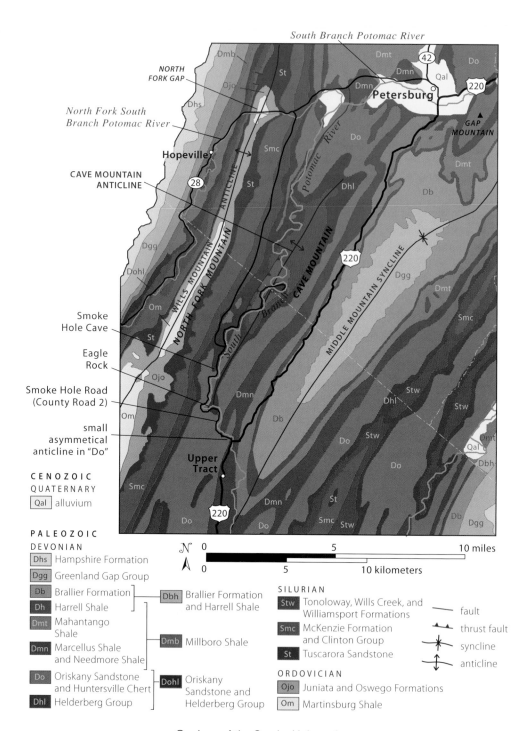

Geology of the Smoke Hole region.

Regardless of the way the rocks were deformed, spectacular outcrops appear almost as soon as Smoke Hole Road turns west and enters the canyon. The first structure encountered is a small asymmetrical anticline just west of the Cave Mountain Anticline. Gentle, southeast-dipping beds of the Oriskany Sandstone line both sides of the gap but then switch to a steep northwest dip a few hundred feet later. The Oriskany reappears, folded several times as the road follows the contour through a smaller tributary of the South Branch. It then turns north following the Oriskany, which contains external molds of brachiopods and other marine fossils. The underlying Helderberg also contains similar fossils, but they were recrystallized, preserving the shell.

As the road turns west again it enters the core of the Cave Mountain Anticline. A cliff of Helderberg limestones can be seen dipping to the southeast about 1,000 feet above the river on the north side of the gap. Quickly, the terrain along the road changes from a tight narrow valley to a more open hilly terrain more typical of karst topography developed on the Helderberg carbonates. Ahead, a tall outcrop of steeply dipping, overturned Oriskany Sandstone, known as Eagle Rock, marks the northwest limb of the asymmetrical Cave Mountain Anticline. Once again the valley walls close in.

The Oriskany Sandstone, steeply dipping on the west limb of the Cave Mountain Anticline, forms Eagle Rock in the foreground, while the gently dipping east limb is visible on Cave Mountain in the background.

The road then turns north and passes in and out of a series of steeply dipping beds of the Helderberg and Oriskany rock that line the valley walls. After about 2 miles is Smoke Hole Cave, carved into the Helderberg limestones. The cave is well above road level and can only be accessed by climbing along a very steep streambed. Continuing north, exposures of the Helderberg now line the road until it begins to leave the South Branch valley, about 2 miles north of the sign for Smoke Hole Cave.

As the route climbs out of the valley, it is ascending North Fork Mountain, a hogback formed by the southeast limb of the Wills Mountain Anticline. As such, rocks get progressively older as the road heads northeast toward the core of the fold. After passing a short row of houses, turn right at the next inter-section to continue on Smoke Hole Road to WV 28. The first rocks along this road are east-dipping limestones of the Tonoloway Limestone of Late Silurian age. The thin bedding of the Tonoloway is very characteristic of the unit and can help distinguish it from the overlying Helderberg Group. There is very little rock exposed for the next few miles until the road passes the first of several exposures of the Rose Hill Formation and Tuscarora Sandstone, both of Early Silurian age. The Tuscarora constitutes the resistant layer that forms the North Fork Mountain hogback, and the contact with the Rose Hill is encountered

Near-vertical beds of the Helderberg Group along the South Branch of the Potomac River.

several times as the road winds first toward it and then away from it as it heads north. About 10 miles from the South Branch valley, the view to the east opens up, and the road quickly negotiates a pair of steep switchbacks as it descends North Fork Mountain at North Fork Gap.

A box turtle on County Road 2 in the Smoke Hole area highlights the need to stay alert for wildlife on the road while driving in the Mountain State.

South of Franklin, US 220 continues to follow the South Branch valley all the way to Virginia. Unlike farther north, the valley here is not carved into Middle Devonian shales but rather limestones of the Helderberg Group, which can be seen in natural exposures along the valley walls and in the riverbed, as well as in an abandoned quarry along the road. As with most limestones, caves are common in the Helderberg and are easily spotted in the quarry. From Harper to the Virginia line, steeply dipping beds of both the Oriskany Sandstone and Marcellus Shale that overlie the Helderberg are exposed.

Cave entrances in a quarry of Helderberg Group carbonate rocks.

US 522

Virginia State Line—Berkeley Springs—Hancock (Maryland)
20 miles

For those making their way from western Virginia to central Pennsylvania, or vice versa, along I-81 and I-70, US 522 shortens the route between Winchester, Virginia, and Hancock, Maryland, by 26 miles. The path of the two-lane highway takes advantage of fairly level terrain along an outcrop belt of soft shales of Middle Devonian age situated between two regional folds: the Cacapon Mountain Anticline to the west and the Timber Ridge Syncline to the east. The rocks dip steeply to the east at about 50 degrees along the route. Two resistant sandstones form ridges west of the highway and help to define the east limb of the Cacapon Mountain Anticline. Immediately west of highway the

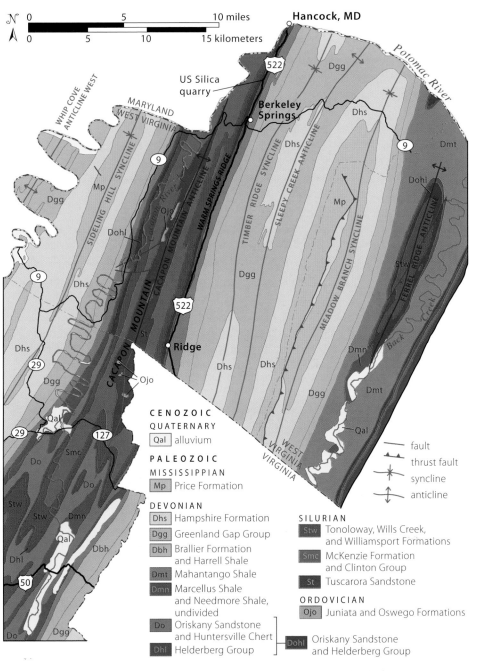

Geology of the Valley and Ridge Province between Virginia and Maryland.

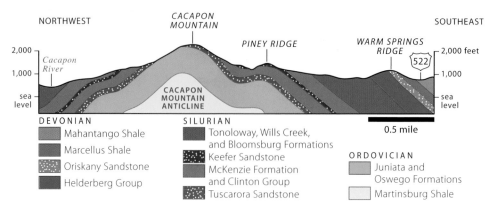

NORTHWEST   CACAPON MOUNTAIN   PINEY RIDGE   WARM SPRINGS RIDGE   SOUTHEAST

Geologic cross section of the Cacapon Mountain Anticline. Resistant, ridge-forming sandstones have been highlighted to show their topographic expression. US 522 lies in a valley of easily eroded Middle Devonian shales. –Modified from Ashton, 2008

Oriskany Sandstone of Early Devonian age forms Warm Springs Ridge, which has an average elevation of 1,100 feet. Just to its west, with an elevation almost twice as high, is Cacapon ("kuh-Kay-pon") Mountain, capped by the Tuscarora Sandstone of Early Silurian age. Near the summit of Cacapon Mountain, exposures of the Tuscarora have weathered into distinctive flat irons that are pointed at the top and widen below.

North of the Virginia state line, US 522 veers to the northwest passing over the Middle Devonian Mahantango Shale. In the town of Ridge, the highway crosses into the oldest of the Devonian shales, the Marcellus and Needmore, with the Oriskany Sandstone capping Warm Springs Ridge immediately to the west. The transition from the Oriskany Sandstone to the shales marks a significant event in the geologic history of the Appalachian Basin.

In the Early Devonian Period, the eastern edge of ancient North America was a tropical passive margin where carbonate sediments of the Helderberg and Tonoloway limestones accumulated in a warm shallow sea. The quartz sand of the Oriskany was a beach deposit that bordered that sea. In the Middle Devonian, a microcontinent collided with the eastern edge of the continent, producing the Acadian Mountains to the east and the Catskill foreland basin in this area. The shallow sea that had occupied the region was replaced by a rapidly subsiding basin that began to fill with sediments eroded from the rising Acadian Mountains. The first sediments to reach this area were the muds that became the Middle Devonian shales. The delivery of sediment was slow at first, allowing the remains of plankton that occupied the foreland basin to accumulate at a high concentration, forming the black, organic-rich muds of the Marcellus and Needmore units. In general, black color in rocks reflects the presence of organic matter—think coals. Eventually, sediment delivery increased, producing the lighter, dark-gray to brown shales of the Mahantango Shale.

Interbedded siltstones and shales of the Middle Devonian Mahantango Shale near Berkeley Springs.

As the highway continues north, outcrops of the Marcellus and Needmore Shales occasionally peek out through the vegetation, although exposure to the atmosphere has oxidized much of the organic matter and they appear tan instead of black. In the Appalachian Plateaus Province, these shales are 6,000 to 9,000 feet below the surface where the organic matter is intact, having been converted to hydrocarbons during subsequent burial. These buried black shales have been a principal source of oil and gas in the Mountain State.

For much of the history of petroleum production from the Devonian units, companies have drilled into the Oriskany Sandstone, a porous unit called a *reservoir rock* where petroleum accumulates. However, within the last decade, the technology of hydraulic fracturing has permitted companies to tap directly into the black shales, creating a recent oil and gas boom in the Appalachian Basin.

Originally called Bath after the city in England, Berkeley Springs was established as a spa in 1748. Within its boundaries there are five thermal springs, at least two of which have a constant temperature of 69.8 degrees Fahrenheit. The waters at Berkeley Springs flow through voids within the porous Oriskany Sandstone on their way to the surface. Because the water flows through sandstone, it is relatively soft compared to that of springs in carbonate rocks, the high solubility of which produces hard water rich in dissolved solids. Geochemical analysis suggests that the temperature of the water does not likely exceed 100 degrees Fahrenheit at depth, but the rapid ascent through the porous Oriskany permits the water to retain much of its heat at the surface, thus producing a warm spring.

Beginning in the late eighteenth century, Berkeley Springs became a popular destination for those wishing to "take the waters." Among its regular patrons was George Washington, who also owned property in town. Located in the center of the community, the 7-acre Berkeley Springs State Park is maintained by the state of West Virginia. It has bathing facilities that tap into three of the springs. Thus, those interested in doing so may still "take the waters."

Because the Oriskany Sandstone dips down to the east, it forms a dip slope along most of the length of Warm Springs Ridge. Silica quarries north of Berkeley Springs have taken advantage of the dip slope to mine the Oriskany for its high quartz content. US Silica still maintains a large quarry on the west side of the highway, where you can see both the Oriskany Sandstone and relatively fresh outcrops of Marcellus Shale, which has retained its black color. Farther north, the highway veers east into the Mahantango outcrop belt, which can be distinguished from the Marcellus by the presence of thin siltstone interbeds. US 522 then descends into the Potomac River valley and crosses the river into Maryland.

One of the entrances to Berkeley Springs State Park, where the historic mineral spa is fed by heated groundwater from the Oriskany Sandstone.

The Oriskany Sandstone dips to the east, forming a dip slope along Warm Springs Ridge for much of its length along US 522.

The distinctive black Marcellus Shale across from the US Silica plant north of Berkeley Springs.

WV 92 AND WV 28
WHITE SULPHUR SPRINGS—PETERSBURG
126 miles

For the most part, the Appalachian Plateaus Province and the Valley and Ridge Province have distinctively different landscapes. With the exception of the Allegheny Mountains region to the north, the topography of the plateaus tend to be quite irregular, with the mountains and valleys largely reflecting the dendritic pattern of streams that have been sculpting this gently folded region for millions of years. In contrast, the rocks of the Valley and Ridge Province are severely deformed, a consequence of it having been closer to the edge of the ancient North American continent and thus the collision zone that accompanied the final assembly of Pangea in Late Paleozoic time. The topography of the Valley and Ridge is strongly influenced by the pattern of folded and faulted rocks. Within these structures, the more resistant sandstones create long linear ridges, while the softer shales and limestones have been eroded more quickly, creating the valleys.

This route explores that part of the Valley and Ridge just east of the Allegheny Front and the Appalachian Plateaus Province. Its general north-northeast direction parallels that of the major fold axes that situate the route within the same rock units for long stretches. Where the highway crosses the axis of an anticline, it encounters older rocks toward the core, where it crosses a syncline, it finds younger rocks at its core.

WV 92 originates at exit 181 of I-64 at White Sulphur Springs. Running up the valley of Howard Creek in the shadow of Bobs Ridge, part of Coles Mountain to the west, it parallels the southeast limb of the Browns Mountain Anticlinorium. As the name suggests, this structure has the overall geometry of an anticline, with older Early Devonian rocks at its core and younger

Soft black shales of Middle Devonian age weather rapidly into small plates and form many of the valleys in the Valley and Ridge Province.

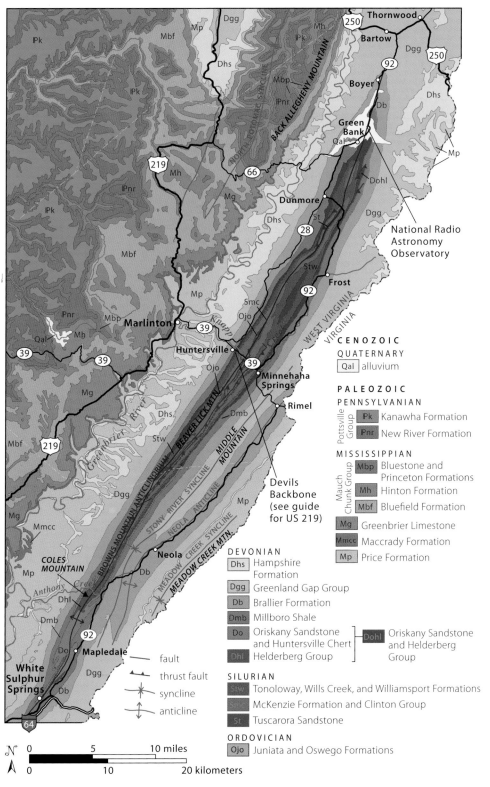

*Geology along WV 92 between White Sulphur Springs and Thornwood.
See the map on page 257 for the route north of Thornwood.*

Middle Devonian rocks along its flanks. WV 92 occupies a valley carved into the Millboro Shale of Middle Devonian age and the Brallier Formation of Late Devonian age. Both units are mostly shale, which is easily weathered and thus makes natural outcrops infrequent. Where the units are exposed in roadcuts north of Mapledale, they tend to look like slopes of platy rock. Although pieces of loose shale make them hard to see, beds of the Millboro Shale are dipping to the southeast away from the anticlinorium. Nine miles north of White Sulphur Springs, the route enters the valley of Anthony Creek, a tributary of the Greenbrier River to the west.

The broad shape of the Anthony Creek valley is somewhat unusual for the Mountain State: it has a comparatively flat floor and is fairly wide, given the size of the stream that has created it. Most routes in the Mountain State travel through V-shaped valleys with little bottomland, requiring numerous cuts into their walls to create a flat surface wide enough to accommodate two lanes, to say nothing of the even wider shelves needed to accommodate four lanes and an intervening median strip for interstate highways.

The valley created by Anthony Creek further reflects the soft nature of shale. Anthony Creek has meandered back and forth across the shale carving out a fairly wide floodplain. These strips of flat ground are an important natural resource for people in the valley. This is not coal country like the region of Pennsylvanian-age rocks to the west, so growing hay and raising cattle are the primary economic activities. So important is the land for agriculture that WV 92 hugs the sides of the valley as much as possible to allow for larger fields for cultivation and grazing.

As the route continues north, Anthony Creek and the road veer away from the valley wall. At Neola, roadcuts expose the southeasterly dipping Brallier Formation. The ridge defining the western horizon is Beaver Lick Mountain, the continuation of Coles Mountain. Neola's location is in part explained by the fact that Anthony Creek forks there, creating a North Fork and a Middle Fork. WV 92 follows the latter.

The creek's valley follows the fold axis of the Neola Anticline, which has been eroded with the passage of time. North of Neola the road runs east of Middle Mountain, a ridge of lower elevation than Beaver Lick Mountain. To the east is Meadow Creek Mountain, a ridge capped by the resistant Price Formation of Early Mississippian age along the axis of the Meadow Creek Syncline.

Ten miles north of Neola, WV 92 crosses into Pocahontas County. A few miles farther, it leaves the valley of the Middle Fork of Anthony Creek, crosses a low drainage divide, passes an excellent exposure of thin-bedded sandstones and shales of the Brallier Formation, and enters the valley of Cochran Creek. The highway intersects with WV 39 at the settlement of Rimel, which lies on the axis of the Neola Anticline. Not more than 1 mile to the east on WV 39 is Rider Gap, Virginia, where beds of the Brallier are severely contorted.

WV 92 and WV 39 run together between Rimel and Minnehaha Springs, perpendicular to the axes of folds in the region. As the road approaches the fold axis of the Stony River Syncline, it passes a large exposure of nearly horizontal sandstone beds of the Foreknobs Formation of Late Devonian time. Although

Tight folding in the Brallier Formation at Rider Gap, just across the Virginia state line east of Rimel, West Virginia.

it may seem odd to find flat-lying rock layers in the midst of all the steeply dipping units encountered thus far, the rocks are only briefly horizontal as they complete the transition from a northwest dip to a southeast dip. Because they are more resistant to weathering than the underlying shaley units, the sandstones have made Middle Mountain an elevated ridge.

As the valley begins to widen, southeast-dipping beds of the Foreknobs Formation are exposed on the north side of the road, which signals that WV 92 is heading away from the axis of the Stony River Syncline and approaching that of the Browns Mountain Anticlinorium. As the road turns northwest, it runs between Douthat Creek and an outcrop of the Oriskany Sandstone of Early Devonian age, which like the last exposure is dipping southeast.

The quartz sand that makes up the Oriskany was deposited on a beach along the edge of a shallow inland sea just prior to the onset of the Acadian Orogeny in the Middle Devonian. The unit contains numerous molds of marine brachiopods and crinoids, as well as burrows, known as trace fossils, of invertebrate animals that inhabited the coastal setting. Minnehaha Springs lies at the confluence of Douthat Creek and Knapp Creek, along which WV 92 will continue its northeasterly course.

The remarkable exposure known as the Devils Backbone, accessed via WV 39 west of Minnehaha Springs, is discussed in a sidebar in the road guide to US 460 and US 219: Bluefield—Lewisburg—Marlinton.

The circular openings in the Oriskany Sandstone near Minne-haha Springs are tubelike burrows of marine organisms.

Northeast of Minnehaha Springs, WV 92 parallels the Browns Mountain Anticlinorium as it hugs the west side of the Knapp Creek valley. As was the case with the lower portion of the Anthony Creek valley, that of Knapp Creek contains the Millboro Shale and Brallier Formation and thus has a fairly broad, flat floor. On the west side of the route exposures of Millboro Shale dip southeast and contain many species of marine fossils. Although both the Oriskany Sandstone and Millboro Shale contain marine fossils, those preserved in the shale inhabited more offshore environments that formed during the Acadian Orogeny in deep, quiet water, where muds could accumulate in the newly formed Catskill foreland basin.

North of the village of Frost, the road leaves Knapp Creek valley for that of a tributary, Sugar Camp Run. Three miles later, WV 92 leaves that valley and crosses over a small drainage divide to the valleys of Shock Run and Sitlington Creek. As the highway passes through a water gap created by Sitlington Creek, it crosses the axis of the Browns Mountain Anticlinorium, marked by a small anticline of the Tuscarora Sandstone in the woods above the road. The fold as a whole is plunging and disappears to the north.

WV 92 merges with WV 28 at Dunmore, located on the northwest limb of the anticlinorium in the valley of Sitlington Creek. Exposures of the Brallier Formation dip to the northwest here, and the combined highways follow the axis of the Browns Mountain fold to the north. More exposures of Millboro Shale appear at the junction with WV 66 near Green Bank. To the east are several small hills that constitute the final topographic expression of the Browns Mountain Anticlinorium as it plunges belowground.

The community of Green Bank is situated in a wide valley resulting from the confluence of several streams, each of which in its own meanderings carved out a part of that valley. To the west can be seen the radio telescopes of the National Radio Astronomy Observatory, among which is the largest steerable radio telescope in the world, named for the late Senator Robert C. Byrd and known to many as the Green Bank Telescope, GBT for short.

Acting as backdrop to the observatory is Back Allegheny Mountain, which constitutes the Allegheny Front here. It is capped by the New River Formation of Early Pennsylvanian age and the Middle Pennsylvanian Kanawha Formation. The mountain continues to dominate the western horizon for a number of miles north of Arbovale as the route heads toward Boyer up the valley created

Small, cone-shaped cephalopod fossils in the Millboro Shale on the east limb of the Browns Mountain Anticlinorium.

This small anticline in the Tuscarora Sandstone is part of the Browns Mountain Anticlinorium, which plunges into the ground just to the east of WV 92 at Green Bank.

by Deer Creek. Rocks of Late Devonian age line the valley south of Boyer, creating bumpy terrain.

At Bartow, WV 92 merges with US 250 and heads northwest. This road guide follows WV 28 as it turns right to merge with US 250 east for a few miles, heading up the valley of the East Fork of the Greenbrier River. The Allegheny Front continues to dominate the western horizon, with the highest elevations between 4,000 and 4,200 feet. At Thornwood, US 250 turns southeast, and WV 28 continues in an east-northeasterly direction along tributaries of the East Fork. The road skirts around the southern edge of the highest elevations of Allegheny Mountain. As it does, it follows a short eastward dog leg in the Allegheny Front that shifts it from Back Allegheny Mountain to Spruce Mountain.

The highway crosses the top of the Allegheny Front into Pendleton County at an elevation of around 4,000 feet. The summit here is also the Eastern Continental Divide, which separates streams that drain to the Gulf of Mexico from those heading to the Atlantic Ocean. East of the divide, the road immediately plunges down the Allegheny Front. Red, cross-bedded sandstones of the Hampshire Formation of Late Devonian age outcrop frequently along the way down and in a series of tall outcrops adjacent to a flagstone quarry.

Between Cherry Grove and a few miles east of Petersburg, WV 28 follows the valley of the North Fork of the South Branch of the Potomac River. At Cherry Grove, the elevation is 2,200 feet, almost 2,000 feet below the highway's highest

Cliffs of the Hampshire Formation of Late Devonian age near the bottom of the Allegheny Front north of Cherry Grove.

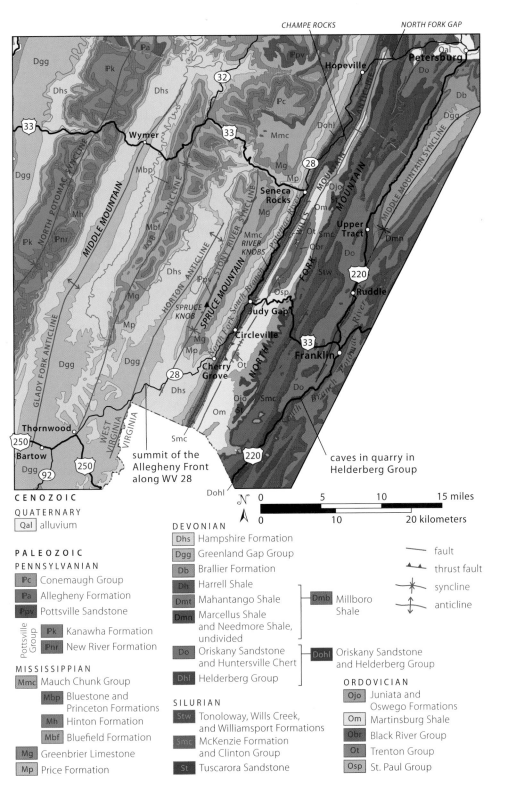

CHAMPE ROCKS   NORTH FORK GAP

Petersburg

Hopeville

Dgg   IPk   IPa

Dhs   Dhs   IPpv   Qal

32   Do

IPc   Db

33   Dgg

Wymer   33   Mmc   Dohl

Dgg   28

Mbp   Mg   MIDDLE MOUNTAIN SYNCLINE

Mp

Mh   IPnr   Seneca   Ojo

IPk   Rocks   Om

Mbf   Mg   Ot   smc   Upper   Dmn

Mmc   Obr   Tract

Dhs   RIVER   Do

KNOBS   Stw   220

IPpv   Ruddle

Mg   Osp

Dgg   Dgg   Judy Gap   33

Mp   Circleville   Franklin

Mg

Cherry   Ot   Do

Mp   Grove   Dhs   Ojo   Smc

Thornwood   Om

250   Smc

Bartow   summit of the

Dgg   250   Allegheny Front   caves in quarry in

92   along WV 28   Helderberg Group

Dohl   220

CENOZOIC   N   0   5   10   15 miles

QUATERNARY   0   10   20 kilometers

Qal alluvium

DEVONIAN

Dhs Hampshire Formation

PALEOZOIC   Dgg Greenland Gap Group   —— fault

PENNSYLVANIAN   Db Brallier Formation   ▲▲ thrust fault

IPc Conemaugh Group   Dh Harrell Shale   ✳ syncline

IPa Allegheny Formation   Dmt Mahantango Shale   Dmb Millboro   ↕ anticline

IPpv Pottsville Sandstone   Shale

IPk Kanawha Formation   Dmn Marcellus Shale

IPnr New River Formation   and Needmore Shale,

undivided

MISSISSIPPIAN   Do Oriskany Sandstone   Dohl Oriskany Sandstone

Mmc Mauch Chunk Group   and Huntersville Chert   and Helderberg Group

Mbp Bluestone and   Dhl Helderberg Group

Princeton Formations   **ORDOVICIAN**

Mh Hinton Formation   **SILURIAN**   Ojo Juniata and

Mbf Bluefield Formation   Stw Tonoloway, Wills Creek,   Oswego Formations

Mg Greenbrier Limestone   and Williamsport Formations   Om Martinsburg Shale

Mp Price Formation   Smc McKenzie Formation   Obr Black River Group

and Clinton Group   Ot Trenton Group

St Tuscarora Sandstone   Osp St. Paul Group

Geology along WV 28 between Thornwood and Petersburg.
See the map on page 251 for the route south of Thornwood.

elevation at the summit of the Allegheny Mountains. The route now runs along the base of the Allegheny Front, and this valley is bordered by mountains in two different physiographic provinces. To the west lies Spruce Mountain and the gently folded rocks on the eastern edge of the Appalachian Plateau; to the east lies the Valley and Ridge.

North of Circleville in the hamlet of Red Lick, look to the west to see the highest point in West Virginia: Spruce Knob, with an elevation of 4,863 feet. To the east is a low ridge called the River Knobs and the taller North Fork Mountain. These landforms are the surface expression of the Wills Mountain Anticline. The River Knobs are formed by vertical beds of the Tuscarora Sandstone on the west limb. North Fork Mountain is the east limb of the anticline, also capped by the Tuscarora Sandstone, which dips about 40 degrees or so to the east. At Judy Gap, where WV 28 joins US 33, there is a small quarry just to the east in which steeply dipping Silurian carbonate rocks are exposed just in front of the Tuscarora Sandstone.

For the 11 miles between Judy Gap and Seneca Rocks, WV 28 and US 33 are joined. The geology and topography of this stretch of highway are discussed in the road guide for US 33: Seneca Rocks—Franklin—Virginia State Line. It includes a sidebar about Seneca Rocks and the Wills Mountain Anticline.

Just north of the split with US 33 at Seneca Rocks, WV 28 curves below terraces, or ancient floodplains, of the North Fork of the South Branch of the Potomac River. The deposits are characterized as ancient because they lie above the recent floodplain and are not subject to erosion by the river at its present elevation. To the east lie the River Knobs and North Fork Mountain, both of which are topographic expressions of the Tuscarora Sandstone in the asymmetrical Wills Mountain Anticline. For much of this route, the core of the Wills Mountain Anticline has been eroded away, and the limbs of the fold, the Tuscarora, as well as the adjacent units do not connect over the top.

Because the route lies west of the Tuscarora Sandstone, most of the rocks that are encountered are younger units of Early to Middle Devonian age. Clearly visible are vertical exposures of the Oriskany Sandstone on the west side of the road, along with contorted shales and sandstones of Middle and Late Devonian age that lie at the base of the Allegheny Front.

About 5 miles north of Seneca Rocks, as the highway continues northeast, the east and west limbs of the Wills Mountain Anticline begin to converge while revealing numerous exposures of white Tuscarora rock. A distinctive formation known as Champe Rocks lies to the east; a historical marker provides a brief discussion. Two miles north of Champe Rocks, as the highway turns west, it passes through a water gap in the Hopeville Anticline, a small, secondary fold on the west limb of the Wills Mountain Anticline. The limbs of the fold are composed of the Helderberg Group and Oriskany Sandstone, both easily visible near the Pendleton-Grant county line. WV 28 continues north to Hopeville, where its namesake anticline is very well exposed behind Cabins Church. At Hopeville, you can take Jordon Run Road/County Road 19 to Dolly Sods Wilderness. See the sidebar in the road guide for WV 32: Thomas—Harman.

The Oriskany Sandstone on the west limb of the Hopeville Anticline dips into the North Fork of the South Branch of the Potomac River on the east side of the river opposite Dolly Town Road.

The Oriskany Sandstone at Hopeville, the type locality of the Hopeville Anticline.

The Tuscarora Sandstone is exposed on both limbs of the Wills Mountain Anticline at North Fork Gap. Here, on the western side of the gap, the rocks in the foreground are nearly vertical on the steep west limb, while the more gently dipping beds in the background on the east limb form the hogback at North Fork Mountain.

The North Fork turns east and passes through North Fork Gap, which in effect makes it possible to look "inside" the Wills Mountain Anticline. On the west side of the gap on the north side of the road, overturned beds of the Tuscarora Sandstone on the west limb come right to the edge of the highway.

East of the overturned rocks, more cliffs of the Tuscarora are visible on both sides of the road and converge to form a distinctive V shape, the result of erosion by the North Fork. The road intersects with Smoke Hole Road just east of the Tuscarora (see the side trip to Smoke Hole in the road guide for US 220: Keyser—Virginia). After passing through the narrow gap in the point of the V, look behind the Smoke Hole Cabins to see exposures of east-dipping Helderberg and Oriskany units lying above the Tuscarora rock in the east limb of the anticline.

WV 28 continues east across a valley of Middle Devonian shales carved by the South Branch of the Potomac in the hinge of the Bedford Syncline. As with most of the shale valleys, little rock is exposed as WV 28 intersects US 220 in Petersburg.

BLUE RIDGE PROVINCE AND THE GREAT VALLEY

The Great Valley stretches from northeastern Pennsylvania south to Georgia. From north to south in Pennsylvania, it is known locally as the Lehigh Valley, the Lebanon Valley, and the Cumberland Valley. In Maryland, it is the Hagerstown Valley. Cross the Potomac River, the boundary between Maryland and West Virginia, and you have entered the northern end of the Shenandoah Valley, which extends into Virginia. Locals in West Virginia refer to this as the lower reaches of the Great Valley, and traveling south is said to be heading "up the valley." The Shenandoah River joins the Potomac River at the northern end of the valley at Harpers Ferry. The confluence is the lowest elevation in the state: a mere 240 feet above sea level. Thus, heading south is traveling up the drainage to higher elevation, to the divide that separates the Shenandoah River drainage basin from that of the James River in Virginia.

The relatively wide and flat Great Valley within West Virginia is not representative of the topography of the state. Elsewhere, rocks and terrain reveal dramatic evidence of the Alleghanian Orogeny that resulted from the North American Plate's encounter with the African Plate during the final stages of the assembly of the supercontinent Pangea in the Late Paleozoic Era. But the surface expression is deceiving. Just beneath the surface, the rocks were folded and faulted to a higher degree than those in the adjacent Valley and Ridge Province because they were closer to the collision zone. Here, the difference is that the rocks are primarily soft shales and carbonates (limestones and dolostones), the latter of which are readily dissolved with exposure to rainwater or groundwater. Thus, the contrast between the weathering of shales and sandstones that gives the Valley and Ridge its distinctive topography is lacking. Here, the rocks have more or less been uniformly weathered, creating a broad, low-relief valley.

The Cambrian and Ordovician carbonates, or more concisely the Cambro-Ordovician carbonates, accumulated along a tropical carbonate shelf on the passive margin of Laurentia that existed following the breakup of the supercontinent Rodinia in Precambrian time. Although the total thickness of these units is greater than 10,000 feet, most were deposited on broad tidal flats and in fairly shallow water that may not have exceeded a few tens of feet. So, how could thousands of feet of carbonate sediment be deposited in such shallow water? The answer is thermal subsidence.

As Rodinia rifted apart, the continental fragments slid away from a spreading ridge on the seafloor. Such ridges are essentially very long submarine volcanoes

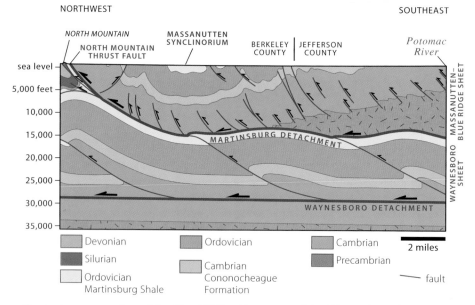

Geologic cross section of the Great Valley. Segments of the Waynesboro thrust sheet overlap at depth, and the sheet, as well as a wedge of Precambrian rock, was thrust over itself, causing the Martinsburg Shale to be exposed at the surface in the core of the Massanutten Synclinorium. It also occurs at a depth between about 17,000 and 5,000 feet. –Modified from Dean and others, 1997

erupting new basaltic oceanic crust that remains relatively warm and elevated near the spreading ridge. As more seafloor is produced, the older seafloor moves farther from the spreading ridge and becomes denser as it cools. Where the oldest seafloor is attached to the passive margin of a continental fragment, this area sinks, or thermally subsides, and allows more and more sediment to accumulate over time. Thus, while the passive margin shelf was shallow for very long periods of time, slow subsidence over millions of years continuously added more room below sea level for the accumulation of the thick Cambro-Ordovician carbonates.

The Great Valley is bound by two geologically significant features. The Blue Ridge uplift to the east and the North Mountain Fault to the west. Both features are marked by linear ridges that extend the length of the valley in West Virginia: the Blue Ridge Mountains and North Mountain. The older crystal-line and clastic rocks of the Blue Ridge and the younger clastic rocks of North Mountain have not weathered as rapidly as the carbonates, thus producing the topographic highs that define the valley.

The Blue Ridge Province is defined by a series of thrust faults, collectively known as the Blue Ridge Fault, which allowed the uplift and westward move-ment of a block of the North American crystalline basement and its overlying rocks during the intense continental collision of the Alleghanian Orogeny. The igneous and metamorphic rocks of the crystalline basement are some of the oldest rocks in the entire Appalachian Mountains, ranging from about 1.2 to 1 billion years old, and were uplifted nearly 30,000 feet. Younger Cambrian to Precambrian layered rocks were folded over the basement during the uplift and, along with the basement as its core, forms the Blue Ridge Anticlinorium. The structure as a whole is an overturned anticline, which, like many of the tight folds in the Valley and Ridge Province, is a fault-propagation fold produced by drag along a thrust fault.

While the basement rocks lie outside of the state's borders, some of the overlying Precambrian and Cambrian layered rocks appear at the surface in and around Harpers Ferry. The layered units are mostly metamorphosed sedimentary rocks, with the exception of the Catoctin Formation. The Catoctin consists of a series of lava flows that erupted into the rift valley that formed as Rodinia broke up in the late Precambrian, about 570 million years ago. These are the oldest rocks at the surface in the state, but there are only a few small exposures of this unit to the south along the eastern border. The other layered units were originally sedimentary and also accumulated in the Precambrian rift valley. They were metamorphosed during the Alleghanian Orogeny and represent the only metamorphic rocks in the state. The youngest, deposited in Early Cambrian time, is the Antietam Formation, a quartzite, or metamorphosed sandstone.

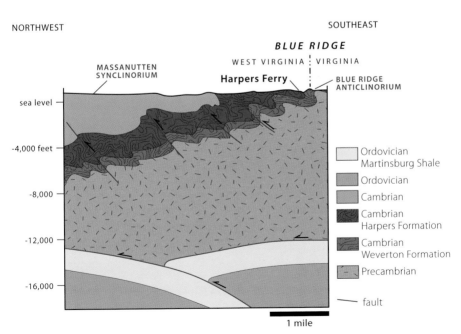

Geologic cross section of the Blue Ridge Anticlinorium near Harpers Ferry.
–Modified from Dean and others, 1990

The geology of the Great Valley was strongly influenced by the westward movement of the Blue Ridge uplift during the Alleghanian Orogeny. As this block was displaced more than 150 miles to the west and tens of thousands of feet upward, the rocks to the west were also shoved westward along subsurface thrust faults. One of these faults, called the Martinsburg Detachment, cut upward through the layers of rock and allowed a section of rock from the east to be shoved westward and thrust upon itself. Thus, the section of rock under the valley was nearly doubled in thickness. The rocks on the surface are part of the Massanutten–Blue Ridge sheet and are the hanging wall of the Martinsburg Detachment. Fifteen thousand feet below the surface, the same rocks, called the Waynesboro sheet, are found in the footwall of the fault. Although the fault continues to the west under the Valley and Ridge, several smaller thrust faults splintered away from the Martinsburg Detachment, one of which is the North Mountain Fault.

The rocks of the Massanutten–Blue Ridge sheet were folded into the large, complex Massanutten Synclinorium, with the Martinsburg Shale of Late Ordovician age composing the core and older Cambrian and Ordovician rocks constituting the flanks. Many smaller-scale folds and faults complicate the geometry of the rocks. To best visualize the near-surface geology, think of the Great Valley as a simple syncline.

Interstate 81
POTOMAC RIVER (MARYLAND BORDER)—
RIDGEWAY (VIRGINIA BORDER)
26 miles

For many traveling up and down the East Coast, I-81 is the preferred route. Unlike I-95, which superseded US 1 and therefore runs close to, if not through, major metropolitan areas, this interstate passes to the west of Philadelphia, Wilmington, Baltimore, Washington DC, and Richmond. It is still a heavily traveled route, primarily for commercial trucks transporting goods from the southern ports of New Orleans and Memphis to the aforementioned cities of the northeast. Its route takes it across the eastern panhandle of the Mountain State, and so for many travelers the 26 miles it takes to do so represents their only encounter with West Virginia.

With the exception of the first few miles south of the Potomac River, I-81 runs along the west limb of the Massanutten Synclinorium along a belt of Martinsburg Shale. The fold axis lies to the east and parallels the highway for much of the route. Like the carbonates, the shales have weathered, so as a consequence there are few exposures of rock. The first outcrops to be seen are south of mile marker 20, where carbonates of the Beekmantown Group of Early Ordovician age are visible to the west. At first glance, these might seem to be isolated boulders. In fact, they are the edges of steep, east-dipping beds that extend many thousands of feet below the surface. Exposures of the Beekmantown continue

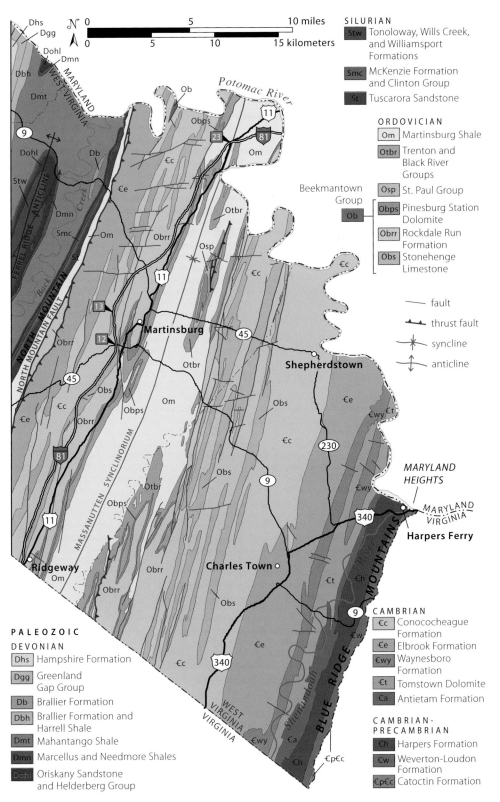

Geology along I-81 and WV 9, and at Harpers Ferry.

to the south, until exit 13 where a small anticline, aptly named the Exit 13 Anticline, exposes carbonates of the Elbrook Formation of Late Cambrian age. By now, the Blue Ridge Mountains—the boundary between the Mountain State and Virginia—can be seen to the east, while North Mountain constitutes the western horizon.

South of Martinsburg, I-81 remains on the west limb of the Massanutten Synclinorium. Small exposures of carbonates of Late Cambrian and Early Ordovician age can be seen here and there, often dipping in different directions as the highway encounters small-scale folds. North Mountain, the western limit of the Great Valley, continues to dominate the western horizon. The North Mountain Fault sheared off a sliver of Late Ordovician and Early Silurian rocks from its footwall and uplifted them next to the older Cambrian and Ordovician rocks of the headwall. One of the units from the footwall is the Tuscarora Sandstone, the resistant quartz-rich unit that forms many of the ridges in the Valley and Ridge Province to the west.

WV 9
Martinsburg—Charles Town
15 miles

East of Martinsburg, WV 9 crosses the axis of the Massanutten Synclinorium, which is marked by the Martinsburg Shale, and enters the part of the Great Valley floored by the east limb of the synclinorium. The highway encounters older Cambrian and Early to Middle Ordovician rocks on the way to the Blue Ridge at Harpers Ferry.

East of exit 12 of I-81, WV 9 passes just north of two industries closely tied to the local geology. The first is the Essroc Cement Plant, which maintains a quarry from which high-calcium Ordovician limestones are extracted as the principal raw material for producing cement. They are also used as road aggregate. Just to the east is the Continental Brick Company, which makes use of clays from the Martinsburg Shale. Though not visible from the highway, the contact between the limestone and shale runs between the two industrial facilities.

At mile marker 54.5 on WV 9 you can see an exposure of weathered Martinsburg Shale, a black to dark-gray shale deposited in a foreland basin during the early stages of the Taconic Orogeny in Ordovician time. However, the shale takes on a tan to brown color when weathered. At mile marker 58.5, the highway crosses onto the carbonate belt marked by bright-red exposures of terra rossa, a common soil type produced by the chemical weathering of iron-rich clays that is often found mixed in with the calcium carbonate of carbonate rocks. The bedrock is exposed a half mile farther east near mile marker 59. At Charles Town, if you take the exit for US 340 eastbound, look for exposures of steeply dipping carbonates.

Harpers Ferry

If you are on US 340 approaching Harpers Ferry from the west, look to the east to see the gap in the Blue Ridge created by the Potomac River, just east of its confluence with the Shenandoah River at Harpers Ferry. The Antietam Formation, a Cambrian quartzite, is resistant enough to produce a subtle ridge just west of the US 340 exit for Harpers Ferry.

There are several options for entering and exploring Harpers Ferry. The first is to continue east on US 340 and turn left onto Shenandoah Street just before the bridge over the Shenandoah River. The second is to turn south off US 340 onto Shoreline Drive and enter the fee area for the Harpers Ferry National Historic Park. The third is to turn north off US 340 onto Washington Street, which leads to downtown Harpers Ferry. Keep in mind that parking is limited in and around downtown Harpers Ferry. If descending into the Potomac River valley along Washington Street, look to the right to see small exposures of the Harpers Formation, which originated as an accumulation of muds in a lake or lagoon in the rift valley that formed as the Precambrian supercontinent Rodinia broke up. The muds were subsequently lithified to form shale after burial and were later metamorphosed into phyllite by heat and pressure.

Phyllite, as far as metamorphic rocks go, is fairly low grade, having been heated just beyond the limits of slate. As such, the Harpers Formation breaks along even planes similar to slate, yet many of the clay minerals have been transformed to micas, which give the rock a greenish tint and a smooth sheen.

The Harpers Formation along Shenandoah Street in Harpers Ferry. Bedding is slightly overturned, dipping to the east. The nearly horizontal lines in the rock were formed by the stress of metamorphism.

When you are at the point where you can see the confluence of the Shenandoah and Potomac Rivers and the Appalachian Trail, look back at the town to observe that many buildings, retaining walls, and sidewalks were constructed using Harpers phyllite.

The Harpers Formation is best exposed along Shenandoah Street, which runs right along the Shenandoah River. It constitutes the tall cliffs that extend upward from road level, as well as a boulder known locally as Jefferson Rock, which has had sandstone columns installed for support. Close to Lower Town, many exposures of this formation dip to the east and are overturned, lying upside down on the west limb of the anticlinorium, although this can be difficult to discern because the effects of metamorphism tend to obscure the original bedding planes

The overturned anticline is also evident across the Potomac River in Maryland at the cliffs of Maryland Heights. Here, the Harpers lies below the older Weverton Formation, a quartzite deposited by streams in the ancient rift valley. On the cliffs, the Harpers Formation, which weathers more readily than the Weverton, is covered by vegetation, unlike the bare rocks above. It is worth crossing the old B&O Railroad bridge on the pedestrian walkway to the Maryland Heights Trailhead. Although the hike to the top of Maryland Heights is strenuous, it offers access to exposures of the younger Harpers Formation that lie under the older cliff-forming Weverton and an excellent view of Harpers Ferry and the surrounding ridges.

Resistant quartzite beds of the Weverton Formation form the cliffs of Maryland Heights.

The younger Harpers Formation below the older Weverton Formation in the overturned Blue Ridge Anticlinorium near the bottom of the Maryland Heights Trail.

The cliffs also provide an opportunity to examine the Weverton Formation up close. As was the case with the Harpers Formation along Shenandoah Street, the effects of metamorphism can make it difficult to discern the orientation of bedding here as well. However, there are a few places where cross beds are visible. They have a consistent concave-up orientation that can be used to determine what is right side up in the beds. Resistant beds of the Weverton, Harpers, and Antietam Formations form a series of steplike rapids, visible from the cliffs, in both the Potomac and Shenandoah Rivers. West of the rapids, the rivers calmly flow over more easily weathered Cambrian rocks.

An interesting aspect of both the Weverton and Harpers Formations is that their exact age is uncertain. They clearly lie above the lavas of the Catoctin Formation, which have been radiometrically dated at 570 million years. They also lie below the younger Antietam Formation, which contains fossils of the ancient trilobite *Olenellus*, a common index fossil of the Early Cambrian. Lacking either minerals that can be radiometrically dated or index fossils that can be used to assign an age, the Harpers and Weverton Formations are considered to be either Precambrian or Cambrian in age, or perhaps one or both units span this important geologic boundary.

The view from Maryland Heights of the confluence of the Potomac River (right) and the Shenandoah River (left) and the town of Harpers Ferry. Resistant beds in the Weverton, Harpers, and Antietam Formations form ripples in both rivers, while the smooth water flows over weathered Early Cambrian carbonate units.

Cross beds in the Weverton Formation at Maryland Heights. These structures form concave-up, providing a useful tool for determining original right-side-up orientation in severely deformed rocks.

GLOSSARY OF TERMS

active margin. The border of a continent that corresponds to a plate boundary, usually a subduction zone, and is characterized by igneous activity and deformation.

alluvial fans. A fan-shaped wedge of sediments beginning where a stream leaves a mountain front and extending out onto the floor of a flat valley.

alluvium. Any combination of sedimentary materials (clay, silt, sand, and gravel) deposited by a stream in the recent past.

anticlinal trap. Where an impermeable layer of rock within the fold of an anticline overlies sedimentary units containing hydrocarbons, resulting in their concentration under that barrier.

anticline. An upward (convex) folding of multiple rock layers, the oldest of which lie at its core. See also **syncline**.

anticlinorium. A regional composite anticlinal structure containing numerous smaller folds and faults.

Appalachian Basin. A depositional basin produced by subsidence during each of the three Paleozoic mountain building events and filled with sediments from the erosion of the resultant mountains. The rocks were deformed by the last of the three events, the Alleghanian Orogeny.

asthenosphere. The upper layer of the Earth's mantle upon which the lithosphere or crust is located. It is a mechanically weak layer where isostatic adjustment takes place and magmas are generated.

axis. The line along which the curvature of a fold is greatest. Also called the **hinge**. The two limbs of a fold meet at the axis or hinge.

basement rock. The undifferentiated rock, igneous or metamorphic, which composes the crust of the Earth and underlies sedimentary deposits.

basin. A depression on the Earth's surface with no outlet, or a low area of tectonic origin in the Earth's crust where successive layers of sediments have accumulated and lithified.

braided streams. Streams characterized by multiple small, shallow, frequently shifting channels that form where riverbanks are easily eroded and where there is more coarse sediment to transport than the stream can easily handle.

carbonates. A group of nonclastic sedimentary rocks composed of various forms of calcium and magnesium carbonate; for example, limestones and dolostones.

channel. That part of a stream system that usually contains water and confines its flow.

clast. An individual grain resulting from the weathering and disintegration of a larger mass of rock.

clastic. A type of sediment composed of the fragments of preexisting rocks.

clastic wedges. Major accumulations of sediment eroded from mountains and transported by streams and rivers. They are thickest near their sources and thin out away from these sources.

coarsening-upward. Describes the gradual increase in particle size from the bottom to the top of a rock unit.

conglomerate. A clastic sedimentary rock consisting of gravel-sized grains greater than 2 millimeters in diameter in a matrix of smaller, usually sand-sized grains.

continental environments. Depositional settings that are either land based or in fresh water.

convergent boundary. A tectonic setting in which two tectonic plates move toward one another.

crust. The outermost layer of the Earth. The granitic continental crust averages 25 miles in thickness. The basaltic oceanic crust averages 5 miles in thickness.

cutbank. The steep, outside edge of a river bend where the current is the fastest, and, as a consequence, there is often rapid and significant erosion of the river's bank.

cyclothem. A sequence of repeating sedimentary units deposited during a sedimentary cycle. These sequences were common during the Pennsylvanian and Permian Periods.

deformation. A general term for the folding, faulting, shearing, extension, or compression of rock.

dendritic drainage. A pattern of surface drainage where tributaries resemble the branching pattern of a tree. It generally forms over rocks with equal resistance to erosion.

detachment. A low-angle fault plane separating undeformed rocks below from folded and faulted rocks above.

dip. The downward angle at which a rock layer tilts from the horizontal, expressed in degrees. See also **strike**.

dip slope. A slope for which the land surface is formed by the upper surface of a dipping rock unit.

displacement. The relative movement of rocks on opposite sides of a fault.

divergent boundary. A tectonic setting in which tectonic plates are moving apart relative to one another.

dolostone. A nonclastic sedimentary rock consisting largely of the mineral dolomite, which is composed of calcium magnesium carbonate.

drainage divide. The boundary, usually a ridge or other topographic high, between adjacent drainage basins.

erosion. The wearing away of soil and rock by various processes. See also **weathering**.

faults. Fractures in rock along which displacement or movement has occurred parallel to the fracture plane.

fining-upward. Describes the gradual decrease in particle size from the bottom to the top of a rock unit.

footwall. A block or mass of rock beneath a fault. See also **headwall**.

foreland basin. A depression that forms where crust adjacent to an orogenic belt receives additional load produced by the overthickened crust.

formation. A body of rock strata with a distinct lithology, or combination of lithologies, that serves as the fundamental unit of stratigraphy; for example, the Allegheny Formation.

geologic time scale. A system of chronological dating that relates geological strata to time and is used to describe the timing and relationships of events that occurred during the whole of Earth history

group. A unit of rock higher in rank than a formation that consists of several formations. For example, the Pennsylvanian-age Pottsville Group consists of the Kanawha, New River, and Pocahontas Formations. See also **formation** and **member**.

headwall. A block or mass of rock above a fault. Also called a **hanging wall**. See also **footwall**.

hinge. The area of maximum curvature or bending in a fold where the two limbs join.

hinge line. The boundary separating a stable region and one that has undergone or is undergoing upward or downward movement. Such a hinge line separates the Northern and Southern Basins of the Appalachian Plateaus, the southern one having dropped in the past, resulting in considerably thicker beds of rock units that are more or less common to both basins.

hogback. A ridge with a summit consisting of both outcrops and steep slopes of resistant rock with roughly the same degree of incline, typically greater than 20 degrees.

igneous. Rocks formed by the cooling of molten material, either magma or lava.

index fossil. A fossil that serves to identify and date the rock unit in which its found because it is easily found, easily distinguished from other fossils, geographically widespread, and preserved in a variety of sedimentary rocks that formed in a restricted period of time. Also called a **guide fossil**.

interbedded. Said of rock units with alternating layers that have different lithologies or characteristics, or both.

isostatic adjustment. The uplift or subsidence of the lithosphere on the asthenosphere to maintain equilibrium, comparable to floating, as erosion removes rock and soil from a particular region and deposits it in another. The amount of adjustment is roughly 82 percent of the weight of the eroded materials.

joint. A fracture, often found in sets, along which there has been little or no movement.

karst. A distinctive type of topography formed by the dissolution of carbonates or other soluble rocks and characterized by sinkholes, caves, and underground streams.

knob. A rounded hill with steep sides that stands out against the prevailing topography.

landform. Any physical feature of the Earth's surface: hills, mountains, plateaus, ridges, valleys, etc.

law of original horizontality. A principle formulated by Nicolaus Steno (1638–1686) that states that sedimentary rock units were generally horizontal when they formed.

law of superposition. A principle formulated by Nicolaus Steno (1638–1686) that states that where rock layers are undisturbed, the oldest lies at the bottom with units becoming progressively younger the higher in the sequence they appear.

lens. A body of rock that is thick in the middle and thin at the edges.

limb. The gently curved area of a fold (either anticline or syncline) between adjacent fold hinges.

lithosphere. The rigid outer, approximately 60-mile-thick layer of the Earth composed of the crust and upper mantle. It comprises the tectonic plates.

magma. Molten rock deep in the Earth that becomes lava when it rises to the surface.

mantle. The middle zone of the Earth between the core and the crust.

margin. The boundary between two bodies. Generally used to refer to the edges of tectonic plates or the edge of a continent or coast.

marine. Environments characterized by seawater of average salinity.

meander bend. The curved part in a stream's course where sediment accumulates on the inner bank and is eroded by currents on the outer bank.

meander loop. The part of a stream's course that includes the bend and adjoining straight segments, which are separated by a thin strip of land.

member. A rock unit of lower rank than a formation. For example, the Nuttall Sandstone is a member of the Kanawha Formation. See also **formation** and **group**.

metamorphic rock. Rock units altered by heat and pressure.

mineral. A solid, crystalline substance that is naturally occurring, is inorganic, and has a specific chemical composition. Rocks are combinations of minerals.

nonclastic. A type of sedimentary rock that forms from the precipitation of either organic or inorganic minerals as opposed to the accumulation of fragments of preexisting rocks.

normal fault. An extensional fault in which the headwall, or hanging wall, moves downward relative to the footwall.

orogeny. A mountain building event resulting from the tectonic compression of continental crust and the addition of igneous material.

paleochannel. What remains of an ancient, abandoned stream channel cut into older rock.

paleodivide. An ancient drainage divide that was eliminated by erosional forces, thus altering the drainage patterns of a region.

paleosol. A fossilized or ancient soil that formed on a landscape in the distant past.

paleovalley. An ancient river valley.

parent rock. In the context of metamorphic rocks, the rock that existed before alteration by heat and pressure.

passive margin. An edge of a continent that lies far away from a tectonic boundary and is not the site of igneous activity or deformation. Sediments tend to accumulate in great quantities on passive margins.

physiographic province. A region of the Earth with distinct topography that is the product of climate and geology. Two such provinces constitute much of the Mountain State: the Appalachian Plateaus Province and the Valley and Ridge Province.

plateau. An expansive area of elevated terrain, consisting of relatively horizontal rock layers, with one margin that is quite steep. The steep side of the Appalachian Plateaus is known as the Allegheny Front.

point bar. Deposits of sediments on the inner bank, or curve, of a meander bend.

radiometric dating. A means of determining the age of rock units by comparing the amount of radioactive and daughter isotopes found in them.

red beds. Sediments of any grain size that are reddish in color, usually due to coatings or cements of hematite or other iron oxide minerals.

regression. The seaward movement of a shoreline as sea level drops or the land rises. See also **transgression**.

reverse fault. A compressional fault in which the headwall moves upward relative to the footwall.

rift. A long narrow valley, generally bound by normal faults, that formed where two tectonic plates diverge; often associated with volcanism.

sandstone. A clastic sedimentary rock consisting primarily of sand-sized grains, usually of the mineral quartz.

sequence. A series of major rock units deposited under the same or closely related environmental conditions within a particular region.

shale. A thin-bedded or platy clastic sedimentary rock consisting primarily of clay- and silt-sized grains.

siltstone. A clastic sedimentary rock consisting primarily of silt-sized grains. It can have texture and composition similar to shale but lacks the thin-bedded, platy appearance and tends to be better cemented.

source area. The place of origin, usually a mountainous region or topographic high, of a particular deposit of clastic sediments.

strata. Rock layers. A single layer is a **stratum**.

stratigraphy. The study of rock layers and their relationships, both in time and space.

stream capture. The natural diversion of the headwaters of one stream into the channel of another that is at a lower elevation. This process often increases the stream gradient.

stress fracture. See **joint**.

strike. The angle of intersection, measured from north, between a dipping rock unit (plane) and a horizontal surface (Earth's surface). See also **dip**.

strike-slip fault. A fault formed by opposing or shear stress in which the displacement of the rocks parallels the fault plane.

structures. Folds, faults, and other geologic features that result from deformational forces in the Earth's crust.

subduction. The process by which the edge of a tectonic plate capped by oceanic crust descends below an adjacent plate into the asthenosphere, where it causes melting. The molten rock can make its way back to the surface through volcanoes or form intrusions in the Earth's crust.

syncline. A downward (concave) folding of multiple rock layers, the youngest of which lies at its core. See also **anticline**.

synclinorium. A regional composite synclinal structure containing numerous smaller folds and faults.

tectonic plate. A fragment of the Earth's lithosphere that moves independently of, and above, the asthenosphere

terrace. A former floodplain that is situated at a higher elevation than a river's current floodplain.

terra rossa. Iron-rich red clays that remain in the soil as carbonate rock weathers.

terrestrial. Refers to land above sea level; a terrace is a terrestrial feature. Terrestrial environments include rivers, alluvial plains, and floodplains.

topographical expression. Where the occurrence of a geological feature is reflected in the contour of the land; for instance, where a resistant sandstone forms a ridge.

transform boundary. Where two tectonic plates slide past one another.

transgression. The landward advance of a shoreline as sea level rises or the land subsides. See also **regression**.

trellis drainage. A drainage pattern in which tributaries join the main channel at approximately right angles. This pattern is characteristic of the Valley and Ridge Province.

type locality. The geographic location where a particular rock unit was first or best recognized and described. For example, Marcellus, New York, is the type locality for the Marcellus Shale.

type section. One or more adjacent outcrops in a particular location displaying a vertical sequence of rock units that are identified by that location's name. For example, a rock outcropping in Pottsville, Pennsylvania, is the type section for the Pottsville Group, which includes the Kanawha, New River, and Pocahontas Formations.

underclay. A layer of clay below a coal bed that represents the old soil in which the coal-forming plants grew; those that are pure enough to be heated in a kiln to high temperatures to manufacture china or other ceramic products are known as **fireclays**.

weathering. The sum total of processes, both chemical and physical, by which rocks are broken down into smaller components. See also **erosion**.

BIBLIOGRAPHY

Algeo, T. J., ed. 2001. *Sedimentology and Sequence Stratigraphy of Foreland Basin Deposits of the Acadian and Alleghenian Orogenies, Central Appalachian Basin.* Cincinnati, OH: University of Cincinnati, Department of Geology.

Arkle, T., Jr. 1972. *I. C. White Memorial Symposium Field Trip, September 27–29, 1972.* Morgantown, WV: West Virginia Geological and Economic Survey.

Arkle, T., Jr. 1974. "Stratigraphy of the Pennsylvanian and Permian Systems of the Central Appalachians." In *Carboniferous of the Southeastern United States*, GSA Special Paper 148, edited by G. Briggs, 5–29. Boulder, CO: Geological Society of America.

Ashton, K. 2008. *The Geology of Cacapon Resort and Lost River State Parks.* Morgantown, WV: West Virginia Geological and Economic Survey.

Avary, K. L. 1986. "Greenland Gap, Grant County, West Virginia." In *Southeastern Section of the Geological Society of America*, Centennial Field Guide, vol. 6, edited by T. L. Neathery, 69–73. Boulder CO: Geological Society of America.

Barlow, J. A. 1974. *Coal and Coal Mining in West Virginia.* Coal Geology Bulletin no. 2. Morgantown, WV: West Virginia Geological and Economic Survey.

Bentley, C., and others. 1914. *Geology of Corridor H, Geological Society of Washington Fall Field Trip, 1914.* Annandale, VA: Geological Society of Washington.

Bierman, P. R., and D. R. Montgomery. 2014. *Key Concepts in Geomorphology.* New York: W. H. Freeman.

Blake, B. M., and others. 1996. *Regional Stratigraphy and Coal Geology of the Kanawha Formation in Southern West Virginia.* Energy Minerals Division Field Trip, Annual Meeting, Eastern Section, American Association of Petroleum Geologists.

Bonnett, R. B., H. C. Noltimier, and D. C. Sanderson. 1991. "A Paleomagnetic Study of the Early Pleistocene Minford Silt Member, Teays Formation, West Virginia." In *Geology and Hydrogeology of the Teays-Mahomet Bedrock Valley System*, GSA Special Paper 258, edited by W. N. Melhorn and J. P. Kempton, 9–18. Boulder, CO: Geological Society of America.

278

Brezinski, D. K. 1989. *Lower Mississippian Foreland Basin Deposits of Western Maryland: Hancock to Keysers Ridge, Maryland, July 14, 1989.* Field Trip Guidebook T226. Washington, DC: American Geophysical Union.

Cardwell, D. H., R. B. Erwin, and H. P. Woodward. 1968. *Geologic Map of West Virginia.* Map 1, scale 1:250,000. Morgantown, WV: West Virginia Geological and Economic Survey.

Cecil, C. B. 1990. "Paleoclimate Controls on Stratigraphic Repetition of Chemical and Siliciclastic Rocks." *Geology* 18 (6): 533–536.

Cecil, C. B., J. C. Cobb, D. R. Chestnut Jr., H. Damberger, and K. J. Englund, eds. 1989. *Carboniferous Geology of the Eastern United States: St. Louis, Missouri to Washington, D.C, June 28–July 8, 1989.* Field Trip Guidebook T143. Washington, DC: American Geophysical Union.

Coolen, J. M. 2003. "Coal Mining along the Warfield Fault, Mingo County, West Virginia: A Tale of Ups and Downs." *International Journal of Coal Geology* 54 (3–4): 193–207.

Dean, S. L., B. R. Kulander, P. Lessing, and D. Barker. 1987. *Geology of the Hedgesville, Keedysville, Martinsburg, Shepherdstown, and Williamsport Quadrangles, Berkeley and Jefferson Counties, West Virginia.* Map WV-31, scale 1:24,000. Morgantown, WV: West Virginia Geological and Economic Survey.

Dean, S. L., P. Lessing, B. R. Kulander, and D. Barker. 1990. *Geology of the Berryville, Charles Town, Harpers Ferry, Middleway, and Round Hill Quadrangles, Berkeley and Jefferson Counties, West Virginia.* Map WV-35, scale 1:24,000. Morgantown, WV: West Virginia Geological and Economic Survey.

Dennison, J. M., ed. 1988. *Geologic Field Guide, Devonian Delta, East-Central West Virginia and Adjacent Virginia, September 12–13, 1988.* Charleston, WV: Appalachian Geological Society.

Diecchio, R. J. 1986. "Taconian Clastic Sequence and General Geology in the Vicinity of the Allegheny Front in Pendleton County, West Virginia." In *Southeastern Section of the Geological Society of America*, Centennial Field Guide, vol. 6, edited by T. L. Neathery, 85–90. Boulder CO: Geological Society of America.

Donaldson, A. C. 1968. "Geology of the Arboretum." *Arboretum Newsletter* 18 (1). Morgantown: Department of Biology, West Virginia University.

Donaldson, A. C., M. W. Presley, and J. J. Renton, eds. 1979. *Field Trip Guidebook for Carboniferous Coal Short Course.* Bulletin 37-1. Morgantown, WV: West Virginia Geological and Economic Survey.

Edmunds, W. E., V. W. Skema, and N. K. Flint. 1999. "Pennsylvanian." In *The Geology of Pennsylvania*, Special Publication 1, edited by C. H. Shultz, 148–169. Harrisburg, PA: Pennsylvania Geological Survey.

Englund, K. J., H. H. Arndt, S. P. Schweinfurth, and W. H. Gillespie. 1986. "Pennsylvanian System Stratotype Sections, West Virginia." In *Southeastern*

Section of the Geological Society of America, Centennial Field Guide, vol. 6, edited by T. L. Neathery, 59–68. Boulder CO: Geological Society of America.

Fedorko, N., and M. Blake. 1998. *A Geologic Overview of Mountaintop Removal Mining in West Virginia*. Executive Summary of a Report to the Committee on Post-Mining Land Use and Economic Aspects of Mountaintop Removal Mining, October, 26, 1998. Morgantown, WV: West Virginia Geological and Economic Survey.

Fedorko, N., and V. Skema. 2011. "Stratigraphy of the Dunkard Group in West Virginia and Pennsylvania." In *Geology of the Pennsylvanian-Permian in the Dunkard Basin*, Guidebook for the Annual Field Conference of Pennsylvania Geologists, edited by J. A. Harper, 1–25. Washington, PA: Pennsylvania Geological Survey/Pittsburgh Geological Society.

Fenneman, N. M. 1938. *Physiography of Eastern United States*. New York: McGraw-Hill.

Fichter, L. S. 1986. "The Catskill Clastic Wedge (Acadian Orogeny) in Eastern West Virginia." In *Southeastern Section of the Geological Society of America*, Centennial Field Guide, vol. 6, edited by T. L. Neathery, 91–96. Boulder CO: Geological Society of America.

Fichter, L. S., and R. J. Diecchio. 1986. "The Taconic Sequence in the Northern Shenandoah Valley, Virginia." In *Southeastern Section of the Geological Society of America*, Centennial Field Guide, vol. 6, edited by T. L. Neathery, 73–78. Boulder CO: Geological Society of America.

Filer, J. K. 1986. "Burning Springs Anticline, West Virginia." In *Southeastern Section of the Geological Society of America*, Centennial Field Guide, vol. 6, edited by T. L. Neathery, 55–58. Boulder CO: Geological Society of America.

Fonner, R. F. 1987. *Geology along I-64, Putnam County, West Virginia*. Morgantown, WV: West Virginia Geological and Economic Survey.

Fonner, R. F., and G. A. Chappell. 1987. *Geology along I-64, Cabell County, West Virginia*. Morgantown, WV: West Virginia Geological and Economic Survey.

Fonner, R. F., and G. A. Chappell. 1987. *Geology along I-64, Wayne County, West Virginia*. Morgantown, WV: West Virginia Geological and Economic Survey.

Fonner, R. F., and N. Fedorko III. 1985. *Geology along I-79, Harrison County, West Virginia*. Morgantown, WV: West Virginia Geological and Economic Survey.

Fonner, R. F., and C. P. Messina. 1981. *Geology along I-79, Marion County, West Virginia*. Morgantown, WV: West Virginia Geological and Economic Survey.

Fonner, R. F., and C. P. Messina. 1981. *Geology along I-79, Monongalia County, West Virginia*. Morgantown, WV: West Virginia Geological and Economic Survey.

Fonner, R. F., and others. 1981. *Geology along the West Virginia Portion of U.S. Route 48*. Morgantown, WV: West Virginia Geological and Economic Survey.

Frye, K. 1986. *Roadside Geology of Virginia*. Missoula, MT: Mountain Press.

Geology Guidebook for Marion County [WV] Teachers Field Trip: West Virginia Side Trip, June 18-21. 1981. Morgantown, WV: West Virginia University, Department of Geology and Geography.

Gerritsen, S. S. 1988. *Structural Analysis of the Silurian-Devonian Cover in the Smoke Holes, West Virginia*. Master's Thesis, West Virginia University.

Gillespie, W. H., G. W. Rothwell, and S. E. Sheckler. 1981. "The Earliest Seeds." *Nature* 293 (October): 462–464.

Green, D. K. 1912. "Geologic Wonder, Historic Landmark: The Burning Springs Anticline." *Wonderful West Virginia*, June, 4–7.

Hansen, M. C. 1995. *The Teays River*. GeoFacts no. 10. Ohio Department of Natural Resources. Available online at https://geosurvey.ohiodnr.gov /portals/geosurvey/PDFs/GeoFacts/geof10.pdf.

Hare, C. E. 1957. *Geology of the Coopers Rock State Forest and Mont Chateau State Park*. State Park Bulletin 5. Morgantown, WV: West Virginia Geological and Economic Survey.

Harper, J. A., ed. 2011. *Geology of the Pennsylvanian-Permian in the Dunkard Basin*. Guidebook for the Annual Field Conference of Pennsylvania Geologists. Washington, PA: Pennsylvanian Geological Survey/Pittsburgh Geological Society.

Haynes, J. T., and others. 2015. *Appalachian Stratigraphy, Tectonics, and Eustasy from the Blue Ridge to the Allegheny Front, Virginia and West Virginia*. Field Trip 408 of the Geological Society of America Meeting, Baltimore, Maryland, October 30–31, 2015.

Jacobson, R. B., ed. 1993. *Geomorphic Studies of the Storm and Flood of November 3–5, 1985, in the Upper Potomac and Cheat River Basins in West Virginia and Virginia*. Bulletin 1981. Reston, VA: US Geological Survey.

Jordan, T. H., and J. P. Grotzinger. 2008. *The Essential Earth*. New York: W. H. Freeman.

Kavage Adams, R., M. D. Swift, D. K. Brezinski, and S. J. Kite. 2017. "Pleistocene Periglacial Features of the Pittsburgh Low Plateau and Upper Youghiogheny Basin." In *Forts, Floods, and Periglacial Features: Exploring the Pittsburgh Low Plateau and Upper Youghiogheny Basin*, GSA Field Guide, vol. 46, edited by J. T. Hannibal and K. C. Fredrick, 29–45. Boulder, CO: Geological Society of America.

Keiser, A. F., and others. 1988. *"Corridor G" (119) Pennsylvanian Stratigraphy: Field Trip #2, September 13, 1988*. Charleston, WV: American Association of Petroleum Geologists Eastern Section Meeting.

Kulander, B. R., and S. L. Dean. 1966. "Structure and Tectonics of Central and Southern Appalachian Valley and Ridge and Plateau Provinces, West Virginia and Virginia." *AAPG Bulletin* 70 (11): 1674–1684.

Kulander, B. R., S. L. Dean, and P. Lessing. 1986. "The Browns Mountain Anti-clinorium, West Virginia." In *Southeastern Section of the Geological Society of America*, Centennial Field Guide, vol. 6, edited by T. L. Neathery, 101–104. Boulder CO: Geological Society of America.

Lutgens, F. K., and E. J. Tarbuck. 2015. *Essentials of Geology*. 12th ed. New York: Pearson.

Martino, R. L. 1994. "Facies Analysis of Middle Pennsylvanian Marine Units, Southern West Virginia." In *Elements of Pennsylvanian Stratigraphy, Central Appalachian Basin*, GSA Special Paper 294, edited by C. L. Rice, 69–86. Boulder, CO: Geological Society of America.

Martino, R. L. 1996. "Stratigraphy and Depositional Environments of the Kanawha Formation (Middle Pennsylvanian), Southern West Virginia, U.S.A." *International Journal of Coal Geology* 31 (1–4): 217–248.

Matchen, D. L., Fedorko, N., and B. M. Blake, Jr. 2008. *Bedrock Geology of Canaan Valley, West Virginia*. Publication OF-9902-A, 2 sheets, scale 1:24,000. Morgantown, WV: West Virginia Geological and Economic Survey.

McColloch, G. H., and J. S. McColloch. 2003. *Bedrock Geology of the West Virginia Portion of the Lake Lynn Quadrangle, Monongalia County, West Virginia*. Publication OF-0405, scale 1:24,000. Morgantown, WV: West Virginia Geological and Economic Survey.

McColloch, J. S., and J. F. Schwietering. 1985. *Geology along U.S. Route 33 Canfield to Bowden, Randolph County, West Virginia*. Morgantown, WV: West Virginia Geological and Economic Survey.

McColloch, J. S., and J. F. Schwietering. 1986. "Devonian to Mississippian Section, Elkins, West Virginia." In *Southeastern Section of the Geological Society of America*, Centennial Field Guide, vol. 6, edited by T. L. Neathery, 79–84. Boulder CO: Geological Society of America.

McCoy, M. L. 1988. "Geology of the Seneca Rocks Recreation Area." In *Mountain State Geology: Seneca Rocks*: 18–28.

McDowell, R. C., and A. P. Schultz. 1990. *Structural and Stratigraphic Framework of the Giles County Area, a Part of the Appalachian Basin of Virginia and West Virginia*. Bulletin 1839-E. Reston, VA: US Geological Survey.

Mcdowell, R. R., and others. 2005. *Bedrock Geologic Map of the Franklin 7.5 Quadrangle, West Virginia*. Morgantown, WV: West Virginia Geological and Economic Survey.

Means, J. 2010. *Roadside Geology of Maryland, Delaware, and Washington, D.C.* Missoula, MT: Mountain Press.

Messina C. P., R. F. Fonner, and N. Fedorko. 1981. *Geology along I-70 and I-470, Ohio County, West Virginia*. Morgantown, WV: West Virginia Geological and Economic Survey.

Nadon, G. C., E. H. Gierlowski-Kordesch, and J. P. Smith. 1998. *Sedimentology and Provenance of Carboniferous and Permian Rocks of Athens County,*

Southeastern Ohio. Guidebook 15. Columbus, OH: Division of Geological Survey, Ohio Department of Natural Resources.

Nature Conservancy. No date. *Cranesville Swamp.* Preserve Guide. Bethesda, MD: Nature Conservancy of Maryland/DC. Available online at https://www.nature.org/ourinitiatives/regions/northamerica/unitedstates/maryland_dc/placesweprotect/preserve-visitors-guide-cranesville-swamp.pdf.

Nichols, G. 2009. *Sedimentology and Stratigraphy.* 2nd ed. Oxford: Wiley-Blackwell.

Patchen, D. G., and others. 1985. *Northern Appalachian Region: Correlation of Stratigraphic Units of North America (COSUNA) Project.* Tulsa, OK: American Association of Petroleum Geologists.

Perry, W. J., Jr. 1975. "Tectonics of the Western Valley and Ridge Foldbelt, Pendleton County, West Virginia—A Summary Report." *Journal of Research of the US Geological Survey* 3 (5): 583–588.

Rauch, H. 2014. *Karst Geology Field Trip Guide Book.* Morgantown, WV: Department of Geology and Geography, West Virginia University.

Reger, D. B. 1931. *Randolph County.* West Virginia Geological and Economic Survey County Report. Morgantown, WV: Morgantown Printing and Binding.

Reger, D. B., and P. H. Price. 1926. *Mercer, Monroe, and Summers Counties.* West Virginia Geological and Economic Survey County Report. Wheeling, WV: Wheeling News Litho.

Renton, J. J. No date. "A Geology Field Trip." Department of Geology and Geography, West Virginia University. Accessed April 27, 2018. http://www.wvgs.wvnet.edu/www/geoeduc/FieldTrip/GeologyFieldTripGuide.pdf.

Repine, T. E., Jr. 1986. "Mining Beneath the Ohio." *Mountain State Geology*: 35–39.

Repine, T. E., Jr. 1989. "Clay Mines of Hancock County." *Mountain State Geology*: 37–44.

Rodd, J. S. 1994. *A Guide to Coopers Rock State Forest.* Moatsville, WV: Barn Echo Press.

Ryder, R. T., and others. 2009. *Geologic Cross Section D-D' through the Appalachian Basin from the Findlay Arch, Sandusky County, Ohio, to the Valley and Ridge Province, Hardy County, West Virginia.* Scientific Investigations Map 3067. Reston, VA: US Geological Survey.

Schwietering, J. F. 1984. "Beneath the New River Gorge." *Mountain State Geology* 84: 23–24.

Simard, C. 1987. "Legacy from the Ice Age." *Mountain State Geology*: 29–32.

Stanley, S. M. 2009. *Earth System History.* 3rd ed. New York: W. H. Freeman.

Sullivan, K., ed. 2006. *The West Virginia Encyclopedia.* Charleston, WV: West Virginia Humanities Council.

Suppe, J. 1985. *Principles of Structural Geology*. Englewood Cliffs, NJ: Prentice-Hall.

Teller, J. T., and R. P. Goldthwait. 1991. "The Old Kentucky River: A Major Tributary to the Teays." In *Geology and Hydrogeology of the Teays-Mahomet Bedrock Valley System*, GSA Special Paper 258, edited by W. N. Melhorn and J. P. Kempton, 29–42. Boulder, CO: Geological Society of America.

Tilton, J. L. 1928. "Geology from Morgantown to Cascade, West Virginia, along State Route Number 7." *Proceedings of the West Virginia Academy of Science* 2: 1–22.

Tso, J., R. McDowell, K. L. Avary, D. Matchen, and G. Wilkes. 2004. "Middle Eocene Igneous Rocks in the Valley and Ridge of Virginia and West Virginia." In *Geology of the National Capital Region—Field Trip Guidebook*, Circular 1264, edited by S. Southworth and W. Burton, 137–162. Reston, VA: US Geological Survey.

Welker, D. 1982. "The Ice Age in West Virginia." *Mountain State Geology*: 26–32.

West Virginia Nature Conservancy. 2006. *Dolly Sods North: West Side*. Map. Elkins, WV: West Virginia Nature Conservancy.

West Virginia Nature Conservancy. 2006. *Dolly Sods Wilderness*. Map. Elkins, WV: West Virginia Nature Conservancy.

Whisonant, R. C., and A. P. Schultz. 1986. "Appalachian Valley and Ridge to Appalachian Plateau Transition Zone in Southwestern Virginia and Eastern West Virginia: Structure and Sedimentology." In *Southeastern Section of the Geological Society of America*, Centennial Field Guide, vol. 6, edited by T. L. Neathery, 113–118. Boulder CO: Geological Society of America.

Woodfork, L. D., and J. F. Schwietering. 1984. *Field Trip for AAPG Trustees to Eastern Greenbrier County and Southern Pocahontas County, West Virginia, April 14, 1984*. Morgantown, WV: West Virginia Geological and Economic Survey.

Writers' Program of the Work Projects Administration in the State of West Virginia. 1941. *West Virginia: A Guide to the Mountain State*. New York: Oxford University Press.

INDEX

JOSEPH LEBOLD earned a BS in geology from West Virginia University in 1994. After completing his master's degree in paleontology at Ohio State University on ancient reef communities, he returned to WVU in 2001 to complete a doctoral dissertation on the marine invertebrate fossils that are found among the vast sequence of sedimentary rocks containing West Virginia's coal reserves. Since 2009, Joe has taught geology at WVU, including a popular course on the geology of West Virginia.

CHRISTOPHER WILKINSON, a musicologist specializing in African American musical culture, taught music history and writing at WVU's School of Music for thirty-seven years, retiring in 2013. Having a layperson's interest in geology ever since taking two courses in the subject at Hamilton College in the 1960s, he encourages others to explore the fascinating geologic history of the Mountain State.

MARIA AF ROLÉN earned her BS in geology from WVU in 2016 and is currently working as a geologist in Morgantown. Maria is a graduate of Fotoskolan i Stockholm (the Stockholm School of Photography), the leading institution of its kind in her native Sweden.